# WORLD HISTORY

## THE HUMAN EXPERIENCE

# Chapter and Unit Tests:
# Forms A and B

NATIONAL
GEOGRAPHIC
SOCIETY

Mounir A. Farah

Andrea Berens Karls

**GLENCOE**

McGraw-Hill

New York, New York   Columbus, Ohio   Woodland Hills, California   Peoria, Illinois

## To the Teacher

This resource booklet provides you with *Chapter and Unit Tests* to accompany *World History: The Human Experience.* Two tests, Form A and Form B, are provided for each chapter and allow you to test and retest student mastery of chapter content and skills. Both test forms include recall questions, higher-level questions to test students' comprehension of main ideas and concepts, and two essay questions calling for critical thinking. Each test is based on a 100-point scoring system. For those students unable to master the test, assign the *Reteaching Activity* that corresponds to the chapter. Upon completion of the activity, students may be retested with the second form of the chapter test.

Comprehensive unit tests are supplied to evaluate student mastery of unit concepts and themes. Each unit test includes higher-level questions calling for students to apply an understanding of concepts learned in the unit. Two essay questions ask students to analyze, interpret, and evaluate the concepts learned in the unit.

Answers to the tests are provided at the back of this booklet.

## Glencoe/McGraw-Hill

*A Division of The McGraw-Hill Companies*

Send all inquiries to:
Glencoe/McGraw-Hill
936 Eastwind Drive
Westerville, OH 43081

ISBN 0-02-821587-7

Printed in the United States of America
2 3 4 5 6 7 8 9 0 045 03 02 01 00 99

# TABLE OF CONTENTS

# TABLE OF CONTENTS

# Chapter 1 : Form
# Test : A

**Score** _____

## Matching

*Match each item in Column A with an item in Column B by writing the correct letters in the blanks.*
*(3 points each)*

**Column A**

_____ **1.** metal mixtures used to create improved tools and weapons

_____ **2.** inhabited the Tigris-Euphrates valley

_____ **3.** period of time before the development of writing

_____ **4.** about 8000 B.C. to 5000 B.C.

_____ **5.** earliest *Homo sapiens*

_____ **6.** oldest hominids known to manufacture tools

_____ **7.** exchange of goods and ideas between peoples

_____ **8.** earliest *Homo sapiens sapiens* in Europe

_____ **9.** studies fossil remains to learn about prehistory

_____ **10.** the Old Stone Age

**Column B**

**a.** Paleolithic period

**b.** prehistory

**c.** Neanderthals

**d.** Neolithic period

**e.** cultural diffusion

**f.** paleontologist

**g.** alloys

**h.** Sumerians

**i.** *Homo habilis*

**j.** Cro-Magnons

## Multiple Choice

*In the blank, write the letter of the choice that best completes the statement or answers the question.*
*(4 points each)*

_____ **11.** Archaeologists would classify all of the following objects as artifacts EXCEPT
  **a.** a stone bead.
  **b.** an antelope skull.
  **c.** a metal blade.
  **d.** the remains of a cooking pit.

_____ **12.** The agricultural lifestyle led to the development of all of the following EXCEPT
  **a.** the calendar.
  **b.** rules of inheritance.
  **c.** land boundaries.
  **d.** cooperative hunting groups.

_____ **13.** Many archaeologists believe that writing developed from the record keeping of urban
  **a.** priests.      **b.** artisans.      **c.** soldiers.      **d.** kings.

_____ **14.** Many scientists date the existence of humanlike creatures to about
  **a.** 5,500 years ago.
  **b.** 10,000 years ago.
  **c.** 50,000 years ago.
  **d.** 4.4 million years ago.

_____ **15.** *Homo erectus* developed all of the following EXCEPT
  **a.** the ability to hunt animals using weapons.
  **b.** the ability to make barbed points and blades.
  **c.** the ability to make clothing.
  **d.** the ability to make fire.

_____ **16.** The process by which people become more proficient at earning a living by performing a single task is referred to as
  **a.** the diffusion of culture.
  **b.** surplus agricultural production.
  **c.** the specialization of labor.
  **d.** domestication.

# Chapter 1 : *Form*
# Test : Ⓐ

_____ **17.** The loom and textile weaving were invented
  **a.** in the Neander Valley.
  **b.** during the Paleolithic period.
  **c.** during the Old Stone Age.
  **d.** during the Neolithic period.

_____ **18.** The disappearance of the Neanderthals was probably caused by
  **a.** inability to adapt to colder climates.
  **b.** intermarriage with *Homo sapiens sapiens*.
  **c.** destructive flooding.
  **d.** the formation of land bridges between continents.

_____ **19.** The Paleolithic period is characterized by the use of
  **a.** stone tools.
  **b.** irrigation systems.
  **c.** advances in agriculture.
  **d.** bronze weapons.

_____ **20.** Social standing in ancient cities can be measured by proximity to the
  **a.** irrigation canal.   **b.** city center.   **c.** city market.   **d.** trade routes.

_____ **21.** The discovery of Cro-Magnons buried with daggers, beads, and other status symbols provides evidence of
  **a.** the existence of leaders in Cro-Magnon society.
  **b.** cooperative big-game hunting.
  **c.** their technological inferiority compared to the Neanderthals.
  **d.** the existence of a spoken language.

_____ **22.** Cultural and lifestyle changes of the Neolithic Revolution were mostly caused by
  **a.** the development of new agricultural methods.
  **b.** severe changes in the global climate.
  **c.** the development of long-distance hunting weapons.
  **d.** the development of spoken language.

_____ **23.** *Australopithecus*, the earliest hominids, probably survived by
  **a.** hunting with primitive wooden weapons.
  **b.** domesticating and cultivating wild plants.
  **c.** building permanent homes along the shores of lakes and rivers.
  **d.** moving constantly in search of food.

_____ **24.** Creation myths have been found
  **a.** only in Asian civilizations.
  **b.** only in the Sumerian civilization.
  **c.** only in prehistoric civilizations.
  **d.** in all civilizations.

_____ **25.** The development of dikes, dams, and irrigation systems did all of the following EXCEPT
  **a.** provide a steadier flow of water.
  **b.** increase farmers' reliance on rainfall.
  **c.** ease destructive flooding.
  **d.** increase grain production.

## Essay
*Answer one of the following questions on a separate sheet of paper. (10 points)*

**26a. Critical Thinking** Describe two reasons why the growth of cities required the formation of governments or ruling bodies.

**26b. Critical Thinking** Identify and describe two techniques scientists use to learn about early hominids from fossilized remains.

Name ........................................................................... Date ........................... Class ...........................

# Chapter 1 : *Form*
# Test : **B**

## Matching
*Match each item in Column A with an item in Column B by writing the correct letters in the blanks.*
*(3 points each)*

**Column A**

_____ **1.** lived from 1.8 million to 30,000 years ago

_____ **2.** all humans and humanlike creatures

_____ **3.** wanderers

_____ **4.** marks and pictures representing products

_____ **5.** people living today

_____ **6.** sites of Cro-Magnon cave paintings

_____ **7.** study objects left behind by prehistoric people

_____ **8.** land bridge between Siberia and Alaska

_____ **9.** probably home of the earliest humans

_____ **10.** site of the earliest cities yet discovered

**Column B**

**a.** hominids

**b.** Tigris-Euphrates valley

**c.** eastern and southern Africa

**d.** archaeologists

**e.** nomads

**f.** *Homo erectus*

**g.** Lascaux and Vallon-Pont-d'Arc

**h.** *Homo sapiens sapiens*

**i.** Beringia

**j.** pictograms

## Multiple Choice
*In the blank, write the letter of the choice that best completes the statement or answers the question.*
*(4 points each)*

_____ **11.** Which of the following were nomadic hunter-gatherers who cared for their sick and aged?
  **a.** Neanderthals    **b.** *Homo habilis*    **c.** Sumerians    **d.** *Homo erectus*

_____ **12.** Bronze became a favored material for tools and weapons because
  **a.** it could be given a sharp cutting edge and was easy to mold.
  **b.** was much less expensive than copper or tin.
  **c.** flint supplies diminished during the Bronze Age.
  **d.** artisans found it difficult to shape liquid metals.

_____ **13.** Complex societies with advanced knowledge of farming, trade, government, and art are called
  **a.** cultures.
  **b.** cooperatives.
  **c.** civilizations.
  **d.** agricultural villages.

_____ **14.** All of the following are innovations of the Neolithic Revolution EXCEPT
  **a.** the domestication of dogs and oxen.
  **b.** the use of graves for burials.
  **c.** improved food storage methods.
  **d.** the development of fertilizers.

_____ **15.** Bones found at the Hadar site indicate that the hominids there
  **a.** could walk upright.
  **b.** could not walk upright.
  **c.** could not climb trees.
  **d.** lived primarily in trees.

_____ **16.** The development of agriculture occurred
  **a.** simultaneously in all parts of the world.
  **b.** at various times in different parts of the world.
  **c.** only between 5,000 B.C. and 3,000 B.C.
  **d.** only in the Indus Valley.

# Chapter 1 : *Form*
# Test : **B**

_____ 17. The exchange of ideas and goods between different groups of people is called
    **a.** the specialization of labor.
    **b.** economic civilization.
    **c.** cultural diffusion.
    **d.** cultural anthropology.

_____ 18. Radiocarbon dating involves determining the age of artifacts by
    **a.** measuring the amount of a radioactive element remaining.
    **b.** examining the sequence in which they were found.
    **c.** comparing the remains to similar discoveries.
    **d.** analyzing differences in the physical features.

_____ 19. All of the following valleys are sites of early urban civilizations EXCEPT
    **a.** Tigris and Euphrates.
    **b.** Huang He.
    **c.** Nile River.
    **d.** Neander.

_____ 20. The founding of Neolithic villages such as Jericho and Çatal Hüyük was made possible by
    **a.** increased competition for land and water.
    **b.** the invention of weaving.
    **c.** the development of agriculture.
    **d.** the ability to control fire.

_____ 21. Land bridges that allowed migration between places now separated by water formed during
    **a.** the New Stone Age.
    **b.** the Ice Ages.
    **c.** the Neolithic Revolution.
    **d.** the Bronze Age.

_____ 22. The first *Homo sapiens* appeared about
    **a.** 200,000 years ago.
    **b.** 1.8 million years ago.
    **c.** 4.4 million years ago.
    **d.** 3.2 million years ago.

_____ 23. Most Neanderthals lived in
    **a.** groups of 5 to 10 people.
    **b.** groups of 35 to 50 people.
    **c.** villages of 50 to 500 people.
    **d.** cities of 1,000 to 5,000 people.

_____ 24. The remains of early *Homo sapiens sapiens* have been found
    **a.** only in Europe.
    **b.** only in Africa.
    **c.** only in Asia.
    **d.** on almost every continent.

_____ 25. A people's way of life, including diet, religious beliefs, artistic achievements, and language, is called their
    **a.** prehistory.
    **b.** technology.
    **c.** culture.
    **d.** archaeology.

## Essay
*Answer one of the following questions on a separate sheet of paper. (10 points)*

**26a. Critical Thinking** Explain how the Neolithic Revolution laid the foundation for the specialization of labor.

**26b. Critical Thinking** Compare and contrast the level of technological development achieved by the Neanderthals and the Cro-Magnons.

Name ............................................................... Date ............... Class ...............

## Matching

*Match each item in Column A with an item in Column B by writing the correct letters in the blanks.*
*(3 points each)*

**Column A**

_____ **1.** capital of Egypt's Middle Kingdom

_____ **2.** the worship of many deities

_____ **3.** title meaning "great house of the king"

_____ **4.** hero of the world's oldest epic

_____ **5.** authority to rule

_____ **6.** made "justice appear in the land"

_____ **7.** first king of a united Egypt

_____ **8.** leader of the Akkadians

_____ **9.** oldest writing system

_____ **10.** political and religious government

**Column B**

**a.** polytheism

**b.** Sargon I

**c.** theocracy

**d.** Narmer

**e.** cuneiform

**f.** mandate

**g.** Gilgamesh

**h.** pharaoh

**i.** Hammurabi

**j.** Thebes

## Multiple Choice

*In the blank, write the letter of the choice that best completes the statement. (4 points each)*

_____ **11.** The Sumerian religion encompassed all of the following beliefs EXCEPT
  **a.** that each god controlled a specific natural force or human activity.
  **b.** the belief in a blissful and peaceful afterlife.
  **c.** that gods could cause great misery if angered.
  **d.** the need to honor the gods through prayer and sacrifice.

_____ **12.** Less is known about the Harappans than the Egyptians or Mesopotamians because of
  **a.** their lack of written records.
  **b.** destruction caused by invaders from Mohenjo-Daro.
  **c.** the loss of the royal archives.
  **d.** scientists' inability to decipher hieroglyphs.

_____ **13.** Egyptian pyramid building began during the period of
  **a.** the New Kingdom.
  **b.** the Middle Kingdom.
  **c.** the Old Kingdom.
  **d.** the Shang dynasty.

_____ **14.** The region known as the Fertile Crescent includes parts of present-day
  **a.** Egypt and the Sudan.
  **b.** Egypt, Israel, Jordan, and Lebanon.
  **c.** Ethiopia and Kenya.
  **d.** Israel, Jordan, Lebanon, Turkey, Syria, and Iraq.

_____ **15.** To irrigate their crops, Egyptian farmers relied on
  **a.** regular year-round rainfall.
  **b.** heavy rain during the monsoon season.
  **c.** the yearly flooding of the Nile River.
  **d.** an irrigation network connected to the Tigris-Euphrates.

# Chapter 2 : Form
# Test : Ⓐ

_____ **16.** The earliest Chinese dynasty that can be dated from written records is the
    **a.** Shang.     **b.** Xia.     **c.** Pan Gu.     **d.** Huang He.

_____ **17.** Achievements of the ancient Egyptians included all of the following EXCEPT
    **a.** a 365-day calendar.
    **b.** medical techniques to treat fractures and wounds.
    **c.** advanced mathematical principles, including geometry.
    **d.** the development of cuneiform writing script.

_____ **18.** The oldest continuous civilization in the world is that of
    **a.** Egypt.     **b.** China.     **c.** India.     **d.** Pakistan.

_____ **19.** Harappan cities are notable for their
    **a.** gridlike layouts and underground sewers.
    **b.** circular design and all-stone construction.
    **c.** slate-roofed wooden houses.
    **d.** palace and temple placement near the city boundaries.

_____ **20.** By the time of the empire, Egyptian women had
    **a.** no legal rights.
    **b.** the right to own property only with the permission of their husbands.
    **c.** no right to own property.
    **d.** the ability to own property, testify in court, and initiate divorce proceedings.

_____ **21.** Claiming to be the sun god's equal, Amenhotep changed his name to
    **a.** Ramses II.     **b.** Ramses III.     **c.** Hatshepsut.     **d.** Akhenaton.

_____ **22.** The mythical founder of China's Xia dynasty was called
    **a.** Shun, the master of elephants.
    **b.** Yang-shao.
    **c.** Yu the Great.
    **d.** Zhou.

_____ **23.** Settlement of the Nile Valley began around
    **a.** 10,000 B.C.     **b.** 5000 B.C.     **c.** 1000 B.C.     **d.** 300 B.C.

_____ **24.** The South Asian subcontinent is separated from the rest of Asia by the
    **a.** Himalayas and the Hindu Kush.
    **b.** Nile Valley.
    **c.** Ganges.
    **d.** Arabian peninsula.

_____ **25.** Sumerian sites such as Ur, Uruk, and Eridu are considered by historians to be
    **a.** among the world's first cities.
    **b.** the birthplace of spoken language.
    **c.** the birthplace of polytheism.
    **d.** the finest examples of Egyptian architecture.

## Essay
_Answer one of the following questions on a separate sheet of paper. (10 points)_

**26a. Critical Thinking** Describe the seasonal flooding of the Huang He and the rivers of the Indus-Ganges plain. Explain why these floods were both beneficial to and feared by area inhabitants.

**26b. Critical Thinking** Identify the three periods into which historians have organized the dynasties that ruled Egypt. Describe the major events that occurred during each period.

Name ........................................................................ Date ............................. Class ...............................

# Chapter 2 : *Form*
# Test : **B**

**Score** _____

## Matching

*Match each item in Column A with an item in Column B by writing the correct letters in the blanks.*
*(3 points each)*

**Column A**

_____ **1.** long reeds used to make rope, baskets, mats

_____ **2.** terraced temple found in Sumerian cities

_____ **3.** a Harappan civilization settlement

_____ **4.** eastern part of the Fertile Crescent

_____ **5.** one of the ancient Chinese capitals

_____ **6.** Nile River valley location

_____ **7.** initially, god of the Nile

_____ **8.** early writing system using picture symbols

_____ **9.** used by the Chinese to make pottery

_____ **10.** site of the Indus Valley civilization

**Column B**

**a.** kaolin

**b.** Egypt

**c.** hieroglyphics

**d.** papyrus

**e.** South Asia

**f.** Anyang

**g.** Osiris

**h.** Mesopotamia

**i.** Mohenjo-Daro

**j.** ziggurat

## Multiple Choice

*In the blank, write the letter of the choice that best completes the statement. (4 points each)*

_____ **11.** The river sometimes called "the Great Sorrow" because of its destructive flooding is the
   **a.** Ganges.
   **b.** Euphrates.
   **c.** Indus.
   **d.** Huang He.

_____ **12.** After conquering Lower Egypt, Narmer set up the capital of his government in
   **a.** Syria.
   **b.** Cairo.
   **c.** Thebes.
   **d.** Memphis.

_____ **13.** The area of China most suitable for agriculture and the development of early civilization was the
   **a.** Gobi region.
   **b.** southwest.
   **c.** east.
   **d.** Kunlun Shan.

_____ **14.** Sumerian innovations include all of the following EXCEPT
   **a.** the umbrella.
   **b.** the wagon wheel.
   **c.** an alphabet-based script.
   **d.** the metal plow.

_____ **15.** At its height, ancient Egypt had a population of around
   **a.** 100,000 people.
   **b.** 1 million people.
   **c.** 5 million people.
   **d.** 100 million people.

_____ **16.** The Egyptians built the pyramids as places to
   **a.** honor and bury their god-kings.
   **b.** store and distribute grain.
   **c.** issue ritual commands.
   **d.** serve as local government headquarters.

# Chapter 2 : *Form*
# Test : **B**

_____ **17.** Shang dynasty kings tried to predict the future by
    **a.** writing in vertical columns.
    **b.** scratching on oracle bones.
    **c.** making sacrifices to Aton.
    **d.** consulting Osiris.

_____ **18.** The existence of trade between the Indus Valley and Mesopotamia is
    **a.** unlikely because of the subcontinent's geographic isolation.
    **b.** indicated by the discovery of Harappan seals in Mesopotamia.
    **c.** thought to have begun as early as 5000 B.C.
    **d.** recorded in the *Gilgamesh* epic.

_____ **19.** The Hyksos were able to invade and defeat the Egyptians because of their
    **a.** political alliance with Ramses II.
    **b.** carved stone obelisks.
    **c.** centralized military bureaucracy.
    **d.** superior military tools such as horse-drawn chariots.

_____ **20.** The legal code of Hammurabi called for
    **a.** specific punishments for each type of violation.
    **b.** monetary fines for all offenses.
    **c.** punishment only for crimes against the government.
    **d.** equal punishment for a crime against a person regardless of class.

_____ **21.** The Indus River civilization dates to about
    **a.** 2500 B.C.
    **b.** 5000 B.C.
    **c.** 7500 B.C.
    **d.** 10,000 B.C.

_____ **22.** According to ancient Chinese belief, just and effective rulers would
    **a.** receive authority from heaven.
    **b.** achieve the stature of gods.
    **c.** never be overthrown.
    **d.** reign for 800 years.

_____ **23.** A major accomplishment of Sargon I was to
    **a.** restore the royal archives at Ebla.
    **b.** unite the city-states of Mesopotamia.
    **c.** develop a 365-day calendar.
    **d.** facilitate the spread of the Sumerian language.

_____ **24.** Harappa was located in present-day
    **a.** Pakistan.
    **b.** India.
    **c.** Syria.
    **d.** Egypt.

_____ **25.** From 3000 B.C. to 332 B.C., Egypt was ruled by a series of 30
    **a.** dynasties.
    **b.** monarchies.
    **c.** Middle Kingdoms.
    **d.** Theban kings.

## Essay

*Answer one of the following questions on a separate sheet of paper. (10 points)*

**26a.** **Critical Thinking** Describe the social hierarchy of Egyptian society. Which groups of people made up each level?

**26b.** **Critical Thinking** Why might it be fair to say that "history begins at Sumer"?

# Chapter 3 : Form
# Test : Ⓐ

**Score** _____

## Matching

*Match each item in Column A with an item in Column B by writing the correct letters in the blanks.*
*(3 points each)*

**Column A**

_____ **1.** reformer of Persian religion

_____ **2.** Israelite judge who defeated the Canaanites near Mount Tabor

_____ **3.** developed monotheistic religion

_____ **4.** seafaring traders

_____ **5.** overland traders

_____ **6.** developers of the three-person chariot

_____ **7.** messengers believed to communicate God's word

_____ **8.** divider of the Persian Empire into provinces

_____ **9.** spoken by most Fertile Crescent people until the A.D. 800s.

_____ **10.** child of David

**Column B**

**a.** Solomon

**b.** Aramaeans

**c.** prophets

**d.** Israelites

**e.** Darius

**f.** Aramaic

**g.** Zoroaster

**h.** Phoenicians

**i.** Hittites

**j.** Deborah

## Multiple Choice

*In the blank, write the letter of the choice that best completes the statement. (4 points each)*

_____ **11.** The Israelite tribes were ruled by judicial and military leaders called
    **a.** god-kings.
    **b.** judges.
    **c.** priests.
    **d.** satraps.

_____ **12.** The gold-rich Asia Minor kingdom that prospered around 600 B.C. was called
    **a.** Canaan.
    **b.** Byblos.
    **c.** Persia.
    **d.** Lydia.

_____ **13.** At its height, the Persian Empire encompassed about
    **a.** 1 million people.
    **b.** 5 million people.
    **c.** 50 million people.
    **d.** 110 million people.

_____ **14.** The holy Jewish writings compiled around 400 B.C. are called the
    **a.** Torah.
    **b.** Diaspora.
    **c.** Micah.
    **d.** Ten Commandments.

_____ **15.** Around 1200 B.C., the Aramaeans settled in what is now central
    **a.** Egypt.
    **b.** Syria.
    **c.** China.
    **d.** Iraq.

_____ **16.** The Jewish festival of Passover celebrates
    **a.** the Israelite Exodus from Egypt.
    **b.** the construction of a temple in Jerusalem.
    **c.** the arrival of Abraham in Canaan.
    **d.** the unification of the northern and southern tribes.

# Chapter 3 : *Form*
# Test : Ⓐ

_____ **17.** By 650 B.C., the Assyrian Empire stretched from
   **a.** the Jordan River to the Mediterranean Sea.   **c.** Tyre south into Asia Minor.
   **b.** Nineveh north into Asia Minor.   **d.** the Persian Gulf to Egypt and into Asia Minor.

_____ **18.** The Israelite king who set up a capital in Jerusalem was
   **a.** Cyrus II.   **c.** David.
   **b.** Saul.   **d.** Solomon.

_____ **19.** The system of trade that involved exchanging goods for other goods is called the
   **a.** money system.   **c.** Lydian system.
   **b.** barter system.   **d.** Phoenician system.

_____ **20.** During the rule of King Nebuchadnezzar, Babylon
   **a.** became capital of the Hittite Empire.   **c.** was destroyed by the Persians.
   **b.** became known as one of the world's most beautiful cities.   **d.** was destroyed by the Chaldeans.

_____ **21.** King Cyrus II allowed the Jews to return to Jerusalem in
   **a.** 1900 B.C.   **c.** 1595 B.C.
   **b.** 1645 B.C.   **d.** 539 B.C.

_____ **22.** Both the Hebrew and Arabic languages are closely related to
   **a.** Greek.   **c.** Aramaic.
   **b.** Sumerian.   **d.** Persian.

_____ **23.** Persepolis, the magnificent capital of Persia, was built by
   **a.** Ahura Mazda.   **c.** Darius I.
   **b.** Cyrus II.   **d.** Cyrus I.

_____ **24.** All of the following were characteristic of the Phoenicians EXCEPT
   **a.** monotheistic belief.   **c.** the harvesting of cedar.
   **b.** setting up trading posts along the Mediterranean coast.   **d.** the use of contracts and bills of sale in business.

_____ **25.** The Hittites contributed little to Middle Eastern civilization except for
   **a.** the Zoroastrian religion.   **c.** the development of a solar calendar.
   **b.** the satrap system of provincial government.   **d.** a legal system emphasizing payment over punishment.

## Essay
*Answer one of the following questions on a separate sheet of paper. (10 points)*

**26a. Critical Thinking** Discuss the teachings of the prophet Zoroaster. Describe how they differed from other religious beliefs predominant in the ancient world.

**26b. Critical Thinking** Describe the major movements of the Israelite people in and out of Canaan. Identify the causes of each movement and the time frame in which each occurred.

# Chapter 3 : *Form*
# Test : **B**

## Matching
*Match each item in Column A with an item in Column B by writing the correct letters in the blanks.*
*(3 points each)*

**Column A**

_____ **1.** group from which Persians originated

_____ **2.** Phoenician city-state

_____ **3.** successor to Moses

_____ **4.** includes the first five books of the Bible

_____ **5.** active trading peoples centered in Damascus

_____ **6.** Jewish escape from Egypt

_____ **7.** divisions of the Israelites

_____ **8.** neighbors in Canaan

_____ **9.** provincial governors of the Persian Empire

_____ **10.** built the Hanging Gardens

**Column B**

**a.** Aramaeans

**b.** Torah

**c.** Tyre

**d.** 12 tribes

**e.** satraps

**f.** Philistines and Phoenicians

**g.** Joshua

**h.** Nebuchadnezzar

**i.** Indo-Europeans

**j.** Exodus

## Multiple Choice
*In the blank, write the letter of the choice that best completes the statement. (4 points each)*

_____ **11.** The Lydians replaced the barter system by
   **a.** using coins as a medium of exchange.
   **b.** using glass and jewelry as a medium of exchange.
   **c.** developing soapstone seals.
   **d.** developing a system of bills and contracts.

_____ **12.** All of the following are Phoenician deities EXCEPT
   **a.** Baal.      **b.** Astarte.      **c.** Yahweh.      **d.** Adonis.

_____ **13.** The capture of Nineveh marked
   **a.** the end of the Assyrian Empire.
   **b.** the beginning of the Diaspora.
   **c.** the end of the Chaldean Empire.
   **d.** the beginning of the Persian Empire.

_____ **14.** All of the following are true of the Persians EXCEPT
   **a.** they were more tolerant of conquered people than the Assyrians were.
   **b.** they possessed a strict moral code.
   **c.** they conquered the Greeks in 480 B.C.
   **d.** they constructed the 1,500-mile-long Royal Road.

_____ **15.** The first Israelites settled in
   **a.** Persia.
   **b.** Egypt.
   **c.** Babylon.
   **d.** Canaan.

_____ **16.** The economy of Phoenician civilization was based on
   **a.** Mediterranean shipping and trade.
   **b.** control of the overland trade between Egypt and Mesopotamia.
   **c.** control of the Persian road network.
   **d.** the agricultural development of western Syria.

# Chapter 3 : Form
# Test : **B**

_____ 17. The Hittites are best known for their
  a. use of the money system in trade.
  b. military technology and techniques.
  c. early alphabetic script.
  d. monotheistic religion.

_____ 18. The scattering of Jewish communities outside their homeland has come to be called
  a. the Diaspora.
  b. Deuteronomy.
  c. Nineveh.
  d. the confederation.

_____ 19. Christianity and Islam were greatly influenced by Judaism's
  a. polytheistic teachings.
  b. monotheistic teachings.
  c. Hammurabic code.
  d. reform of the Persian religion.

_____ 20. The Assyrians earned a reputation for
  a. seafaring talent.
  b. allowing conquered peoples to retain their customs.
  c. extreme cruelty.
  d. scientific achievement.

_____ 21. Portions of the Bible were written in
  a. Arabic.
  b. Lydian.
  c. Babylonian.
  d. Aramaic.

_____ 22. According to the teachings of Zoroaster,
  a. the world was ruled by one all-powerful deity.
  b. an afterlife did not exist.
  c. the world was ruled by many deities representing natural forces.
  d. humans had to choose between the forces of good and evil.

_____ 23. The Chaldean capital where Jews were taken into exile was
  a. Assyria.
  b. Jerusalem.
  c. Carthage.
  d. Babylon.

_____ 24. Around 2000 B.C., the Persians settled in the site of present-day
  a. Iran.
  b. Lebanon.
  c. Greece.
  d. Egypt.

_____ 25. The Greek alphabet was based on the easy-to-learn 22-character writing system of
  a. the Chinese.
  b. the Phoenicians.
  c. the Persians.
  d. Zoroaster.

## Essay
_Answer one of the following questions on a separate sheet of paper. (10 points)_

**26a. Critical Thinking** Identify two significant Israelite leaders. Relate the major events that occurred during the leadership of each.

**26b. Critical Thinking** Choose one early Middle Eastern civilization, and describe how geographic and environmental factors such as an abundance or lack of certain natural resources played a role in shaping its development.

Name ................................................ Date ................ Class ................

## Matching
*Match each item in Column A with an item in Column B by writing the correct letters in the blanks.*
*(3 points each)*

**Column A**

_____ **1.** legendary blind poet

_____ **2.** site of devastating defeat for the Persians

_____ **3.** kidnap victim

_____ **4.** very cruel law

_____ **5.** Athenian system for removing bad politicians from office

_____ **6.** paid for Spartan naval fleet

_____ **7.** famous temple of Athena

_____ **8.** cruel rule

_____ **9.** extended citizenship to the landless

_____ **10.** Greek formation of soldiers

**Column B**

**a.** phalanx

**b.** Persia

**c.** tyrannical

**d.** Helen of Troy

**e.** ostracism

**f.** Peisistratus

**g.** draconian

**h.** Homer

**i.** Parthenon

**j.** Marathon

## Multiple Choice
*In the blank, write the letter of the choice that best completes the statement. (4 points each)*

_____ **11.** Spartan society was notable for
**a.** a higher standard of living than most Greek city-states.
**b.** an emphasis on military and athletic ability.
**c.** great intellectual and artistic accomplishment.
**d.** the complete political control of its two kings.

_____ **12.** All of the following are characteristic of Greek religion EXCEPT
**a.** a belief in gods with human forms and humanlike behavior.
**b.** the use of oracles to predict the future.
**c.** a belief in the existence of powerful goddesses.
**d.** a belief in a female chief deity, the Earth Mother.

_____ **13.** The public square where meetings took place in Greek city-states was called the
**a.** agora.          **b.** acropolis.          **c.** Assembly.          **d.** phalanx.

_____ **14.** Athens was defeated during the Peloponnesian War by an alliance led by the
**a.** Macedonians.          **b.** Persians.          **c.** Spartans.          **d.** Delian League.

_____ **15.** Ancient Greece included a group of islands and
**a.** the northern part of the Balkan Peninsula.          **c.** the entire Balkan Peninsula.
**b.** the southern part of the Balkan Peninsula.          **d.** all of Asia Minor.

_____ **16.** Spartan men were allowed to retire from the army at age
**a.** 20.          **b.** 30.          **c.** 40.          **d.** 60.

# Chapter 4 : Form
# Test : Ⓐ

_____ **17.** In most Greek city-states before 500 B.C., citizenship and voting rights were usually extended to
  **a.** male landowners only.
  **b.** landowners over the age of 30 only.
  **c.** all native-born adult residents.
  **d.** all adult residents except slaves.

_____ **18.** Most Greek goods were transported
  **a.** overland by pack animal.
  **b.** overland by slave labor.
  **c.** overland by chariot.
  **d.** in cargo ships.

_____ **19.** The women allowed greatest participation in Athenian public life were members of
  **a.** the ostracon.  **b.** the Assembly.  **c.** the *metic* class.  **d.** the symposium.

_____ **20.** Minoan civilization flourished between
  **a.** 3900 B.C. and 2500 B.C.
  **b.** 2500 B.C. and 1450 B.C.
  **c.** 1000 B.C. and 700 B.C.
  **d.** 750 B.C. and 612 B.C.

_____ **21.** Hellenic traditions and stories were recorded in epic poems composed by
  **a.** oracles.  **b.** bards.  **c.** traders.  **d.** choruses.

_____ **22.** Solon promoted the growth of Athenian industry by
  **a.** urging farmers to produce more grain.
  **b.** extending citizenship to foreign-born artisans.
  **c.** ordering all slaves to learn a trade.
  **d.** abolishing the institution of slavery.

_____ **23.** The period from 461 B.C. to 429 B.C. is called the Golden Age of Athens because during this time
  **a.** democratic laws were introduced.
  **b.** the Persians were defeated at Salamis and Marathon.
  **c.** the *Iliad* and *Odyssey* were composed.
  **d.** the greatest achievements in the arts and sciences were produced.

_____ **24.** Despite Greece's mild climate, transport and communication were difficult because
  **a.** of numerous rocky harbors.
  **b.** no community was located more than 50 miles from the coast.
  **c.** of the rugged mountainous terrain.
  **d.** of the constant threat of armed nomadic groups.

_____ **25.** All of the following are true of the Mycenaeans EXCEPT that
  **a.** their kingdoms centered around hilltop fortresses.
  **b.** they intermarried with the local Hellenes.
  **c.** they adopted many aspects of Minoan culture.
  **d.** they conquered the Dorians around 1100 B.C.

## Essay

*Answer one of the following questions on a separate sheet of paper. (10 points)*

**26a. Critical Thinking** Identify the opposing forces in the Peloponnesian War, and describe two factors that led to the war.

**26b. Critical Thinking** Compare and contrast the Athenian and Spartan educational systems.

# Chapter 4 : *Form*
# Test : **B**

Score _____

## Matching

*Match each item in Column A with an item in Column B by writing the correct letters in the blanks.*
*(3 points each)*

**Column A**

_____ **1.** anti-Persian alliance

_____ **2.** where Olympic champions usually came from

_____ **3.** location of Athens

_____ **4.** Greek hiding place

_____ **5.** Greek city-states in Asia Minor

_____ **6.** head Greek god

_____ **7.** site of Minoan civilization

_____ **8.** hill in center of Greek city

_____ **9.** where Leonidas made his valiant stand

_____ **10.** tried and failed to defeat the Athenians

**Column B**

**a.** acropolis

**b.** Delian League

**c.** Crete

**d.** Ionia

**e.** Darius

**f.** Sparta

**g.** Zeus

**h.** Attica peninsula

**i.** Trojan horse

**j.** Thermopylae

## Multiple Choice

*In the blank, write the letter of the choice that best completes the statement. (4 points each)*

_____ **11.** Words such as *police* and *politics* derive from the Greek word *polis*, meaning
   **a.** soldier.   **b.** fortress.   **c.** democracy.   **d.** city-state.

_____ **12.** The Greeks adopted a money economy during the
   **a.** 1200s B.C.   **b.** 800s B.C.   **c.** 600s B.C.   **d.** 300s B.C.

_____ **13.** The Minoans did not need to build walls around their cities because
   **a.** their control of the sea discouraged invaders.
   **b.** they possessed the largest army in the Mediterranean.
   **c.** they had formed an alliance with the Mycenaeans.
   **d.** they had formed an alliance with the Spartans.

_____ **14.** Citizens of democratic Athens favored lotteries over elections because
   **a.** citizens were not expected to participate in government.
   **b.** few citizens were considered competent to run for office.
   **c.** they believed elections could be dominated by the wealthy or well spoken.
   **d.** many citizens were unwilling to run for elected office.

_____ **15.** A major factor in Greece's victories during the Persian Wars was
   **a.** the cooperation of the independent city-states.
   **b.** the antagonistic relationship between Ionia and Sparta.
   **c.** the antagonistic relationship between Athens and Sparta.
   **d.** its vastly greater number of warships.

_____ **16.** The ruler who introduced laws establishing Athenian democracy was named
   **a.** Solon.   **b.** Cleisthenes.   **c.** Pericles.   **d.** Leonidas.

# Chapter 4 : Form
# Test : **B**

_____ **17.** Most of the Greek mainland is made up of
    **a.** rugged mountains.
    **b.** a wide floodplain.
    **c.** low-lying hills.
    **d.** unusually fertile farmland.

_____ **18.** The _Iliad_ tells the story of
    **a.** the Peloponnesian War.
    **b.** a war between the Mycenaeans and the Trojans.
    **c.** the discovery of the ancient city of Troy.
    **d.** the return of a Mycenaean king to his homeland.

_____ **19.** Farmers on the Greek mainland could concentrate on growing export crops because
    **a.** grain was supplied by the Minoans.
    **b.** vineyards and olive groves required more laborers.
    **c.** grain was supplied by the colonies.
    **d.** the production of grain required very few laborers.

_____ **20.** All of the following are true of Spartan women EXCEPT that
    **a.** they married much later than most Greek women.
    **b.** they had greater personal and political rights than most Greek women.
    **c.** they trained in gymnastics, wrestling, and boxing.
    **d.** they had limited voting rights.

_____ **21.** Two Aegean civilizations that preceded the Greeks were the
    **a.** Minoans and the Macedonians.
    **b.** Macedonians and the Thebans.
    **c.** Athenians and the Spartans.
    **d.** Minoans and the Mycenaeans.

_____ **22.** All of the following are true of the Golden Age of Athens EXCEPT that
    **a.** men and women discussed public issues at forums called symposia.
    **b.** great public buildings including the Parthenon were built.
    **c.** slaves worked as teachers, servants, miners, and craftsmen.
    **d.** the city-state was led by a general named Pericles.

_____ **23.** From 500 B.C. to 336 B.C., many Greek city-states were ruled by a small group of wealthy people. Such political systems are referred to as
    **a.** democracies.    **b.** oligarchies.    **c.** tyrannies.    **d.** republics.

_____ **24.** The "dark age" refers to the period after the fall of
    **a.** the Dorians.    **b.** Troy.    **c.** the Mycenaeans.    **d.** Athens.

_____ **25.** Draco's code of law was considered an improvement because it
    **a.** applied only to aristocrats.
    **b.** eliminated the death penalty for minor offenses.
    **c.** signaled the end of tyranny.
    **d.** eliminated inconsistent laws and punishment.

## Essay
_Answer one of the following questions on a separate sheet of paper. (10 points)_

**26a. Critical Thinking** Describe the effects of the Peloponnesian War on the Greek city-states.

**26b. Critical Thinking** Provide an overview of Greek religious belief. Identify and describe two Greek gods or goddesses.

Name _____ Date _____ Class _____

## Matching

Match each item in Column A with an item in Column B by writing the correct letters in the blanks.
(3 points each)

**Column A**

_____ **1.** sculptors

_____ **2.** advocated rest, hygiene, and a good diet

_____ **3.** son of Olympias

_____ **4.** domain rulers

_____ **5.** temple to Athena

_____ **6.** battled Seleucids for Jerusalem

_____ **7.** comic playwright

_____ **8.** mathematician who explained triangles

_____ **9.** philosopher who was sentenced to death

_____ **10.** student of Plato, tutor of Alexander

**Column B**

**a.** Socrates

**b.** Parthenon

**c.** Judah Maccabee

**d.** Aristophanes

**e.** Pythagoras

**f.** Alexander the Great

**g.** Aristotle

**h.** Myron, Phidias, and Praxiteles

**i.** Ptolemy, Seleucus, and Antigonus

**j.** Hippocrates

## Multiple Choice

In the blank, write the letter of the choice that best completes the statement. (4 points each)

_____ **11.** The first Greek scientist, Thales, formulated a theory that
   **a.** disease had natural causes.
   **b.** disease had supernatural causes.
   **c.** the world revolved around a fixed point.
   **d.** water was the basic substance of all things.

_____ **12.** The earliest Greek plays tended to be
   **a.** comedies.   **b.** trilogies.   **c.** tragedies.   **d.** Euripides.

_____ **13.** Alexander the Great accomplished all of the following EXCEPT
   **a.** freeing the Ionian city-states and capturing Persepolis.
   **b.** encouraging his soldiers to intermarry with the Persians.
   **c.** convincing his Macedonian troops to continue beyond the Indus River valley.
   **d.** establishing 70 cities and making his capital in Babylon.

_____ **14.** The first historian to try to separate fact from legend was
   **a.** Aristotle.   **b.** Herodotus.   **c.** Homer.   **d.** Thucydides.

_____ **15.** Greece's Golden Age occurred during
   **a.** the mid-700s B.C.
   **b.** the mid-600s B.C.
   **c.** the mid-500s B.C.
   **d.** the mid-400s B.C.

_____ **16.** The Hellenistic age was characterized by all of the following EXCEPT
   **a.** soldiers and bureaucrats roaming freely in search of job opportunities.
   **b.** Hellenistic women gaining greater freedom.
   **c.** philosophical inquiry focused on questions of personal behavior.
   **d.** deterioration of trade links between the cities built by Alexander.

# Chapter 5 : Form
# Test : Ⓐ

_____ 17. The architecture of the Parthenon is notable for its
   a. unusual asymmetrical design.
   b. graceful proportions and use of perspective.
   c. 46 black marble columns.
   d. 100 black marble columns.

_____ 18. The subject of the *Historia* was
   a. the Persian Wars.
   b. the Peloponnesian War.
   c. a comparison of systems of government.
   d. the conquests of Alexander the Great.

_____ 19. The Hellenistic philosophy advocating the avoidance of both joy and pain is called
   a. Cynicism.
   b. Epicureanism.
   c. Stoicism.
   d. the Hippocratic Oath.

_____ 20. All of the following are types of Greek pottery EXCEPT a(n)
   a. amphora.     b. *kylix*.     c. *krater*.     d. phalanx.

_____ 21. Sophist teaching can best be characterized by the phrase
   a. "there is one absolute law."
   b. "moral codes are developed by the gods."
   c. "truth is different for each individual."
   d. "freedom results in social disorder."

_____ 22. The mixture of Greek and Middle Eastern culture that formed during and after Alexander is called
   a. Septuagint.     b. Hellenistic.     c. Ptolemaic.     d. Stoic.

_____ 23. The Macedonian king who had conquered most of Greece by 338 B.C. was
   a. Alexander the Great.
   b. Demosthenes.
   c. Darius III.
   d. Philip II.

_____ 24. Plato preferred the Spartan government to the Athenian because
   a. he believed the state as a whole was more important than the individual.
   b. he resented Athenian philosophers such as Socrates.
   c. he had great trust in the opinions of the majority.
   d. Sparta emphasized military prowess rather than intellectual ability.

_____ 25. All of the following are true of the ancient Olympics EXCEPT
   a. women were not permitted to watch.
   b. non-Athenians were not allowed to compete.
   c. they were held in honor of Zeus.
   d. they did not include team events.

## Essay
*Answer one of the following questions on a separate sheet of paper. (10 points)*

**26a. Critical Thinking** Discuss two playwrights of ancient Greece. What were their major concerns and themes?

**26b. Critical Thinking** Describe the Greeks who revolutionized the field of writing history. What were their historical techniques?

# Chapter 5 : Form
# Test : B

Score _____

## Matching

*Match each item in Column A with an item in Column B by writing the correct letters in the blanks.*
*(3 points each)*

**Column A**

_____ **1.** traveling professional teacher of relative truth

_____ **2.** author of *The Republic*

_____ **3.** capital of Alexander's empire

_____ **4.** appealed in vain for Greek cooperation

_____ **5.** narrow-necked pot

_____ **6.** run, jump, throw, wrestle, hurl

_____ **7.** designed Parthenon's sculptures

_____ **8.** wide-mouth jar

_____ **9.** critic of materialism

_____ **10.** developed the syllogism

**Column B**

**a.** Demosthenes

**b.** *leythos*

**c.** Diogenes

**d.** *krater*

**e.** Phidias

**f.** Plato

**g.** pentathlon

**h.** Babylon

**i.** Aristotle

**j.** Sophist

## Multiple Choice

*In the blank, write the letter of the choice that best completes the statement. (4 points each)*

_____ **11.** A teacher using the Socratic method would
  **a.** help students polish their rhetorical skills.
  **b.** encourage students to memorize information.
  **c.** force students to defend their statements.
  **d.** demand payment from all students.

_____ **12.** Ptolemy and his descendants ruled
  **a.** Macedonia and Greece.
  **b.** Egypt, Libya, and part of Syria.
  **c.** Mesopotamia and Iran.
  **d.** Mesopotamia and Afghanistan.

_____ **13.** All of the following were Greek tragedians EXCEPT
  **a.** Sophocles.
  **b.** Euripides.
  **c.** Aristophanes.
  **d.** Aeschylus.

_____ **14.** The Alexandrian author of *The Elements of Geometry* was
  **a.** Euclid.
  **b.** Archimedes.
  **c.** Eratosthenes.
  **d.** Aristarchus.

_____ **15.** All of the following factors contributed to Macedonia's conquest of Greece EXCEPT
  **a.** Philip II's use of Greek-style military techniques.
  **b.** lack of cooperation among the Greek city-states.
  **c.** Greece's weakened state after the Peloponnesian War.
  **d.** the Macedonians' alliance with the Persians.

_____ **16.** The construction of the Parthenon began in
  **a.** 700 B.C.
  **b.** 609 B.C.
  **c.** 536 B.C.
  **d.** 447 B.C.

Name ............................................... Date ................................ Class ..............................

# Chapter 5 : *Form*
# Test : Ⓑ

_____ **17.** The translation of the Hebrew Bible into Greek was done by Jewish scholars in
   **a.** Alexandria.     **b.** Jerusalem.     **c.** Athens.     **d.** Babylon.

_____ **18.** The code of conduct still practiced by modern doctors was developed by
   **a.** Thales.     **b.** Zeno.     **c.** Herodotus.     **d.** Hippocrates.

_____ **19.** Unlike much other Greek pottery, a *kylix* was often decorated with
   **a.** mythological figures.            **c.** scenes of everyday life.
   **b.** scenes from history.            **d.** plain geometrical designs.

_____ **20.** All of the following is true of Aristotle EXCEPT that
   **a.** he wrote about political science.      **c.** he wrote the *Historia.*
   **b.** he believed that the earth was the center      **d.** he believed that an ideal government
   of the solar system.            would include monarchy, aristocracy,
                  and democracy.

_____ **21.** The *Oresteia* illustrated how
   **a.** the consequences of one's deeds could      **c.** gods and goddesses rarely influenced the
   affect future generations.            lives of humans.
   **b.** the gods were often merciless toward      **d.** war brought misery to both the victor
   humans.            and the vanquished.

_____ **22.** The sculptures of Praxiteles reflected
   **a.** a belief in unlimited Greek power.      **c.** the ideals of the Golden Age of Athens.
   **b.** Greece's diminished confidence after the      **d.** an ideal called the "golden mean."
   Peloponnesian War.

_____ **23.** Thucydides' historical technique was revolutionary because he
   **a.** checked the reliability of his sources.      **c.** tried to separate fact from legend.
   **b.** traveled to the sites about which he      **d.** rejected the idea of gods having a role in
   wrote.            history.

_____ **24.** After defeating the Persians at the Granicus River and at Issus, Alexander and his troops
   **a.** headed south toward Egypt.      **c.** returned to Athens.
   **b.** headed east toward the Persian capital.      **d.** returned to Macedonia.

_____ **25.** At his trial, Socrates argued that
   **a.** the search for truth was most important.      **c.** he should not receive the death penalty.
   **b.** he would never obey the laws of the state.      **d.** the state should never try to determine
                  truth.

## Essay
*Answer one of the following questions on a separate sheet of paper. (10 points)*

**26a. Critical Thinking** Describe the factors that led to the mixing of Greek and Middle Eastern cultures into a culture referred to as Hellenistic.

**26b. Critical Thinking** How similar were the political philosophies of Aristotle and Plato? In which social class did each prefer to place government control?

Name ................................................ Date .................... Class ...................

## Matching

*Match each item in Column A with an item in Column B by writing the correct letters in the blanks.*
*(3 points each)*

**Column A**

_____ **1.** overthrew the Etruscans

_____ **2.** originally Byzantium

_____ **3.** assassinated Caesar

_____ **4.** led by Attila

_____ **5.** one of the Good Emperors

_____ **6.** one of Rome's legendary twins

_____ **7.** elephant man

_____ **8.** Aphrodite to the Greeks

_____ **9.** what a Roman bishop was called

_____ **10.** book of Jewish law

**Column B**

**a.** Venus

**b.** Brutus and Cassius

**c.** Huns

**d.** Talmud

**e.** Latins

**f.** Marcus Aurelius

**g.** *papa*

**h.** Remus

**i.** Constantinople

**j.** Hannibal

## Multiple Choice

*In the blank, write the letter of the choice that best completes the statement. (4 points each)*

_____ **11.** The representatives of the plebeians were called
    **a.** consuls.     **b.** senators.     **c.** tribunes.     **d.** praetors.

_____ **12.** Christians stirred Roman opposition in all of the following ways EXCEPT by
    **a.** refusing to honor the emperor as a god.     **c.** rejecting Roman belief in a messiah.
    **b.** refusing to serve in the military.     **d.** regarding their religion as the only
        true faith.

_____ **13.** Roman generals improved on Greek military tactics by employing
    **a.** the phalanx system.     **c.** smaller, more mobile divisions of troops.
    **b.** larger, more powerful divisions of troops.     **d.** a tolerant attitude toward deserters,
        which boosted morale.

_____ **14.** The Italian Peninsula is located
    **a.** on the Mediterranean's southern coast.     **c.** just east of the Balkan Peninsula.
    **b.** almost at the east-west midpoint of the     **d.** just east of the Fertile Crescent.
        Mediterranean.

_____ **15.** The Christian Church in Rome was probably founded by
    **a.** Paul.     **b.** Peter.     **c.** Jesus.     **d.** Pontius Pilate.

_____ **16.** After the death of Theodosius, the eastern part of the Roman Empire became known as the
    **a.** Ottoman Empire.     **c.** Visigoth Empire.
    **b.** Byzantine Empire.     **d.** Christian Empire.

# Chapter 6 : Form
# Test : Ⓐ

_____ **17.** The reign of Augustus Caesar was marked by all of the following EXCEPT
  **a.** the construction of magnificent public buildings.
  **b.** the beginning of the *Pax Romana*.
  **c.** the importation of North African grain to Rome.
  **d.** the renewed war with Carthage.

_____ **18.** Diocletian issued the Edict of Prices in an attempt to
  **a.** raise wages among the Roman poor.
  **b.** encourage farmers to leave provincial farms.
  **c.** control severe inflation.
  **d.** please the merchant class.

_____ **19.** Early Rome was divided into two main social classes,
  **a.** the plebeians and the patricians.
  **b.** the Etruscans and the Etrurians.
  **c.** the Latins and the patricians.
  **d.** the slaves and the free citizens.

_____ **20.** In A.D. 455, Rome was completely ransacked by the
  **a.** Vandals.   **b.** Visigoths.   **c.** Huns.   **d.** Byzantines.

_____ **21.** The author of *Confessions*, who described his conversion to Christianity, was
  **a.** Augustine.
  **b.** Constantine.
  **c.** Paul.
  **d.** Antioch.

_____ **22.** Tiberius Gracchus was killed after proposing a law to
  **a.** reduce provincial taxes.
  **b.** limit the size of the latifundia.
  **c.** give more power to the poor.
  **d.** sell grain at low prices.

_____ **23.** By the A.D. 200s, the *jus gentium* became unnecessary because
  **a.** most free males in the provinces had been made citizens of Rome.
  **b.** Marcus Aurelius had rescinded the *jus civile*.
  **c.** Hadrian had strengthened Rome's fortifications.
  **d.** provincial residents demanded their own sets of laws.

_____ **24.** During the *Pax Romana*, Romans did all of the following EXCEPT
  **a.** build the Colosseum and Circus Maximus.
  **b.** trade with places as distant as China and Britain.
  **c.** build a series of stone water channels called aqueducts.
  **d.** adopt a new calendar based on the Egyptian year of 365 ¼ days.

_____ **25.** In 49 B.C., Julius Caesar began a civil war by
  **a.** crossing the Alps with troops and elephants.
  **b.** adopting the Julian calendar.
  **c.** leading his troops across the Rubicon River.
  **d.** driving Pompey out of Italy.

## Essay
*Answer one of the following questions on a separate sheet of paper. (10 points)*

**26a. Critical Thinking** How do the geographic features of the Italian Peninsula explain why the people of Italy did not become a seafaring people?

**26b. Critical Thinking** Summarize the events of the three Punic Wars.

Name _____ Date _____ Class _____

# Chapter 6 : *Form*
# Test : **B**

Score _____

## Matching
*Match each item in Column A with an item in Column B by writing the correct letters in the blanks.*
*(3 points each)*

**Column A**

_____ **1.** Roman soldiers

_____ **2.** emperors who ruled from A.D. 14 to A.D. 68

_____ **3.** tended to live by Stoic principles

_____ **4.** island southwest of the Italian peninsula

_____ **5.** defeated Hannibal near Carthage

_____ **6.** Rome's upper class

_____ **7.** Caesar crossed this

_____ **8.** Rome's German ruler

_____ **9.** refused to fight in the army

_____ **10.** North African-born Christian scholar

**Column B**

**a.** patricians

**b.** Scipio

**c.** legionaries

**d.** Augustine

**e.** Sicily

**f.** Good Emperors

**g.** plebeians

**h.** Rubicon

**i.** Odoacer

**j.** Julio-Claudians

## Multiple Choice
*In the blank, write the letter of the choice that best completes the statement or answers the question.*
*(4 points each)*

_____ **11.** The First Punic War began when Rome resisted
   **a.** Hannibal's attack on a Spanish ally.
   **b.** Carthage's attempt to seize the Strait of Messina.
   **c.** Hannibal's attempt to cross the Alps.
   **d.** the revolt of the latifundia owners.

_____ **12.** Christianity was adopted as the official religion of the Roman Empire by
   **a.** Theodosius.
   **b.** Constantine.
   **c.** Claudius.
   **d.** Augustine.

_____ **13.** After a rebellion in A.D. 132 , the Romans forbade
   **a.** the practice of any monotheistic religion.
   **b.** Christians to live in Rome.
   **c.** Jews to live in Jerusalem.
   **d.** the worship of the emperor.

_____ **14.** Which of the following cultures had begun to form on the Italian Peninsula as early as 5000 B.C.?
   **a.** Etruscan
   **b.** Indo-European
   **c.** Neolithic
   **d.** Roman

_____ **15.** In 60 B.C., Caesar, Pompey, and Crassus formed a governing group called
   **a.** a triumvirate.
   **b.** the Republic.
   **c.** the Dictatorship.
   **d.** a legion.

_____ **16.** In 451 B.C., the patricians finally
   **a.** put Roman law into writing.
   **b.** eliminated the Assembly of Tribes.
   **c.** eliminated the Assembly of Centuries.
   **d.** allowed intermarriage between plebeians and Etruscans.

# Chapter 6 : *Form*
# Test : **B**

_____ **17.** The first emperor of Rome took the title
   **a.** Julius Caesar.
   **b.** Proconsul.
   **c.** Claudius.
   **d.** Augustus.

_____ **18.** All of the following occurred in Rome during the period between A.D. 192 and A.D. 284 EXCEPT
   **a.** a succession of 28 emperors.
   **b.** the minting of more coins to try to pay soldiers.
   **c.** repeated attacks by Germanic tribes.
   **d.** a cut in land taxes to stimulate agricultural production.

_____ **19.** The growing success of provincial and mainland latifundia resulted in
   **a.** the destruction of Carthage.
   **b.** the migration of landless farmers into Rome.
   **c.** opposition to plebeian rule.
   **d.** a reduction in the power of the army.

_____ **20.** *Christos* was the Greek word for
   **a.** messiah.
   **b.** rebel.
   **c.** religion.
   **d.** Jews.

_____ **21.** The religious beliefs of republic-era Romans were greatly influenced by the beliefs of
   **a.** Persians.
   **b.** Jews.
   **c.** Christians.
   **d.** Greeks.

_____ **22.** The Visigoth chief who captured Rome in A.D. 410 was
   **a.** Attila.
   **b.** Odoacer.
   **c.** Constantine.
   **d.** Alaric.

_____ **23.** More than 150,000 spectators could watch charioteers race in
   **a.** the Colosseum.
   **b.** the Circus Maximus.
   **c.** the Forum.
   **d.** the Pantheon.

_____ **24.** The writings of Paul and other early Christians are collected in
   **a.** the Talmud.
   **b.** the Torah.
   **c.** the New Testament.
   **d.** *Meditations*.

_____ **25.** All of the following are true of Latin EXCEPT that it
   **a.** was the official language of Rome.
   **b.** was the *lingua franca* of Europe until the A.D. 1500s.
   **c.** had a larger vocabulary than Greek.
   **d.** forms the basis of the Italian, French, and Romanian languages.

## Essay
*Answer one of the following questions on a separate sheet of paper. (10 points)*

**26a. Critical Thinking** Describe the factors involved in the fall of the Roman Empire.

**26b. Critical Thinking** Describe the structure and institutions of the Roman government during the period of the Republic. Which social classes did these institutions represent?

# Chapter 7 : Form
# Test : Ⓐ

**Score** _____

## Matching

*Match each item in Column A with an item in Column B by writing the correct letters in the blanks.*
*(3 points each)*

**Column A**

____ **1.** capital of Kush

____ **2.** Bantu-based, Arabic-influenced language

____ **3.** port that controlled gold trade with the interior

____ **4.** highest mountain in Africa

____ **5.** early Malian king

____ **6.** island off East African coast

____ **7.** made Christianity the religion of Axum

____ **8.** defeated the Songhai

____ **9.** world's largest desert

____ **10.** a monotheistic faith

**Column B**

**a.** Kilwa

**b** Morocco

**c.** Napata

**d.** Sahara

**e.** Islam

**f.** Ezana

**g.** Sundiata Keita

**h.** Zanzibar

**i.** Swahili

**j.** Kilimanjaro

## Multiple Choice

*In the blank, write the letter of the choice that best completes the statement. (4 points each)*

____ **11.** Axum's growth as a trading power was facilitated by its
    **a.** location on the Red Sea.
    **b.** location on the Indian Ocean.
    **c.** alliance with Kush.
    **d.** alliance with Nubia.

____ **12.** European exploration of the East African coast was motivated by desire to control the
    **a.** silk trade.
    **b.** sources of gold, ivory, and copper.
    **c.** salt caravans.
    **d.** Malian kingdom.

____ **13.** The great central plateau just south of the Sahara is known as
    **a.** the Sahel.
    **b.** the Great Rift Valley.
    **c.** Nubia.
    **d.** Axum.

____ **14.** The Islamic religion spread through North Africa
    **a.** beginning around A.D. 100.
    **b.** during the A.D. 300s and 400s.
    **c.** during the A.D. 600s and 700s.
    **d.** beginning around A.D. 1500.

____ **15.** The Songhai Empire reached its height under the rule of
    **a.** Mansa Musa.
    **b.** Sunni Ali.
    **c.** Askia Muhammad.
    **d.** Malindi.

____ **16.** Three hundred stone fortresses, including the Great Zimbabwe, were built by the
    **a.** Mombasans.
    **b.** Karanga.
    **c.** Songhai.
    **d.** Persians.

# Chapter 7 Form
# Test A

_____ **17.** The kingdom established around 3000 B.C. in the southern Nile River valley was called
   **a.** Nubia.          **b.** Kush.          **c.** Axum.          **d.** Ghana.

_____ **18.** The capital of the Malian kingdom was
   **a.** Benin.          **b.** Nok.          **c.** Adulis.          **d.** Timbuktu.

_____ **19.** The strongest of the two empires that divided Karanga territories was called the
   **a.** Monomotapa.                    **c.** Bantu.
   **b.** Swahili.                       **d.** Changamire.

_____ **20.** Matrilineal societies refer to groups of people who
   **a.** use metal tools to increase agricultural       **c.** trace their descent through their
       production.                                          mothers rather than their fathers.
   **b.** formed villages after migrating from          **d.** share the same beliefs, traditions, and
       West Africa.                                         marriage and family customs.

_____ **21.** By the A.D. 1300s, the city-states of coastal East Africa were populated
   **a.** only by Bantu speakers.        **c.** mainly by Arab merchants.
   **b.** only by Muslims.               **d.** by a multicultural mixture of Africans,
                                             Persians, and Arabs.

_____ **22.** During the A.D. 1000s, the Ghanaian kingdom
   **a.** achieved domination of the salt and    **c.** splintered into small
       gold trades.                                  independent states.
   **b.** defeated the Almoravid invaders.       **d.** officially adopted a polytheistic religion.

_____ **23.** The African continent is approximately
   **a.** half the size of the United States.    **c.** twice as large as the United States.
   **b.** the same size as the United States.    **d.** three times larger than the United States.

_____ **24.** All of the following are East African ports EXCEPT
   **a.** Mombasa.                       **c.** Malindi.
   **b.** Djenne.                        **d.** Kilwa.

_____ **25.** The laws introduced by Askia Muhammad were based on
   **a.** a respect for ancestor worship.        **c.** the teachings of Sundiata Keita.
   **b.** the teachings of the Quran.            **d.** the social code of the Berbers.

## Essay
_Answer one of the following questions on a separate sheet of paper. (10 points)_

**26a. Critical Thinking** Discuss the role of trade in shaping the culture of the East African city-states.

**26b. Critical Thinking** Describe the location and importance of Timbuktu. Identify the regional powers that controlled the city.

# Chapter 7 : Form
# Test : B

Score _____

## Matching

*Match each item in Column A with an item in Column B by writing the correct letters in the blanks.*
*(3 points each)*

**Column A**

_____ **1.** succeeded the Malians

_____ **2.** northern Karanga became this empire

_____ **3.** 40 miles wide and 3,000 miles long

_____ **4.** name for ruler and a region

_____ **5.** center of Islamic learning

_____ **6.** location of the Nubian kingdom

_____ **7.** holy book of Islam

_____ **8.** means "stone house"

_____ **9.** ancient Egypt may have learned much from this culture

_____ **10.** location of Sofala

**Column B**

**a.** Timbuktu

**b.** Quran

**c.** Songhai

**d.** Great Zimbabwe

**e.** present-day Mozambique

**f.** present-day Sudan

**g.** Monomotapa

**h.** Great Rift Valley

**i.** Ghana

**j.** Nubia

## Multiple Choice

*In the blank, write the letter of the choice that best completes the statement. (4 points each)*

_____ **11.** All of the following are true of Mansa Musa EXCEPT
   **a.** he introduced Islamic culture to Mali.
   **b.** his lavish gift giving on the way to Makkah caused a drop in the world price of gold.
   **c.** he defeated his rival Sundiata Keita for control of the Malian kingdom.
   **d.** he encouraged the growth of Timbuktu as a center of arts and learning.

_____ **12.** The Bantu migrations involved the mass movements of people from
   **a.** Southern Africa to Central Africa.
   **b.** Africa, south of the Sahara to West Africa.
   **c.** Africa, south of the Sahara to Egypt.
   **d.** West Africa to other parts of the continent.

_____ **13.** The treeless grasslands that constitute about 40 percent of Africa are called
   **a.** plateaus.     **b.** savannas.     **c.** sahels.     **d.** highlands.

_____ **14.** Trade between coastal East Africa and South Asia began as early as
   **a.** 500 B.C.     **b.** A.D. 1200     **c.** A.D. 1500     **d.** 2500 B.C.

_____ **15.** The Swahili people served as intermediaries between
   **a.** people of the Sahel and Moroccan traders.
   **b.** people of the East African interior and Asian traders.
   **c.** the Egyptians and people of the lower Sudan.
   **d.** the Songhai and the Malian Kingdom.

# Chapter 7 Form
# Test B

_____ **16.** Under Sundiata Keita, Mali grew to include
    **a.** the territory of the old Ghanaian kingdom. **c.** much of North Africa.
    **b.** all of Africa south of the Sahara.     **d.** the lower Nile River valley.

_____ **17.** Many Africans believed in a single supreme god
    **a.** who had little influence on the life of   **c.** who created all social laws and
    most villagers.     traditions.
    **b.** who struggled to control many lesser   **d.** whose only responsibility was determin-
    deities.     ing the success of the harvest.

_____ **18.** Caravans originating in Ghana often carried produce and gold to
    **a.** North Africa.     **b.** Zimbabwe.     **c.** Axum.     **d.** East Africa.

_____ **19.** The kingdom of Karanga was centered
    **a.** just south of the Niger River.     **c.** on Zanzibar.
    **b.** just north of the Niger River.     **d.** between the Zambezi and Limpopo
        Rivers.

_____ **20.** The area of Africa near the Equator is the location of
    **a.** an arid central plateau.     **c.** the Sahara.
    **b.** lush tropical rain forests.     **d.** the Niger River.

_____ **21.** The Malian kingdom had dissolved under external and internal pressures by the
    **a.** A.D. 500s.     **b.** A.D. 1000s.     **c.** A.D. 1300s.     **d.** A.D. 1500s.

_____ **22.** East African trade with Asia declined rapidly after
    **a.** the conversion of many Africans to Islam.  **c.** the Bantu migrations began.
    **b.** the beginning of the caravan trade     **d.** a Chinese policy prohibited ocean
    between Ghana and North Africa.     sailing.

_____ **23.** In 724 B.C., King Piankhi led Kush to victory over neighboring
    **a.** Axum.     **b.** Timbuktu.     **c.** Egypt.     **d.** Nubia.

_____ **24.** The Bantu kingdoms of Central and Southern Africa produced
    **a.** silk and porcelain.     **c.** carpets and sorghum.
    **b.** salt.     **d.** copper and gold.

_____ **25.** Ghana became a trade-based empire largely because of
    **a.** its proximity to the Red Sea.     **c.** its proximity to Morocco.
    **b.** its location between Saharan salt mines  **d.** the conversion of its rulers to Islam.
    and tropical gold mines.

## Essay
_Answer one of the following questions on a separate sheet of paper. (10 points)_

**26a. Critical Thinking** Describe the regions and commodities involved in the trans-Saharan
caravan trade.

**26b. Critical Thinking** Provide an overview of the geography of the African continent.

# Chapter 8 : Form
# Test : A

Score _____

## Matching
*Match each item in Column A with an item in Column B by writing the correct letters in the blanks.*
*(3 points each)*

**Column A**

_____ **1.** play about a king and a forest maiden

_____ **2.** the practice of nonviolence

_____ **3.** the Enlightened One

_____ **4.** leader of each Aryan tribe

_____ **5.** dominant Buddhists in China, Japan, Korea

_____ **6.** leader whose death signaled end of Golden Age

_____ **7.** laws of Asoka

_____ **8.** empire that dissolved by A.D. 600

_____ **9.** oldest Aryan religious text

_____ **10.** occupational group

**Column B**

**a.** Chandragupta II

**b** rajah

**c.** *Rig-Veda*

**d.** Rock Edicts

**e.** *jati*

**f.** ahimsa

**g.** Mahayana

**h.** the Buddha

**i.** *Shakuntala*

**j.** Gupta

## Multiple Choice
*In the blank, write the letter of the choice that best completes the statement. (4 points each)*

_____ **11.** The concepts of zero and infinity were developed during the reign of the
    **a.** Mauryans.
    **b.** Aryans.
    **c.** Guptas.
    **d.** Sudras.

_____ **12.** Initially, the highest *varna* of ancient India's social system was made up of
    **a.** artisans.
    **b.** warriors.
    **c.** priests.
    **d.** cattle herders.

_____ **13.** The Buddhist religion originated during the
    **a.** 800s B.C.
    **b.** 500s B.C.
    **c.** 400s B.C.
    **d.** 100s B.C.

_____ **14.** After crossing the mountains, Aryan invaders moved
    **a.** through the Indus River valley into the Ganges Plain.
    **b.** north to the Caspian Sea.
    **c.** across the Ganges Plain into the Hindu Kush.
    **d.** north to the Black Sea.

_____ **15.** Most people in India today are
    **a.** Hindus.
    **b.** Buddhists.
    **c.** Christians.
    **d.** Muslims.

_____ **16.** The Buddha rejected all of the following EXCEPT
    **a.** belief in Hindu deities.
    **b.** the idea that a person's place in life was determined by his or her birth.
    **c.** the *varna* system.
    **d.** belief in reincarnation.

# Chapter 8 | Form
# Test | Ⓐ

_____ **17.** In Hindu belief, the form a person will take in the next life is determined by
  **a.** dharma.
  **b.** *moksha.*
  **c.** karma.
  **d.** ahimsa.

_____ **18.** Most of India was first brought under unified rule by the
  **a.** Gupta Empire.
  **b.** Aryan Empire.
  **c.** Mauryan Empire.
  **d.** Sanskrit Empire.

_____ **19.** The collection of moral tales written during the Gupta period is called the
  **a.** *Shakuntala.*
  **b.** *Panchatantra.*
  **c.** "Books of Knowledge."
  **d.** *Bhagavad Gita.*

_____ **20.** Most of our knowledge about Aryan life is derived from the study of
  **a.** their holy books.
  **b.** Indus River valley ruins.
  **c.** excavated artifacts.
  **d.** the ancient cities of the Ganges Plain.

_____ **21.** The Gupta rulers encouraged learning based on
  **a.** Buddhist principles.
  **b.** Aryan principles.
  **c.** Arabic principles.
  **d.** Hindu principles.

_____ **22.** For followers of the Eightfold Path, the main goal is to
  **a.** eliminate desire.
  **b.** obey one's duties.
  **c.** be reborn in a higher form.
  **d.** practice nonviolence.

_____ **23.** The founder of Buddhism was named
  **a.** Rama.
  **b.** Ramayana.
  **c.** Siddhartha Gautama.
  **d.** Chandragupta Maurya.

_____ **24.** Asoka adopted Buddhism after
  **a.** the collapse of the Hindu caste system.
  **b.** witnessing the aftermath of a brutal battle.
  **c.** seven years of wandering.
  **d.** witnessing scenes of shocking poverty outside his palace.

_____ **25.** The two great epics of ancient Indian literature are
  **a.** the *Ramayana* and the *Mahabharata.*
  **b.** the *Bhagavad Gita* and the *Upanishads.*
  **c.** the *Bhagavad Gita* and the *Rig-Veda.*
  **d.** the *Panchatantra* and the *Shakuntala.*

## Essay
*Answer one of the following questions on a separate sheet of paper. (10 points)*

**26a. Critical Thinking** Identify and describe two major principles of Hinduism.

**26b. Critical Thinking** Describe the importance of cattle to the Aryans.

# Chapter 8 : *Form*
# Test : **B**

Score _____

## Matching
*Match each item in Column A with an item in Column B by writing the correct letters in the blanks.*
*(3 points each)*

**Column A**

_____ **1.** ruler of Magadha in Darius's time

_____ **2.** commoners

_____ **3.** Buddhists follow these practices

_____ **4.** the warriors

_____ **5.** the social classes

_____ **6.** "Books of Knowledge"

_____ **7.** both infinity and zero were invented in this era

_____ **8.** Buddhist mound

_____ **9.** outcasts or "untouchables"

_____ **10.** release from the cycle of rebirth

**Column B**

**a.** Vedas

**b.** *moksha*

**c.** pariahs

**d.** Kshatriyas

**e.** Eightfold Path

**f.** Gupta

**g.** Vaisyas

**h.** stupa

**i.** Bimbisara

**j.** *varnas*

## Multiple Choice
*In the blank, write the letter of the choice that best completes the statement. (4 points each)*

_____ **11.** The period known as the Vedic Age is from
  **a.** 1500 B.C. to 1000 B.C.
  **b.** 1200 B.C. to 500 B.C.
  **c.** 542 B.C. to 495 B.C.
  **d.** 321 B.C. to 184 B.C.

_____ **12.** The transformation of Magadha from a small state into the center of an empire was begun by
  **a.** Alexander the Great.
  **b.** Asoka.
  **c.** Chandragupta II.
  **d.** Chandragupta Maurya.

_____ **13.** The main ideas of Buddhism are found in the
  **a.** Four Noble Truths.
  **b.** Vedas.
  **c.** *Ramayana.*
  **d.** *varnas.*

_____ **14.** Members of India's priestly class were called
  **a.** Sudras.
  **b.** *Upanishads.*
  **c.** Brahmans.
  **d.** *jati.*

_____ **15.** The reign of Asoka was characterized by all of the following EXCEPT the
  **a.** prohibition of Hindu practices.
  **b.** promotion of Buddhism through the use of missionaries.
  **c.** continuation of the caste system.
  **d.** building of roads, hospitals, and rest houses.

_____ **16.** The concept of dharma refers to the
  **a.** rebirth of the soul.
  **b.** practice of meditation.
  **c.** preservation of family honor.
  **d.** carrying out of one's personal duty.

# Chapter 8 : Form
# Test : B

_____ **17.** The Aryans are best described as
  **a.** hunter-gatherers.
  **b.** warrior-herders.
  **c.** merchant traders.
  **d.** farmers-agriculturalists.

_____ **18.** The oldest major religion to originate in India is
  **a.** Hinduism.    **b.** Buddhism.    **c.** Islam.    **d.** _Rig-Veda._

_____ **19.** One cause of the Mauryan Empire's collapse was
  **a.** the death of Chandragupta II.
  **b.** Hindu resentment of pro-Buddhist policies.
  **c.** invasions along the northwestern border.
  **d.** popular unrest generated by heavy taxation.

_____ **20.** According to tradition, Gautama began his search for truth after
  **a.** experiencing a flash of insight while meditating under a tree.
  **b.** witnessing scenes of human misery for the first time.
  **c.** suffering greatly during an impoverished childhood.
  **d.** becoming a charioteer for a Kshatriya prince.

_____ **21.** All of the following are true of the Rock Edicts EXCEPT that they
  **a.** were issued by Asoka.
  **b.** were written in the Sanskrit language.
  **c.** were carved on rocks and stone pillars.
  **d.** stressed having concern for other human beings.

_____ **22.** The Golden Age of India refers to the
  **a.** period of peace following Asoka's renunciation of war.
  **b.** development of written language by the Aryans.
  **c.** flourishing of arts and sciences during the Gupta dynasty.
  **d.** period in which the independent kingdoms of India were first united.

_____ **23.** After the fall of the Mauryan Empire, India remained fragmented until an empire was formed by
  **a.** Alexander.
  **b.** Asoka.
  **c.** Chandragupta I.
  **d.** Chandragupta II.

_____ **24.** Buddhism's founder was born around
  **a.** 566 B.C.    **b.** 184 B.C.    **c.** A.D. 26.    **d.** A.D. 100.

_____ **25.** The language of the Aryans was called
  **a.** Veda.    **b.** Gupta.    **c.** Sanskrit.    **d.** Indo-European.

## Essay
_Answer one of the following questions on a separate sheet of paper. (10 points)_

**26a. Critical Thinking** Describe the content and importance of two ancient Indian texts.

**26b. Critical Thinking** Describe the caste system in India as it existed in 500 B.C. How had it evolved since its introduction to the region?

Name ................................................................. Date ..................... Class .......................

**Score** _____

## Matching
*Match each item in Column A with an item in Column B by writing the correct letters in the blanks.*
*(3 points each)*

**Column A**

_____ 1. First Emperor

_____ 2. 400-year period of stability

_____ 3. founder of Daoism

_____ 4. ruled for more than 800 years

_____ 5. one of the Thirteen Classics

_____ 6. inventor of first seismograph

_____ 7. represented society in miniature to Kongfuzi

_____ 8. the majority of Chinese

_____ 9. author of China's first true history

_____ 10. Chinese civil servants

**Column B**

**a.** the Zhou

**b.** *Pax Sinica*

**c.** mandarins

**d.** peasants

**e.** Zhang Heng

**f.** the *Analects*

**g.** Qin Shihuangdi

**h.** Sima Qian

**i.** the family

**j.** Laozi

## Multiple Choice
*In the blank, write the letter of the choice that best completes the statement. (4 points each)*

_____ **11.** Confucian teachings were accepted in China
  **a.** during the Shang dynasty.
  **b.** during the early Zhou dynasty.
  **c.** only after Confucius's death.
  **d.** after Confucius became adviser to the emperors.

_____ **12.** Daoism emphasizes
  **a.** the central role of the emperor.
  **b.** harmony between the individual and nature.
  **c.** respect for one's parents and siblings.
  **d.** finding the proper place in the social order.

_____ **13.** Before their defeat by the Qin, the Zhou
  **a.** had lost much of their power to independent city-states.
  **b.** were the undisputed rulers of northern China.
  **c.** were the undisputed rulers of all of China.
  **d.** had finished construction of the Great Wall of China.

_____ **14.** A diet of millet, rice, beans, turnips, and fish was typical of
  **a.** peasants.
  **b.** merchants.
  **c.** landowners.
  **d.** government officials.

_____ **15.** Daoism and Confucianism shared an emphasis on
  **a.** the supernatural.
  **b.** life in this world.
  **c.** social structure.
  **d.** nature.

_____ **16.** Candidates for civil service were required to master
  **a.** the Five Classics.
  **b.** the *Dao De Jing*.
  **c.** the Eightfold Path.
  **d.** the *Historical Record*.

# Chapter 9 : Form
# Test : Ⓐ

_____ **17.** Under Wudi's rule, the Han did all of the following EXCEPT
   **a.** conquer Korea and Manchuria.
   **b.** develop a civil service system.
   **c.** execute hundreds of scholars.
   **d.** require candidates for office to take written examinations.

_____ **18.** During the Han period, the second-ranking family member was usually the
   **a.** father.    **b.** mother.    **c.** grandmother.    **d.** oldest son.

_____ **19.** A standardized system of weights and measures was introduced by
   **a.** the first Qin dynasty ruler.
   **b.** the last Shang dynasty ruler.
   **c.** Wudi.
   **d.** Confucius.

_____ **20.** The Chinese remained far ahead of Europe in science and technology until the
   **a.** A.D. 100s.    **b.** A.D. 600s.    **c.** A.D. 1300s.    **d.** A.D. 1900s.

_____ **21.** The Zhou justified their rule by claiming that the last Shang dynasty had
   **a.** lost the Mandate of Heaven.
   **b.** challenged the king's authority.
   **c.** been ruled by the Son of Heaven.
   **d.** acted in accordance with Daoist principles.

_____ **22.** The concepts of yin and yang involve
   **a.** Confucian formalism.
   **b.** the interplay between society and the individual.
   **c.** the idea of the Eightfold Path.
   **d.** the opposing forces present in nature.

_____ **23.** During the Han era, the civil service was open to
   **a.** all Chinese citizens.
   **b.** members of the landholding class only.
   **c.** members of the peasant class only.
   **d.** all social groups except the merchants.

_____ **24.** According to Confucius, ethics began with respect for
   **a.** nature.    **b.** the family.    **c.** the state.    **d.** the emperor.

_____ **25.** The Qin government was overthrown by
   **a.** Zhang Quian.    **b.** Wudi.    **c.** Laozi.    **d.** Liu Bang.

## Essay
*Answer one of the following questions on a separate sheet of paper. (10 points)*

**26a. Critical Thinking** Compare the concerns and teachings of Daoism and Confucianism. In what areas of Chinese life did each philosophy have lasting impact?

**26b. Critical Thinking** Identify and describe the different classes that comprised the Han-era social hierarchy.

# Chapter 9 : *Form*
# Test : B

**Score** _____

## Matching

*Match each item in Column A with an item in Column B by writing the correct letters in the blanks.*
*(3 points each)*

**Column A**

_____ **1.** the order of importance

_____ **2.** what the Zhou called their king

_____ **3.** the term "China" comes from

_____ **4.** collection of speeches

_____ **5.** Kongfuzi

_____ **6.** reached China at end of Han Empire

_____ **7.** written between 1000 B.C. and 600 B.C.

_____ **8.** restores the balance of yin and yang

_____ **9.** contains the ideas of Laozi

_____ **10.** linked East and West

**Column B**

**a.** *Dao De Jing*

**b.** Son of Heaven

**c.** Silk Road

**d.** hierarchy

**e.** *Book of Documents*

**f.** acupuncture

**g.** Qin

**h.** Confucius

**i.** *Book of Songs*

**j.** Buddhism

## Multiple Choice

*In the blank, write the letter of the choice that best completes the statement. (4 points each)*

_____ **11.** Qin Shihuangdi reorganized the empire into military districts in order to
   **a.** expand the influence of the Zhou government.
   **b.** prevent attacks by nomadic invaders.
   **c.** deter landowners from using forced-labor gangs.
   **d.** limit the ability of local lords to challenge the central government.

_____ **12.** The growth of Buddhism in China
   **a.** began during the last stages of the Han Empire.
   **b.** was universally opposed by Confucianists.
   **c.** was hindered by its emphasis on personal salvation.
   **d.** was universally opposed by Daoists.

_____ **13.** Confucianism was a major philosophical foundation of Chinese society and government through the
   **a.** 400s B.C.    **b.** 100s B.C.    **c.** A.D. 1300s.    **d.** A.D. 1900s.

_____ **14.** The group that occupied the lowest level of the Chinese social hierarchy was the
   **a.** peasants.
   **b.** merchants.
   **c.** civil servants.
   **d.** inhabitants of rural villages.

_____ **15.** The dynasty that ruled China for the longest was the
   **a.** Qin.    **b.** Zhou.    **c.** Han.    **d.** Laozi.

# Chapter 9 : Form
# Test : **B**

_____ **16.** The term *Pax Sinica* refers to
  **a.** the unification of China by the Zhou dynasty.
  **b.** the social stability of the Confucian era.
  **c.** the extended rule of the Qin dynasty.
  **d.** a period of peace and prosperity during the Han dynasty.

_____ **17.** According to Confucius, the primary ethical relationships include all of the following EXCEPT
  **a.** friend and friend.
  **b.** ruler and subject.
  **c.** man and nature.
  **d.** parent and child.

_____ **18.** All of the following are included in the Five Classics EXCEPT
  **a.** the *Book of Changes*.
  **b.** *Spring and Autumn Annals*.
  **c.** the *Book of Songs*.
  **d.** the *Historical Record*.

_____ **19.** All of the following occurred during the Zhou dynasty EXCEPT
  **a.** the use of the iron plow.
  **b.** the invention of paper.
  **c.** the development of the crossbow.
  **d.** advances in flood-control systems.

_____ **20.** The typical Han home consisted of
  **a.** an extended family dominated by the grandfather.
  **b.** an extended family dominated by the father.
  **c.** a nuclear family dominated by the father.
  **d.** a nuclear family dominated by the mother.

_____ **21.** Han peasants had difficulty entering government service because of
  **a.** the high cost of education.
  **b.** government restrictions.
  **c.** the opposition of the landowners.
  **d.** social prejudice against farmers.

_____ **22.** The philosophy of Daoism was developed by
  **a.** Wudi.    **b.** Kongfuzi.    **c.** Laozi.    **d.** Sima Qian.

_____ **23.** All of the following were ancient chinese inventions EXCEPT
  **a.** paper.    **b.** silk.    **c.** wheelbarrows.    **d.** porcelain.

_____ **24.** The Great Wall of China was completed during the rule of
  **a.** Zhang Quian.    **b.** Wudi.    **c.** Qin Shihuangdi.    **d.** Confucius.

_____ **25.** Daoist teaching rejected the idea that
  **a.** the changing seasons resulted from the interplay between yin and yang.
  **b.** man must live in harmony with nature.
  **c.** people should renounce worldly ambition.
  **d.** people must fill specific societal roles.

## Essay
*Answer one of the following questions on a separate sheet of paper. (10 points)*

**26a. Critical Thinking** Identify three groups that might have been unhappy with the rule of Qin Shihuangdi. Explain the reason for their unhappiness.

**26b. Critical Thinking** Describe the location and importance of the Silk Road.

# Chapter 10 : *Form*
# Test : Ⓐ

**Score** _____

## Matching

*Match each item in Column A with an item in Column B by writing the correct letters in the blanks.*
*(3 points each)*

**Column A**

_____ **1.** ruled the Byzantine Empire at its height

_____ **2.** built independent Armenian kingdom

_____ **3.** known as New Rome

_____ **4.** Byzantine legal expert

_____ **5.** include Russians

_____ **6.** masterpiece of Byzantine architecture

_____ **7.** took Byzantine capital in A.D. 1453

_____ **8.** Mongols

_____ **9.** one of a missionary pair

_____ **10.** Rurik's successor

**Column B**

**a.** Constantinople

**b.** Eastern Slavs

**c.** Methodius

**d.** Tigran II

**e.** Ottomans

**f.** Justinian

**g.** Oleg

**h.** Tatars

**i.** Hagia Sophia

**j.** Tribonian

## Multiple Choice

*In the blank, write the letter of the choice that best completes the statement. (4 points each)*

_____ **11.** Vladimir I ruled Kievan Rus from
  **a.** A.D. 491 to A.D. 502.
  **b.** A.D. 805 to A.D. 841.
  **c.** A.D. 980 to A.D. 1015.
  **d.** A.D. 1210 to A.D. 1224.

_____ **12.** Theodora persuaded Justinian to ignore his advisers who advocated
  **a.** fleeing Constantinople.
  **b.** burning Constantinople.
  **c.** crushing the rebellion of taxpayers.
  **d.** annexing Rome.

_____ **13.** The alphabet for Slavic languages was devised by
  **a.** Justinian.
  **b.** Manzikert.
  **c.** Cyril.
  **d.** Tamara.

_____ **14.** The form of Christianity that developed in the Byzantine Empire became known as
  **a.** Byzantium.
  **b.** Eastern Orthodox.
  **c.** Roman Catholic.
  **d.** the Western Church.

_____ **15.** The Byzantine capital was strategically located
  **a.** where Europe meets Asia.
  **b.** on the Dnieper River.
  **c.** on the Mediterranean Coast.
  **d.** on an Aegean island.

_____ **16.** After A.D. 550, the major Byzantine industry was the production of
  **a.** porcelain.
  **b.** silk.
  **c.** mosaic tile.
  **d.** fur.

_____ **17.** The *Primary Chronicle* is a collection of
  **a.** Byzantine laws.
  **b.** Greek and Roman laws.
  **c.** Eastern Slavic history and legends.
  **d.** Eastern Orthodox religious texts.

# Chapter 10 : *Form*
# Test : Ⓐ                                    Score _____

_____ **18.** Georgia's "golden age" occurred during the reign of
    **a.** Tamara.
    **b.** Tiridates III.
    **c.** Vartan Mamikonian.
    **d.** Mesorb.

_____ **19.** Alexander, prince of Novgorod, became famous for
    **a.** bringing all the Slavic principalities under his control.
    **b.** defeating the Swedes at the Neva River.
    **c.** converting the Eastern Slavs to Catholicism.
    **d.** repelling the Tatars at Kiev.

_____ **20.** Supporters of Leo III's ban on religious images became known as
    **a.** laity.
    **b.** patriarchs.
    **c.** regents.
    **d.** iconoclasts.

_____ **21.** The Byzantines requested the pope's aid after being attacked by
    **a.** Seljuk Turks.
    **b.** Slavs.
    **c.** Avars.
    **d.** Venetians.

_____ **22.** Byzantine goods could travel overland through Asia after being shipped by boat across the
    **a.** Caspian Sea.
    **b.** Dnieper.
    **c.** Black Sea.
    **d.** Danube.

_____ **23.** The Slavic territories along the Dnieper River trade route became known as
    **a.** Novgorod.
    **b.** Bosporus.
    **c.** Venetia.
    **d.** Kievan Rus.

_____ **24.** The immense plain north of the Black Sea is called the
    **a.** laity.
    **b.** steppe.
    **c.** boyar.
    **d.** *izbas*.

_____ **25.** In 1054, a schism, or complete break, separated
    **a.** Christians and iconoclasts.
    **b.** Greeks and Byzantines.
    **c.** the South Slavs and the Eastern Slavs.
    **d.** the Eastern and Western Churches.

## Essay
*Answer one of the following questions on a separate sheet of paper. (10 points)*

**26a. Critical Thinking** Describe the Byzantine role in preserving Greek and Roman knowledge after the fall of the Roman Empire.

**26b. Critical Thinking** Describe two factors that contributed to the fall of the Byzantine Empire.

# Chapter 10 : *Form*
# Test : **B**

Score _____

## Matching

*Match each item in Column A with an item in Column B by writing the correct letters in the blanks.*
*(3 points each)*

**Column A**

_____ **1.** religious images

_____ **2.** developed Armenian alphabet

_____ **3.** Slavic god of lightning and thunder

_____ **4.** first czar of Moscow

_____ **5.** Byzantine capital is named for him

_____ **6.** location of many Black Sea ports

_____ **7.** Slavic script

_____ **8.** Viking leader who accepted Slav invitation to rule

_____ **9.** Theodora's husband

_____ **10.** members of the church but not the clergy

**Column B**

**a.** Rurik

**b.** Ivan

**c.** laity

**d.** Georgia

**e.** Perun

**f.** Mesrob

**g.** Justinian

**h.** icons

**i.** Constantine

**j.** Cyrillic

## Multiple Choice

*In the blank, write the letter of the choice that best completes the statement. (4 points each)*

_____ **11.** The Byzantines were frequently attacked from the east by
  **a.** the Avars.
  **b.** Germanic tribes.
  **c.** the Persians.
  **d.** the Slavs.

_____ **12.** The descendants of the West Slavs became the peoples of
  **a.** Poland, Slovakia, and the Czech Republic.
  **b.** Serbia, Croatia, and Bosnia.
  **c.** Ukraine and Belarus.
  **d.** Russia and Slovenia.

_____ **13.** Those Byzantine women who received an education usually
  **a.** attended the University of Constantinople.
  **b.** were taught by private tutors.
  **c.** attended Eastern Church schools.
  **d.** attended Western Church schools.

_____ **14.** The Byzantines created elaborate decorated books called
  **a.** mosaics.
  **b.** illuminated manuscripts.
  **c.** icons.
  **d.** embroidered regents.

_____ **15.** The first country officially to adopt Christianity was
  **a.** Italy.
  **b.** Persia.
  **c.** Armenia.
  **d.** Georgia.

_____ **16.** After the fall of Constantinople, Moscow became the center of the
  **a.** Eastern Orthodox Church.
  **b.** Ottoman Empire.
  **c.** Kievan Rus.
  **d.** Mongol territories.

# Chapter 10 : *Form*
# Test : **B**

_____ **17.** Byzantine anger toward the Western Church grew when the pope
   **a.** ordered icons removed from all churches.
   **b.** stated that the patriarch was the supreme leader of the Church.
   **c.** supported Emperor Leo III.
   **d.** gave Pepin the Short the title of emperor.

_____ **18.** The language used by the later Byzantine emperors was
   **a.** Latin.
   **b.** Persian.
   **c.** Greek.
   **d.** German.

_____ **19.** In A.D. 1240, Kiev was captured by the
   **a.** Byzantines.
   **b.** Eastern Slavs.
   **c.** Vikings.
   **d.** Mongols.

_____ **20.** Justinian became the Byzantine emperor in
   **a.** A.D. 330.
   **b.** A.D. 527.
   **c.** A.D. 726.
   **d.** A.D. 1054.

_____ **21.** Ivan III's marriage to Sophia helped to legitimize his claim as
   **a.** successor to the Byzantines.
   **b.** protector of the Tatars.
   **c.** ruler of the South Slavs.
   **d.** head of the Roman Catholic Church.

_____ **22.** In A.D. 1453, Constantinople fell to the
   **a.** Serbs.
   **b.** Bulgars.
   **c.** Seljuk Turks.
   **d.** Ottomans.

_____ **23.** In general, Byzantine art depicted
   **a.** nature scenes.
   **b.** historic scenes.
   **c.** everyday life.
   **d.** religious subjects.

_____ **24.** The *Corpus of Civil Law* was compiled by a commission appointed by
   **a.** Constantine.
   **b.** Justinian.
   **c.** Pepin the Short.
   **d.** Leo III.

_____ **25.** Eastern Slavs accepted Eastern Orthodox religion under the leadership of
   **a.** Oleg.
   **b.** Rurik.
   **c.** Vladimir.
   **d.** Yaroslav.

## Essay

*Answer one of the following questions on a separate sheet of paper. (10 points)*

**26a. Critical Thinking** Describe the ways the Eastern Slavs were influenced by the Byzantines.

**26b. Critical Thinking** Discuss the areas of conflict between the Eastern and Western Churches. Identify the time frame in which they occurred. What was the outcome of these conflicts?

# Chapter 11 : Form
# Test : A

**Score** _____

## Matching
*Match each item in Column A with an item in Column B by writing the correct letters in the blanks.*
*(3 points each)*

**Column A**

_____ **1.** bedouin tribal leader

_____ **2.** son of Ali

_____ **3.** capital of Umayyad dynasty

_____ **4.** geometric designs used in decoration

_____ **5.** author of the *Rubaiyat*

_____ **6.** original name of Madinah

_____ **7.** Tigris River city

_____ **8.** author of *Canon of Medicine*

_____ **9.** Umayyad center with 70 libraries

_____ **10.** prayer leaders

**Column B**

**a.** Yathrib

**b.** Ibn Sina

**c.** Baghdad

**d.** sheikh

**e.** Córdoba

**f.** Damascus

**g.** Khayyám

**h.** imams

**i.** arabesques

**j.** Husayn

## Multiple Choice
*In the blank, write the letter of the choice that best completes the statement. (4 points each)*

_____ **11.** The spread of Islam into Europe was halted by Charles Martel's victory in
    **a.** Spain.
    **b.** France.
    **c.** Greece.
    **d.** Syria.

_____ **12.** The first caliph was Muhammad's
    **a.** wife Khadija.
    **b.** father-in-law Abu Bakr.
    **c.** son-in-law Ali.
    **d.** daughter Fatimah.

_____ **13.** The holiest city of Islam is
    **a.** Makkah.
    **b.** Madinah.
    **c.** Yathrib.
    **d.** Quran.

_____ **14.** The first year of the Muslim calendar marks the
    **a.** birth of Muhammad.
    **b.** death of Muhammad.
    **c.** migration to Yathrib.
    **d.** appearance of the angel Gabriel.

_____ **15.** The symbols known as Arabic numerals were developed in
    **a.** Damascus.
    **b.** the House of Wisdom.
    **c.** North Africa.
    **d.** India.

_____ **16.** The great Jewish philosopher who wrote in Egypt during the A.D. 1100s was
    **a.** Ibn Sina.
    **b.** Ibn-Rushd.
    **c.** Maimonides.
    **d.** Omar Khayyám.

# Chapter II : Form
# Test : Ⓐ

_____ **17.** The capital of the Abbasid Empire was
    **a.** Damascus.
    **b.** Baghdad.
    **c.** Bukhara.
    **d.** Makkah.

_____ **18.** The House of Wisdom was founded by
    **a.** al-Razi.
    **b.** Ma'mun.
    **c.** Ibn Sina.
    **d.** Abu Bakr.

_____ **19.** The Arabian Peninsula is composed mainly of arid plains and deserts with the exception of the
    **a.** north.
    **b.** eastern coast.
    **c.** central highlands.
    **d.** southwestern region.

_____ **20.** The Kaaba became a place for Islamic worship after the
    **a.** destruction of polytheistic idols.
    **b.** death of Muhammad.
    **c.** death of Ali.
    **d.** death of Abu Bakr.

_____ **21.** Islamic artists used Arabic script to create an art form called
    **a.** arabesques.
    **b.** Ma'mun.
    **c.** _shari'ah_.
    **d.** calligraphy.

_____ **22.** Followers who backed Ali's claim to Islamic leadership became known as
    **a.** the Shiites.
    **b.** Mu'awiyah.
    **c.** Abbasids.
    **d.** the Sunni.

_____ **23.** Muhammad was born around
    **a.** A.D. 330.
    **b.** A.D. 570.
    **c.** A.D. 732.
    **d.** A.D. 1054.

_____ **24.** Substances were classified as animal, mineral, or vegetable by the chemist
    **a.** Ibn Sina.
    **b.** Maimonides.
    **c.** al-Razi.
    **d.** Ibn al-Haytham.

_____ **25.** During Ramadan, Muslims are expected to
    **a.** make a pilgrimage to Makkah.
    **b.** make a pilgrimage to Madinah.
    **c.** fast from sunrise to sunset.
    **d.** refrain from almsgiving.

## Essay
_Answer one of the following questions on a separate sheet of paper. (10 points)_

**26a. Critical Thinking** Provide an overview of the role of women in early Islamic society. How did their position compare to that of the pre-Islamic period?

**26b. Critical Thinking** List two fields in which Islamic scholars made great intellectual progress during the Abbasid Empire. Identify achievements in each field.

# Chapter 11 : *Form*
# Test : **B**

Score _____

## Matching

*Match each item in Column A with an item in Column B by writing the correct letters in the blanks.*
*(3 points each)*

**Column A**

_____ **1.** theological schools

_____ **2.** improved navigation and measurement

_____ **3.** Islamic law

_____ **4.** its polytheistic idols were destroyed

_____ **5.** Ali's rival

_____ **6.** burned Baghdad in A.D. 1258

_____ **7.** revealed divine messages over 22 years

_____ **8.** wife of Muhammad

_____ **9.** marketplace

_____ **10.** monotheistic Arab holy men

**Column B**

**a.** *shari'ah*

**b.** bazaar

**c.** Kaaba

**d.** hanifs

**e.** Gabriel

**f.** *madrasas*

**g.** Khadija

**h.** Mongols

**i.** astrolabe

**j.** Mu'awiyah

## Multiple Choice

*In the blank, write the letter of the choice that best completes the statement. (4 points each)*

_____ **11.** After the deaths of Ali and Husayn, Muslims split into two branches,
  **a.** Umayyads and Arabs.
  **b.** Arabs and Sunnis.
  **c.** Sunnis and Shiites.
  **d.** caliphs and hanifs.

_____ **12.** The birthplace of Muhammad was
  **a.** Makkah.
  **b.** Madinah.
  **c.** Damascus.
  **d.** Baghdad.

_____ **13.** The Islamic world experienced a great scientific awakening during the rule of the
  **a.** Abbasids.
  **b.** Guptas.
  **c.** Umayyads.
  **d.** Rightly Guided Caliphs.

_____ **14.** All Muslims are expected to make a pilgrimage called
  **a.** Ramadan.
  **b.** hajj.
  **c.** *shari'ah.*
  **d.** Hadith.

_____ **15.** All of the following actions were taken by the Umayyads EXCEPT
  **a.** making Arabic the official language of their empire.
  **b.** minting the first Arabic currency.
  **c.** tolerating the practice of other monotheistic religions.
  **d.** conquering the Abbasids.

_____ **16.** The nomadic herders who inhabited the Arabian Peninsula were called
  **a.** imams.
  **b.** sheikhs.
  **c.** bedouin.
  **d.** hanifs.

# Chapter 11 : *Form*
# Test : Ⓑ

_____ **17.** Homes in Muslim cities were typically constructed
  **a.** around a central courtyard.
  **b.** out of wood.
  **c.** below street level.
  **d.** in residential districts called bazaars.

_____ **18.** Islam improved the position of women by
  **a.** prohibiting the practice of female-infanticide.
  **b.** prohibiting polygamy.
  **c.** encouraging their full participation in public life.
  **d.** prohibiting divorce.

_____ **19.** The departure of Muhammad from Makkah to Yathrib is known as the
  **a.** *Hijrah.*
  **b.** Kaaba.
  **c.** Madinah.
  **d.** Quran.

_____ **20.** Islamic mathematicians invented
  **a.** Arabic numerals.
  **b.** the concept of infinity.
  **c.** geometry.
  **d.** algebra.

_____ **21.** After the death of Muhammad, Muslims chose a new leader called
  **a.** an imam.
  **b.** a caliph.
  **c.** a hanif.
  **d.** a jihad.

_____ **22.** Muslim control of the Persian Empire was achieved by
  **a.** A.D. 507.
  **b.** A.D. 550.
  **c.** A.D. 632.
  **d.** A.D. 650.

_____ **23.** The Abbasid Empire reached its height under the rule of
  **a.** Samanid.
  **b.** Abu Bakr.
  **c.** Harun al-Rashid.
  **d.** Khalid ibn al-Walid.

_____ **24.** The great Islamic historian who examined cause-and-effect in history was
  **a.** Maimonides.
  **b.** Ibn-Khaldun.
  **c.** Ibn al-Athir.
  **d.** Omar Khayyám.

_____ **25.** The holy scriptures of Islam are called
  **a.** the Madinah Compact.
  **b.** the Hadith.
  **c.** the Quran.
  **d.** *Kalila and Dimna.*

## Essay
*Answer one of the following questions on a separate sheet of paper. (10 points)*

**26a. Critical Thinking** Describe the importance of Makkah to both the history and practice of the Islamic faith.

**26b. Critical Thinking** To whom does the term "Rightly Guided Caliphs" refer? Explain the significance of these caliphs, identifying at least two by name.

# Chapter 12 *Form*
# Test Ⓐ

**Score** _____

## Matching
*Match each item in Column A with an item in Column B by writing the correct letters in the blanks.*
*(3 points each)*

**Column A**

_____ **1.** formal church ritual

_____ **2.** led defense of Tours

_____ **3.** a Holy Roman emperor

_____ **4.** opposed the Albigensians

_____ **5.** derived from the Latin for "middle" and "age"

_____ **6.** named for the Anglo-Saxon kingdoms

_____ **7.** bound to the manor

_____ **8.** archbishop who opposed Henry II

_____ **9.** crossed mountains to seek papal pardon

_____ **10.** monastery head

**Column B**

**a.** medieval

**b.** abbot

**c.** Pope Innocent III

**d.** Otto the Great

**e.** Charles Martel

**f.** Thomas à Becket

**g.** Henry IV

**h.** sacrament

**i.** serf

**j.** England

## Multiple Choice
*In the blank, write the letter of the choice that best completes the statement. (4 points each)*

_____ **11.** Near-total authority within a fief was wielded by the
  **a.** king.
  **b.** lord.
  **c.** homage.
  **d.** knight.

_____ **12.** William the Conqueror earned his title by
  **a.** repelling the Danish invaders in England.
  **b.** defeating the Magyars at the Battle of Lechfeld.
  **c.** leading the Normans to victory in the Battle of Hastings.
  **d.** seizing Viking territory in Scandinavia.

_____ **13.** The strongest Germanic group to emerge during the A.D. 400s was the
  **a.** Carolingians.
  **b.** Franks.
  **c.** Vikings.
  **d.** Lombards.

_____ **14.** The wandering preachers who encouraged Catholic loyalty during the A.D. 1200s were called
  **a.** friars.     **b.** cardinals.     **c.** Benedictines.     **d.** abbots.

_____ **15.** Charlemagne did all of the following EXCEPT
  **a.** expand the Frankish Empire to include northern Spain and most of Italy.
  **b.** set up a palace school at his capital.
  **c.** defend Pope Leo III against Roman nobles.
  **d.** divide Carolingian lands by the Treaty of Verdun.

_____ **16.** The reform-minded monastery at Cluny was located in
  **a.** Ireland.
  **b.** Germany.
  **c.** Monte Cassino.
  **d.** France.

# Chapter 12 : *Form*
# Test : Ⓐ

_____ **17.** The behavior of knights was governed by a code of honor called
    **a.** homage.                **c.** manorialism.
    **b.** chivalry.               **d.** vassalage.

_____ **18.** Feudalism began to take hold in Europe in the
    **a.** A.D. 700s.     **b.** A.D. 900s.     **c.** A.D. 1100s.     **d.** A.D. 1200s.

_____ **19.** Viking expeditions out of Scandinavia were triggered by
    **a.** overpopulation and land pressure at home.      **c.** their desire to defeat the Magyars.
    **b.** the Slav invasion of their homeland.      **d.** their desire to defeat the Muslims.

_____ **20.** The Benedictine Rule specified, among other things, that
    **a.** masses would be conducted in Latin.      **c.** local lords could not appoint relatives as abbots.
    **b.** the clergy must live *in saeculo.*      **d.** monks could not own goods.

_____ **21.** The first Germanic ruler to accept Catholicism was
    **a.** Clovis.     **b.** Charles Martel.     **c.** Merowig.     **d.** Eric Bloodax.

_____ **22.** The denial of basic church teachings is called
    **a.** lay investiture.             **c.** excommunication.
    **b.** heresy.                 **d.** the Inquisition.

_____ **23.** Primarily intended to protect feudal rights, the Magna Carta eventually
    **a.** gave the king freedom to tax nobles without their consent.      **c.** guaranteed the rights of all English people.
    **b.** eliminated the power of the monarchy.      **d.** placed all governing authority with the House of Commons.

_____ **24.** Most western Europeans had become Catholics by the
    **a.** A.D. 600s.               **c.** A.D. 900s.
    **b.** A.D. 700s.               **d.** A.D. 1000s.

_____ **25.** Feudal society was characterized by
    **a.** a hierarchical system of relationships and obligations.      **c.** increasing consolidation of power by Frankish kings.
    **b.** the rule of a strong central government.      **d.** the absence of hostility between neighboring fiefs.

## Essay
*Answer one of the following questions on a separate sheet of paper. (10 points)*

**26a. Critical Thinking** Summarize the history of the Carolingian kingdoms. Explain the origins of the name, and describe the forces that caused their collapse.

**26b. Critical Thinking** Identify the powers traditionally held by kings that were gained by local lords during the feudal era. Why were monarchs willing to give up these powers? What did they receive in return?

# Chapter 12 : *Form*
# Test : **B**

**Score** _____

## Matching

*Match each item in Column A with an item in Column B by writing the correct letters in the blanks.
(3 points each)*

**Column A**

_____ **1.** code of the knights

_____ **2.** defeated the Danes in A.D. 886

_____ **3.** introduced by Henry II

_____ **4.** conducted a census of western Europe

_____ **5.** doubled the size of Frankish territory

_____ **6.** site of Benedict's model monastery

_____ **7.** describes the deeds of Viking gods

_____ **8.** an estate with peasants included

_____ **9.** Harald Bluetooth's native home

_____ **10.** cemented ties between lord and vassal

**Column B**

**a.** petit jury

**b.** Monte Cassino

**c.** fief

**d.** chivalry

**e.** *Eddas*

**f.** William the Conqueror

**g.** homage

**h.** Scandinavia

**i.** Alfred the Great

**j.** Charlemagne

## Multiple Choice

*In the blank, write the letter of the choice that best completes the statement. (4 points each)*

_____ **11.** The goal of the Inquisition was to
  **a.** eliminate the growing practice of excommunication.
  **b.** seek out and punish heretics.
  **c.** encourage monks to lead lives of poverty, chastity, and obedience.
  **d.** prevent secular rulers from using the symbols of the Church.

_____ **12.** During the feudal era, noblewomen
  **a.** were prohibited from hunting or fishing.
  **b.** had full responsibility for supervising the manor.
  **c.** possessed few, if any, rights.
  **d.** had a lower standard of living than most serfs.

_____ **13.** All of the following are characteristic of medieval castles EXCEPT
  **a.** habitation by both humans and animals.
  **b.** all-wooden construction through the A.D. 1200s.
  **c.** a square tower called a keep.
  **d.** a large open area called a bailey.

_____ **14.** "Charles the Hammer" defeated Muslim forces in France in
  **a.** A.D. 481.
  **b.** A.D. 732.
  **c.** A.D. 1066.
  **d.** A.D. 1215.

_____ **15.** The term *in saeculo* referred to those members of the clergy who lived
  **a.** in monasteries.
  **b.** a life of poverty.
  **c.** in Rome.
  **d.** as a part of society.

# Chapter 12 : *Form*
## Test : **B**

_____ **16.** The self-sufficiency of the manor was important during the feudal era because
   **a.** carpenters and blacksmiths could not leave the manor without permission.
   **b.** war and invasion made trade difficult.
   **c.** heavy taxation made manufactured goods expensive.
   **d.** few peasants were skilled as artisans.

_____ **17.** The North Atlantic island of Greenland was settled by the
   **a.** Franks.    **b.** Carolingians.    **c.** Norwegians.    **d.** Danes.

_____ **18.** All of the following were Frankish kings EXCEPT
   **a.** Pepin the Short.    **b.** Charlemagne.    **c.** Clovis.    **d.** Alfred the Great.

_____ **19.** The French king who strengthened the monarchy during the period A.D. 1180 to A.D. 1223 was
   **a.** Louis IX.    **b.** Louis VI.    **c.** Philip Augustus.    **d.** Otto the Great.

_____ **20.** In the A.D. 500s, the Benedictine Rule was adopted by
   **a.** Pope Gregory I.
   **b.** Pope Innocent III.
   **c.** Francis of Assisi.
   **d.** the Dominicans.

_____ **21.** Those farmers who could not leave the manor without permission were called
   **a.** vassals.    **b.** squires.    **c.** peasants.    **d.** serfs.

_____ **22.** In return for receiving powers previously held by government, feudal lords
   **a.** gave up the power to mint coins.
   **b.** surrendered their authority to raise armies.
   **c.** swore an oath of loyalty to the king.
   **d.** gave a portion of their income to the vassals.

_____ **23.** Under Henry II, feudal rules in England were replaced by
   **a.** the *Domesday Book*.
   **b.** a common law.
   **c.** the Magna Carta.
   **d.** unlimited royal power.

_____ **24.** The reform movement that began in the A.D. 900s was aimed at
   **a.** allowing secular leaders to appoint church officials.
   **b.** limiting the power of abbots.
   **c.** loosening the ties between the Church and feudal lords.
   **d.** encouraging the practice of lay investiture.

_____ **25.** The pope cut ties with the Byzantine Empire after
   **a.** Pepin gave land in central Italy to the Church.
   **b.** the Viking conversion to Christianity.
   **c.** Charlemagne accepted the title of Roman emperor.
   **d.** the defeat of Muslim forces in Rome.

## Essay
*Answer one of the following questions on a separate sheet of paper. (10 points)*

**26a. Critical Thinking** Describe the factors that made Europe vulnerable to Viking attacks.

**26b. Critical Thinking** Describe the lives of friars and monks during the Middle Ages. What differences were there between the two groups?

# Chapter 13 : *Form*
# Test : Ⓐ

## Matching

*Match each item in Column A with an item in Column B by writing the correct letters in the blanks.*
*(3 points each)*

**Column A**

_____ **1.** united the Muslim forces

_____ **2.** moved to Avignon

_____ **3.** northern European trading center

_____ **4.** wrote of journey from hell to heaven

_____ **5.** monster in Anglo-Saxon epic

_____ **6.** called for First Crusade

_____ **7.** their name originally referred to all town-dwellers

_____ **8.** Slavs of Bohemia

_____ **9.** this house bore the red rose

_____ **10.** followers of John Wycliffe

**Column B**

**a.** Grendel

**b.** bourgeoisie

**c.** Saladin

**d.** Clement V

**e.** Urban II

**f.** Lollards

**g.** Flanders

**h.** Lancaster

**i.** Czechs

**j.** Dante

## Multiple Choice

*In the blank, write the letter of the choice that best completes the statement. (4 points each)*

_____ **11.** Mediterranean trade after A.D. 1200 was controlled by Italian towns including
   **a.** Champagne.
   **b.** Alighieri.
   **c.** Genoa.
   **d.** Calais.

_____ **12.** The Crusades were undertaken to
   **a.** keep the Holy Land out of Muslim control.
   **b.** free Rome from the Byzantines.
   **c.** end the Great Schism.
   **d.** reform the medieval Church.

_____ **13.** Craft guild members who received pay but were not allowed to open their own shops were called
   **a.** apprentices.
   **b.** freeholders.
   **c.** artisans.
   **d.** journeymen.

_____ **14.** Under the leadership of Joan of Arc, the French broke the siege at
   **a.** Crécy.
   **b.** Agincourt.
   **c.** Calais.
   **d.** Orléans.

_____ **15.** The last Muslim stronghold on the Iberian Peninsula was
   **a.** Castile.
   **b.** Granada.
   **c.** Aragon.
   **d.** Portugal.

_____ **16.** The need for a common medium of exchange led to the rise of
   **a.** the barter system.
   **b.** a money economy.
   **c.** the guild system.
   **d.** the *burgesses*.

# Chapter 13 : *Form*
# Test : Ⓐ

_____ **17.** Peasants were enticed to join the Crusades for all of the following reasons EXCEPT

    **a.** freedom from feudal bonds.

    **b.** the promise of immediate salvation if killed.

    **c.** the possibility of wealth.

    **d.** the opportunity to become noblemen.

_____ **18.** The First Crusade was led by

    **a.** Richard I.

    **b.** French nobles.

    **c.** Saladin.

    **d.** Frederick Barbarossa.

_____ **19.** The Great Schism refers to the controversy caused by the

    **a.** simultaneous claim to church leadership of two different popes.

    **b.** courts of the Spanish Inquisition.

    **c.** movement of the Church from Rome to Avignon.

    **d.** translation of the Bible from Latin into English.

_____ **20.** The Hundred Years' War was fought between

    **a.** Christians and Muslims.

    **b.** France and Italy.

    **c.** France and England.

    **d.** Czechs and Bohemians.

_____ **21.** In the A.D. 1000s, Jerusalem was taken over by

    **a.** Ferdinand and Isabella.

    **b.** the Syrians.

    **c.** the Byzantines.

    **d.** the Seljuk Turks.

_____ **22.** Demand for reform of the Bohemian Catholic Church was led by

    **a.** Queen Anne.

    **b.** Clement V.

    **c.** John Wycliffe.

    **d.** Jan Hus.

_____ **23.** The Wars of the Roses were caused by

    **a.** conflict between rivals for the English throne.

    **b.** fear of the Spanish Inquisition.

    **c.** a power struggle between Spanish nobles and the Crown in Castile.

    **d.** France's attempt to recapture Burgundy.

_____ **24.** Between 1348 and 1350, almost one-third of the population of Europe

    **a.** migrated to urban trading centers.

    **b.** bought their freedom from feudal landholders.

    **c.** died in an epidemic of bubonic plague.

    **d.** joined the Third Crusade.

_____ **25.** Many commoners disliked the sale of church positions, a practice called

    **a.** simony.

    **b.** pilgrimage.

    **c.** papal approval.

    **d.** guild association.

## Essay
*Answer one of the following questions on a separate sheet of paper. (10 points)*

**26a. Critical Thinking** Describe three ways Europe benefited from the Crusades.

**26b. Critical Thinking** Explain how the Hundred Years' War demonstrated the obsolescence of feudal military organization and technology.

# Chapter 13 : *Form*
# Test : **B**

Score _____

## Matching

*Match each item in Column A with an item in Column B by writing the correct letters in the blanks. (3 points each)*

**Column A**

_____ **1.** reviewed the policies of Spanish monarchs

_____ **2.** returned the Church to Rome

_____ **3.** struggled alone against Saladin

_____ **4.** forced Jews and Muslims out of Spain

_____ **5.** 30,000 left western Europe at end of eleventh century

_____ **6.** maintained local monopolies

_____ **7.** those not bound to the land

_____ **8.** the sale of church positions

_____ **9.** ravaged Europe in mid-1300s

_____ **10.** supported the Lollards

**Column B**

**a.** Richard I

**b.** merchant guilds

**c.** the Black Death

**d.** Gregory XI

**e.** *cortes*

**f.** Ferdinand and Isabella

**g.** Queen Anne

**h.** Crusaders

**i.** freeholders

**j.** simony

## Multiple Choice

*In the blank, write the letter of the choice that best completes the statement. (4 points each)*

_____ **11.** The Iberian Peninsula is the location of
   **a.** Castile.
   **b.** Burgundy.
   **c.** Flanders.
   **d.** Bohemia.

_____ **12.** Agricultural advances of the later Middle Ages included all of the following EXCEPT
   **a.** the heavy plow.
   **b.** the collar harness.
   **c.** the ox yoke.
   **d.** the three-field system.

_____ **13.** During the A.D. 600s, Jerusalem and Palestine were captured by
   **a.** Arabs.
   **b.** Spaniards.
   **c.** Seljuk Turks.
   **d.** Anglo-Saxons.

_____ **14.** By the end of the Hundred Years' War,
   **a.** a series of victories had given the English a new sense of national unity.
   **b.** the use of feudal soldiers had made national armies obsolete.
   **c.** the French monarchy had lost much of its power and prestige.
   **d.** France had driven the English out of most of its territory.

_____ **15.** The Hussites demanded
   **a.** translation of the Bible into English.
   **b.** reform of the Catholic Church in Bohemia.
   **c.** an end to Slav influence in Germany.
   **d.** elimination of the guild system in Prague.

_____ **16.** Thomas Aquinas became famous as
   **a.** a poet-musician.
   **b.** chief adviser to the French monarchy.
   **c.** a scholastic thinker.
   **d.** leader of the Lollards.

# Chapter 13 : *Form*
# Test : Ⓑ

_____ **17.** The site of the most famous medieval trade fair was
    **a.** Orléans.
    **b.** Pisa.
    **c.** Bologna.
    **d.** Champagne.

_____ **18.** The period in the A.D. 1300s called the Babylonian Captivity refers to
    **a.** the ongoing civil wars in Italy.
    **b.** the expulsion of the Moors from Spain.
    **c.** the exile of the popes in Avignon.
    **d.** German control of Czech territory.

_____ **19.** The First Crusade took place between
    **a.** A.D. 596 and A.D. 609.
    **b.** A.D. 1096 and A.D. 1099.
    **c.** A.D. 1147 and A.D. 1149.
    **d.** A.D. 1189 and A.D. 1192.

_____ **20.** The battle at Crécy is notable for the
    **a.** English use of longbows and firearms.
    **b.** victory of the French despite having fewer soldiers.
    **c.** emergence of Spain as a European military power.
    **d.** leadership of Joan of Arc.

_____ **21.** Followers of John Wycliffe agreed with his criticism of
    **a.** the English monarchy.
    **b.** the Lollards.
    **c.** Queen Anne.
    **d.** church corruption.

_____ **22.** The Crusades contributed to all of the following EXCEPT
    **a.** the growth of Mediterranean trading cities.
    **b.** improvement in the level of European technology.
    **c.** greater contact between Europe and the Byzantine and Muslim civilizations.
    **d.** an increase in the power of feudal lords.

_____ **23.** French unity and power increased in the late A.D. 1400s under
    **a.** Richard III.
    **b.** Charles the Bold.
    **c.** Louis XI.
    **d.** Urban II.

_____ **24.** The Second Crusade ended with the
    **a.** defeat of the Crusaders by the Seljuks.
    **b.** capture of Jerusalem by the Crusaders.
    **c.** capture of Jerusalem by Saladin.
    **d.** formation of a surprising alliance between Louis VII and Conrad III.

_____ **25.** The epic poem that celebrates the exploits of Charlemagne's knights is called
    **a.** *Beowulf.*
    **b.** the *Divine Comedy.*
    **c.** the *Song of Roland.*
    **d.** *Sic et Non.*

## Essay
*Answer one of the following questions on a separate sheet of paper. (10 points)*

**26a. Critical Thinking** Describe the history and functions of merchant and craft guilds.

**26b. Critical Thinking** Explain the meaning of the vernacular. Describe the impact of its use in literary and religious texts of the medieval period.

# Chapter 14 : Form
# Test : Ⓐ

## Matching
Match each item in Column A with an item in Column B by writing the correct letters in the blanks.
(3 points each)

**Column A**

_____ **1.** Tang dynasty military genius

_____ **2.** Kublai Khan was part of this

_____ **3.** halted Mongol advance in Middle East

_____ **4.** ruled Sukhothai kingdom in late A.D. 1200s

_____ **5.** "a shrimp between whales"

_____ **6.** groups bound by family ties

_____ **7.** the *za* associations

_____ **8.** stressed living in harmony with nature

_____ **9.** founded by Yang Jian

_____ **10.** the Khmer capital

**Column B**

**a.** Mamluks

**b.** Sui dynasty

**c.** Angkor

**d.** Yuan dynasty

**e.** clans

**f.** guilds

**g.** Tai Cong

**h.** Zen

**i.** Korea

**j.** Ramkhamhaeng

## Multiple Choice
In the blank, write the letter of the choice that best completes the statement. (4 points each)

_____ **11.** The Tang dynasty was established by
   **a.** Li Yuan.
   **b.** Emperor Wen.
   **c.** Tai Cong.
   **d.** Marco Polo.

_____ **12.** Temujin codified Mongol laws into a new code called the
   **a.** yurt.
   **b.** *yasa.*
   **c.** Helagu.
   **d.** samurai.

_____ **13.** Pagan, the capital of the Tibeto-Burman civilization, became a center for
   **a.** Confucian scholarship.
   **b.** Islamic scholarship.
   **c.** the shogunate.
   **d.** Buddhist learning and culture.

_____ **14.** Southeast Asia was influenced by cultural contact with India beginning in the
   **a.** A.D. 100s.
   **b.** A.D. 600s.
   **c.** A.D. 800s.
   **d.** A.D. 900s.

_____ **15.** Entrance into the Tang dynasty civil service was supposed to be based on
   **a.** social standing.
   **b.** wealth.
   **c.** merit.
   **d.** age.

_____ **16.** Among the artists who flourished in Xuanzang's court was the poet
   **a.** Ngo Quyen.
   **b.** Duo Fu.
   **c.** Suryavarman.
   **d.** Shotoku.

_____ **17.** The Turk-Mongol conquests of the late A.D. 1300s were led by
   **a.** Kublai Khan.
   **b.** Helagu.
   **c.** Samarkand.
   **d.** Timur Lenk.

# Chapter 14 : Form
# Test : Ⓐ

_____ **18.** Under King Sejong, Koreans developed their own alphabet, although scholars continued to use
   **a.** Sanskrit.
   **b.** Japanese characters.
   **c.** Chinese characters.
   **d.** Arabic.

_____ **19.** Vietnamese independence from China was briefly achieved in A.D. 39 in a revolt led by
   **a.** Ngo Quyen.
   **b.** King Sejong.
   **c.** Tai Cong.
   **d.** the Trung sisters.

_____ **20.** The wealth of the Khmer Empire was built on
   **a.** trade with India.
   **b.** rice production.
   **c.** porcelain and silk.
   **d.** control of the Pacific Ocean ports.

_____ **21.** The "Great Change" refers to the
   **a.** attempt to reclaim land from Japanese clan leaders.
   **b.** adoption of Buddhism by the Japanese.
   **c.** adoption of Confucian ideas by the Japanese.
   **d.** shift from a seafaring economy to one based on rice production in Japan.

_____ **22.** Changan was the capital of the
   **a.** Mongol Empire.
   **b.** Khmer Empire.
   **c.** Tang dynasty.
   **d.** Yi dynasty.

_____ **23.** In A.D. 668 the kingdom of Silla conquered all of Korea, marking the end of the
   **a.** Yamato clan.
   **b.** Hermit Kingdom.
   **c.** Three Kingdoms.
   **d.** Yi dynasty.

_____ **24.** The most important city in Timur Lenk's empire was beautiful
   **a.** Kyoto.
   **b.** Changan.
   **c.** Angkor.
   **d.** Samarkand.

_____ **25.** Despite the death of Genghis Khan, by A.D. 1279 China was conquered by the
   **a.** Abbasids.
   **b.** Seljuk Turks.
   **c.** Tibeto-Burmans.
   **d.** Mongols.

## Essay
_Answer one of the following questions on a separate sheet of paper. (10 points)_

**26a. Critical Thinking** Identify and describe the religion followed by the Japanese samurai. What made it useful to warriors?

**26b. Critical Thinking** Describe the cultural influence of the Chinese on two other Asian countries.

# Chapter 14 : *Form*
# **T**est : **B**

**Score** _____

## Matching

*Match each item in Column A with an item in Column B by writing the correct letters in the blanks.*
*(3 points each)*

**Column A**

_____ **1.** Song dynasty capital

_____ **2.** became known as Genghis

_____ **3.** central Asian city that flourished under Timur Lenk

_____ **4.** a home for guardian spirits

_____ **5.** Mongol law code

_____ **6.** ordered construction of Angkor Wat

_____ **7.** the Korean alphabet

_____ **8.** rebuilt the Han capital at Changan

_____ **9.** great Hindu-Buddhist empire in Cambodia

_____ **10.** chain of islands

**Column B**

**a.** *yasa*

**b.** *dinh*

**c.** *hangul*

**d.** Hangzhou

**e.** Khmer

**f.** Wen

**g.** Samarkand

**h.** archipelago

**i.** Suryavarman

**j.** Temujin

## Multiple Choice

*In the blank, write the letter of the choice that best completes the statement. (4 points each)*

_____ **11.** The oldest observatory in Asia was built in
  **a.** Korea.
  **b.** China.
  **c.** Vietnam.
  **d.** India.

_____ **12.** All of the following countries are part of Southeast Asia EXCEPT
  **a.** Malaysia.
  **b.** Japan.
  **c.** Indonesia.
  **d.** the Philippines.

_____ **13.** The Mongols learned the techniques of siege warfare from the
  **a.** Seljuk Turks.
  **b.** Carpathians.
  **c.** Vietnamese.
  **d.** Chinese.

_____ **14.** By the end of the A.D. 1200s, most Mongol territories had
  **a.** been lost to the Turks.
  **b.** been consolidated under Timur Lenk's rule.
  **c.** adopted Islam as the official religion.
  **d.** developed into independent kingdoms.

_____ **15.** The dominant foreign cultural influence on Vietnam was
  **a.** China.
  **b.** India.
  **c.** Cambodia.
  **d.** Burma.

_____ **16.** Marco Polo is believed to have received a position in the court of the
  **a.** Tang.
  **b.** Song.
  **c.** Yuan.
  **d.** Khmer.

# Chapter 14 : Form
# Test : Ⓑ

_____ **17.** The Heian-era Japanese novel *The Tale of Genji*
- **a.** contains many poems about the beauty of nature.
- **b.** tells the story of the first shogun.
- **c.** is a retelling of the Japanese creation myth.
- **d.** chronicles the adventures of a female samurai.

_____ **18.** The use of forced labor by Sui dynasty rulers led to uprisings that allowed
- **a.** Emperor Wen to seize power.
- **b.** Timur Lenk to escape.
- **c.** Li Yuan to take control of China.
- **d.** the Mongols to defeat the Chinese.

_____ **19.** A major goal of Timur Lenk was to
- **a.** unite the Seljuk Turks.
- **b.** spread the Islamic faith.
- **c.** defeat his rival, Genghis Khan.
- **d.** defeat his rival, Kublai Khan.

_____ **20.** Early Japanese clans practiced a form of animism called
- **a.** Zen.
- **b.** Heian.
- **c.** Shinto.
- **d.** Ashikaga.

_____ **21.** In A.D. 1258, Baghdad was captured by the Mongol commander
- **a.** Ogadai.
- **b.** Helagu.
- **c.** Kublai Khan.
- **d.** Tai Cong.

_____ **22.** The belief that spirits inhabit living and nonliving things is called
- **a.** animism.
- **b.** Hinduism.
- **c.** Buddhism.
- **d.** daimyo.

_____ **23.** Peasants' lives improved during Tang dynasty rule chiefly because they were
- **a.** provided with free education.
- **b.** finally allowed to take the civil service examinations.
- **c.** provided with free military training.
- **d.** given land and the peace necessary to farm it.

_____ **24.** The powerful woman behind Tang ruler Gaozong was
- **a.** Empress Wu.
- **b.** Lady Shikibu Murasaki.
- **c.** Heian Kyo.
- **d.** Trung Trak.

_____ **25.** The adoption of neo-Confucianism as state doctrine in Korea resulted in
- **a.** diminished Chinese cultural influence.
- **b.** a reduction in the status and influence of women.
- **c.** an end to the Yi Dynasty.
- **d.** an increase in shamanistic belief.

## Essay
*Answer one of the following questions on a separate sheet of paper. (10 points)*

**26a. Critical Thinking** Describe Japan's location and geography. How did these factors affect the culture, history, and development of its inhabitants?

**26b. Critical Thinking** Describe the dominant religious influences on the seafaring kingdoms of Southeast Asia.

# Chapter 15 : Form
# Test : Ⓐ

## Matching

*Match each item in Column A with an item in Column by writing the correct letters in the blanks.*
*(3 points each)*

**Column A**

_____ **1.** used potatoes and quinoa as staple foods

_____ **2.** Mesoamerican ball game

_____ **3.** used irrigation to farm present-day Arizona

_____ **4.** confederation that included five groups

_____ **5.** capital of Toltec Empire

_____ **6.** "plumed serpent" god

_____ **7.** capital of Inca Empire

_____ **8.** Pacific Coast residents

_____ **9.** believed in the Otherworld

_____ **10.** maize farmers and adobe builders

**Column B**

**a.** Cuzco

**b.** *pok-a-tok*

**c.** Hohokam

**d.** Inca

**e.** Pueblo

**f.** Maya

**g.** Kwakiutl

**h.** Iroquois

**i.** Tula

**j.** Quetzalcoatl

## Multiple Choice

*In the blank, write the letter of the choice that best completes the statement. (4 points each)*

_____ **11.** The city of Teotihuacán was located in present-day
  **a.** California.
  **b.** Peru.
  **c.** Mexico.
  **d.** Arizona.

_____ **12.** Early American peoples began to build permanent settlements once they learned how to
  **a.** build houses.
  **b.** hunt and trap.
  **c.** use tools.
  **d.** plant food.

_____ **13.** The language of the Inca Empire was called
  **a.** Guata.
  **b.** Potlatch.
  **c.** Quinoa.
  **d.** Quechua.

_____ **14.** The Moche were skilled artisans who produced ornaments out of
  **a.** weirs.
  **b.** obsidian.
  **c.** whalebone.
  **d.** gold and silver.

_____ **15.** Great stone heads discovered at La Venta and San Lorenzo were created by the
  **a.** Olmec.
  **b.** Aztec.
  **c.** Pueblo.
  **d.** Quechua.

_____ **16.** One Native American group that inhabited present-day California was the
  **a.** Chumash.
  **b.** Hohokam.
  **c.** Pueblo.
  **d.** Iroquois.

_____ **17.** The Aztec founded their capital on a Lake Texcoco island in
  **a.** A.D. 1325.    **b.** A.D. 1105.    **c.** A.D. 865.    **d.** A.D. 595.

## Chapter 15 : Form
# Test : Ⓐ

_____ **18.** By around A.D. 1500, the present-day United States and Canada were home to about
    **a.** 10,000 inhabitants.
    **b.** 50,000 to 200,000 inhabitants.
    **c.** 1 million to 3 million inhabitants.
    **d.** 15 million to 20 million inhabitants.

_____ **19.** The decisive period of Inca expansion began during the rule of
    **a.** Quetzalcoatl.
    **b.** Pachacuti.
    **c.** Cuzco.
    **d.** Tezcatlipoca.

_____ **20.** The Mound Builders inhabited the
    **a.** Pacific Northwest.
    **b.** Great Plains.
    **c.** Ohio and Mississippi Valleys.
    **d.** Rocky Mountains.

_____ **21.** The frequent appearance of Chac on Mayan temples indicates the importance to the Maya of
    **a.** potatoes.
    **b.** rain.
    **c.** the sea.
    **d.** bison.

_____ **22.** The term _Mesoamerican_ refers to the civilizations that emerged in the
    **a.** Pacific Northwest.
    **b.** land area between North and South America.
    **c.** Arctic.
    **d.** Peruvian Andes.

_____ **23.** Mayan pyramids were used primarily for
    **a.** religious ceremonies.
    **b.** grain storage.
    **c.** the houses of royalty.
    **d.** athletic events.

_____ **24.** All of the following are characteristic of Aztec society EXCEPT
    **a.** religious practices that included human sacrifice.
    **b.** a serf class that was bound to the land.
    **c.** pyramid building.
    **d.** the separation of military and political power.

_____ **25.** Bison were the most important resource of the
    **a.** Northwest peoples.
    **b.** Pueblo.
    **c.** Plains peoples.
    **d.** Olmec.

## Essay
_Answer one of the following questions on a separate sheet of paper. (10 points)_

**26a. Critical Thinking** Explain how a Native American group adapted its lifestyle to the natural resources available.

**26b. Critical Thinking** Explain how the religious beliefs of the Maya shaped their culture.

# Chapter 15 : Form
# Test : Ⓑ

Score _____

## Matching
Match each item in Column A with an item in Column B by writing the correct letters in the blanks.
(3 points each)

**Column A**

_____ **1.** an early people of the Peruvian coast

_____ **2.** floating island garden

_____ **3.** located 30 miles from present-day Mexico City

_____ **4.** wooden salmon trap

_____ **5.** one of the earliest Mesoamerican civilizations

_____ **6.** once a land bridge, now a strait

_____ **7.** now site of Mexico City

_____ **8.** occasion to display, trade, celebrate

_____ **9.** father of Topa Inca Yupanqui

_____ **10.** used by Teotihuacános to make tools

**Column B**

**a.** Teotihuacán

**b.** *chinampa*

**c.** Bering

**d.** Olmec

**e.** Tenochtitlán

**f.** weir

**g.** obsidian

**h.** Pachacuti

**i.** potlatch

**j.** Moche

## Multiple Choice
In the blank, write the letter of the choice that best completes the statement. (4 points each)

_____ **11.** Northwest societies were organized by lineages that traced descent to a
 **a.** maternal ancestor.
 **b.** paternal ancestor.
 **c.** mythical ancestor.
 **d.** group chief.

_____ **12.** Quechua was the language of
 **a.** the Inca.
 **b.** the Aztec.
 **c.** several Mesoamerican peoples.
 **d.** the Mound Builders.

_____ **13.** All of the following were Mesoamerican peoples EXCEPT the
 **a.** Maya.
 **b.** Teotihuacános.
 **c.** Toltec.
 **d.** Moche.

_____ **14.** The trading network of the Northwest peoples stretched from
 **a.** the Arctic to southern California.
 **b.** the Arctic to Mexico.
 **c.** southern Alaska to northern California.
 **d.** southern Alaska to South America.

_____ **15.** The following groups that joined to form the League of the Iroquois lived in the
 **a.** Great Plains.
 **b.** Northeast.
 **c.** Southwest.
 **d.** Northwest.

_____ **16.** The Aztec Empire grew to reach the borders of present-day
 **a.** New Mexico.
 **b.** Colombia.
 **c.** Panama.
 **d.** Guatemala.

_____ **17.** The most important natural resource to the Plains peoples was
 **a.** bison.
 **b.** maize.
 **c.** abalone.
 **d.** squash.

# Chapter 15 : Form
# Test : B

_____ **18.** Until the A.D. 1500s, the Native American population grew mainly as a result of
  **a.** a decreasing number of infant deaths.   **c.** a preference for large families.
  **b.** an increasing food supply.   **d.** an expanding knowledge of natural medicine.

_____ **19.** Two Native American empires destroyed by Spanish invaders were the
  **a.** Aztec and Maya.   **c.** Maya and Olmec.
  **b.** Aztec and Inca.   **d.** Olmec and Toltec.

_____ **20.** The Aztec Empire gained power in all of the following ways EXCEPT by
  **a.** establishing a common language throughout the empire.   **c.** demanding tribute from conquered peoples.
  **b.** forming alliances with neighbors.   **d.** attacking distant rivals.

_____ **21.** Many Olmec carvings display a human with the face of a
  **a.** bison.   **c.** serpent.
  **b.** eagle.   **d.** jaguar.

_____ **22.** The Toltec gods Quetzalcoatl and Tezcatlipoca were later adopted by the
  **a.** Inca.   **c.** Olmec.
  **b.** Aztec.   **d.** Moche.

_____ **23.** The Mayan civilization had begun to collapse by
  **a.** 100 B.C.   **c.** A.D. 900.
  **b.** A.D. 300.   **d.** A.D. 1500.

_____ **24.** The Inca ruler Pachacuti united his empire in all of the following ways EXCEPT by
  **a.** establishing Quechua as the common language.   **c.** moving rebellious peoples to safer locations.
  **b.** building a network of roads and bridges.   **d.** replacing all conquered rulers with Inca officials.

_____ **25.** The Maya developed all of the following EXCEPT
  **a.** *pok-a-tok.*   **c.** wheeled carts.
  **b.** a 365-day calendar.   **d.** a writing system.

## Essay
*Answer one of the following questions on a separate sheet of paper. (10 points)*

**26a. Critical Thinking** Describe the role of the emperor in the Inca Empire.

**26b. Critical Thinking** Give the location of one Mesoamerican civilization, and identify the time period in which it existed. Then describe several achievements of that civilization.

# Chapter 16 : Form
# Test : Ⓐ

**Score** _____

## Matching

*Match each item in Column A with an item in Column B by writing the correct letters in the blanks.*
*(3 points each)*

**Column A**

_____ **1.** author of *The Prince*

_____ **2.** excommunicated Luther

_____ **3.** inventor of the printing press

_____ **4.** earned Reformation title "City of God"

_____ **5.** his divorce precipitated English/Catholic rift

_____ **6.** author of *Utopia*

_____ **7.** painter of *The Last Supper*

_____ **8.** Zwingli was a religious leader of these people

_____ **9.** founder of the Jesuits

_____ **10.** nationality of Jan and Hubert van Eyck

**Column B**

**a.** Thomas More

**b.** Leonardo da Vinci

**c.** Henry VIII

**d.** Swiss

**e.** Machiavelli

**f.** Flemish

**g.** Geneva

**h.** Leo X

**i.** Gutenberg

**j.** Ignatius of Loyola

## Multiple Choice

*In the blank, write the letter of the choice that best completes the statement. (4 points each)*

_____ **11.** German princes met at Worms in order to
  **a.** condemn the sale of indulgences by Pope Leo X.
  **b.** force Luther to recant his criticisms of the papacy.
  **c.** raise money to rebuild St. Peter's Basilica.
  **d.** overthrow Prince Frederick of Saxony.

_____ **12.** The term *Renaissance* refers to the period from about
  **a.** A.D. 550 to A.D. 1050.
  **b.** A.D. 550 to A.D. 1300.
  **c.** A.D. 950 to A.D. 1550.
  **d.** A.D. 1350 to A.D. 1600.

_____ **13.** The wealth of Venice during the Renaissance stemmed from its position as
  **a.** trading capital of northern Europe.
  **b.** center for Italy's banking and textile industries.
  **c.** capital of Italy's national government.
  **d.** trade link between Europe and Asia.

_____ **14.** Francesco Petrarca was famous for writing
  **a.** *The Last Supper.*
  **b.** sonnets expressing his love for a woman who died.
  **c.** a political and economic analysis of Italy.
  **d.** the first autobiography.

_____ **15.** According to the doctrine of predestination,
  **a.** God determines the fate of every person.
  **b.** salvation can be achieved only by good works.
  **c.** salvation can be achieved only by faith.
  **d.** political rulers had to obey papal authority.

# Chapter 16 *Form*
# Test Ⓐ

_____ **16.** All of the following are part of the Low Countries EXCEPT
    **a.** Belgium.
    **b.** the Netherlands.
    **c.** Luxembourg.
    **d.** England.

_____ **17.** *The Institutes of the Christian Religion* expressed the theological beliefs of
    **a.** John Calvin.
    **b.** Martin Luther.
    **c.** Ignatius of Loyola.
    **d.** Pope Paul III.

_____ **18.** Italian interest in classical tradition was fueled by
    **a.** the concentration of the Italian population in rural villages.
    **b.** the Roman heritage in Italy and contact with Byzantine scholars.
    **c.** Italy's use of Latin as the vernacular language.
    **d.** centuries of Greek rule in Sicily.

_____ **19.** Europe from the 1500s on could be roughly described as religiously divided between
    **a.** a Protestant south and a Catholic north.
    **b.** a Protestant north and a Catholic south.
    **c.** a Protestant east and a Catholic west.
    **d.** a Protestant west and a Catholic east.

_____ **20.** Although expert in many fields, Rabelais is best known as the author of
    **a.** personal essays.
    **b.** treatises on law and government.
    **c.** comic tales, satires, and parodies.
    **d.** sonnets and other poetry.

_____ **21.** Zwingli's defeat by Catholics ended his hope of creating a theocracy in
    **a.** Zurich.
    **b.** Münster.
    **c.** Wittenberg.
    **d.** Geneva.

_____ **22.** Opponents of Catholic rituals in the Protestant English Church became known as
    **a.** Anglicans.
    **b.** Anabaptists.
    **c.** Puritans.
    **d.** Calvinists.

_____ **23.** Martin Luther criticized the sale of
    **a.** Catholic Church land.
    **b.** printed texts.
    **c.** freedom to the serfs.
    **d.** certificates of indulgence.

_____ **24.** The Society of Jesus was characterized by
    **a.** its emphasis on Calvinist doctrine including predestination.
    **b.** its rigorous offensive against the Catholic Reformation.
    **c.** strict discipline and complete obedience to the pope.
    **d.** a belief in the strict separation between church and state.

_____ **25.** The city that lost its Renaissance leadership after the interruption of Medici rule was
    **a.** Venice.
    **b.** Florence.
    **c.** Rome.
    **d.** Milan.

## Essay
*Answer one of the following questions on a separate sheet of paper. (10 points)*

**26a. Critical Thinking** Identify two Renaissance artists and their places of origin. Describe the achievements of each artist.

**26b. Critical Thinking** Describe the movement that came to be known as the Counter-Reformation.

Name ................................................ Date ................ Class ................

# Chapter 16 : *Form*
# Test : Ⓑ

Score _____

## Matching
*Match each item in Column A with an item in Column B by writing the correct letters in the blanks.*
*(3 points each)*

**Column A**

_____ 1. espoused rejection of Catholic ritual

_____ 2. French country castles

_____ 3. blended Protestant beliefs and Catholic features

_____ 4. designed dome for Cathedral of Florence

_____ 5. a church-run state

_____ 6. Luther posted his theses on a church here

_____ 7. Italian political leaders

_____ 8. established universities throughout Europe

_____ 9. excelled at the personal essay

_____ 10. site where Anabaptists briefly seized power

**Column B**

a. Jesuits

b. Puritanism

c. signori

d. Elizabeth I

e. Montaigne

f. châteaux

g. Münster

h. theocracy

i. Brunelleschi

j. Wittenberg

## Multiple Choice
*In the blank, write the letter of the choice that best completes the statement. (4 points each)*

_____ 11. All of the following were Renaissance sculptors EXCEPT
   a. Donatello.
   b. Michelangelo Buonarroti.
   c. Lorenzo Ghiberti.
   d. Benvenuto Cellini.

_____ 12. The idea of justification by faith is credited to
   a. Martin Luther.   b. Huldrych Zwingli.   c. Thomas More.   d. John Calvin.

_____ 13. During the Renaissance, Italian government was characterized by
   a. the rule of a strong central government.
   b. the political rule of the Catholic Church.
   c. division into independent city-states.
   d. regional rule of feudal lords.

_____ 14. Many Anabaptists believed that
   a. citizens should respect the God-given authority of government.
   b. children should be baptized.
   c. church members should enter public office in order to spread the faith.
   d. church members should live apart from a sinful society.

_____ 15. Ties between the Catholic Church and England were weakened by
   a. Henry VIII's decision to execute Anne Boleyn.
   b. Queen Mary's decision to bring Protestant doctrine into the English Church.
   c. Henry VIII's decision to divorce Catherine of Aragon.
   d. the death of young Edward VI.

_____ 16. All of the following wrote in England during the Renaissance EXCEPT
   a. Thomas More.
   b. William Shakespeare.
   c. Christopher Marlowe.
   d. Pieter Brueghel.

# Chapter 16 : Form
# Test : B

_____ **17.** Gutenberg facilitated the spread of Renaissance ideas by
   **a.** developing a revolutionary printing method.
   **b.** opening a school in Venice for northern Europeans.
   **c.** opening a school in Florence for sculptors.
   **d.** bringing Leonardo da Vinci and other scholars to Paris.

_____ **18.** The purchase of a certificate of indulgence was supposed to provide
   **a.** a position in the Catholic Church.
   **b.** a position in the civil service.
   **c.** a reduction of punishment for sins.
   **d.** freedom from feudal obligations.

_____ **19.** The Catholic Reformation sparked the growth of the baroque style that emphasized
   **a.** simplicity.
   **b.** the classical influences of ancient Rome and Greece.
   **c.** realism.
   **d.** emotion, complexity, and exaggeration.

_____ **20.** Lutheranism emphasized all of the following EXCEPT
   **a.** the importance of occupations outside the Church.
   **b.** the use of the Bible as the sole source of religious truth.
   **c.** the achievement of salvation by faith alone.
   **d.** the use of Latin as the language of church services.

_____ **21.** During the 1540s, Catholic Church leaders
   **a.** accepted many new translations of the Bible.
   **b.** curtailed censorship of humanist texts.
   **c.** embarked on an ambitious reform program.
   **d.** abolished the Inquisition.

_____ **22.** The Renaissance began in the city-states of
   **a.** France.   **b.** Italy.   **c.** Greece.   **d.** England.

_____ **23.** Erasmus's *The Praise of Folly* attacked
   **a.** the spread of humanist ideas.
   **b.** Medici family rule.
   **c.** papal corruption.
   **d.** medieval artistic traditions.

_____ **24.** The Geneva-based leader of the Reformation in Switzerland was
   **a.** Huldrych Zwingli.
   **b.** John Calvin.
   **c.** Anne Boleyn.
   **d.** Ignatius of Loyola.

_____ **25.** Humanism encompassed all of the following beliefs EXCEPT
   **a.** an admiration for classical culture.
   **b.** people should expect fulfillment only in the afterlife.
   **c.** every individual had dignity and worth.
   **d.** people should participate in a variety of activities.

## Essay
*Answer one of the following questions on a separate sheet of paper. (10 points)*

**26a  Critical Thinking** Describe John Calvin's attempt to create a model religious community.

**26b.  Critical Thinking** Identify three ways in which the ideals of classical antiquity expressed themselves in Renaissance art and thought.

# Chapter 17 : *Form*
# Test : Ⓐ

**Score _____**

## Matching
*Match each item in Column A with an item in Column B by writing the correct letters in the blanks.*
*(3 points each)*

**Column A**

_____ **1.** explored the southern tip of Africa

_____ **2.** first permanent French settlement in the Americas

_____ **3.** French navigator who explored the St. Lawrence River

_____ **4.** treaty that divided the unexplored world in two

_____ **5.** sponsored Columbus

_____ **6.** killed in the Philippines during an attempt at circumnavigation

_____ **7.** banking family of Florence

_____ **8.** English sea captain who raided Spanish ships

_____ **9.** objected to abuse of Native Americans

_____ **10.** conquistador who took over Mexico

**Column B**

**a.** Magellan

**b.** Bartolomé de Las Casas

**c.** Isabella

**d.** Bartholomeu Dias

**e.** Cortés

**f.** Quebec

**g.** Cartier

**h.** Drake

**i.** Tordesillas

**j.** Medici

## Multiple Choice
*In the blank, write the letter of the choice that best completes the statement. (4 points each)*

_____ **11.** Pedro Alvares Cabral's defeat of the Arab fleet helped to establish
  **a.** Portuguese control of the Indian Ocean.
  **b.** Spanish dominance in South America.
  **c.** Spanish control of the Spice Islands.
  **d.** the spread of Christianity in the Americas.

_____ **12.** The Inca leader Atahualpa was defeated by
  **a.** Hernán Cortés.
  **b.** Montezuma II.
  **c.** Samuel de Champlain.
  **d.** Francisco Pizarro.

_____ **13.** The formation of joint-stock companies allowed private investors to
  **a.** make government-chartered banks obsolete.
  **b.** share the risks and profits of an undertaking.
  **c.** obtain church support for voyages of exploration.
  **d.** use coins as a medium of exchange.

_____ **14.** The compass was invented by the
  **a.** Chinese.
  **b.** Portuguese.
  **c.** Arabs.
  **d.** Italians.

_____ **15.** In the early seventeenth century, Henry Hudson claimed North American land for the
  **a.** Portuguese.
  **b.** English.
  **c.** Dutch.
  **d.** French.

# Chapter 17 : Form
# Test : Ⓐ

_____ **16.** Spanish injustice against Native Americans included
  **a.** the practice of indigenous religion.
  **b.** the destruction of native temples.
  **c.** forced conversion to Christianity.
  **d.** forced labor and the confiscation of land.

_____ **17.** The first European sailor to reach India by sailing around Africa was
  **a.** Prince Henry the Navigator.
  **b.** Vasco da Gama.
  **c.** Ferdinand Magellan.
  **d.** Bartholomeu Dias.

_____ **18.** By 1650, the population of Europe had reached about
  **a.** 20 million.    **b.** 50 million.    **c.** 55 million.    **d.** 100 million.

_____ **19.** The islands of Hispaniola, which Columbus explored, include
  **a.** the Bahamas.
  **b.** the Spice Islands.
  **c.** Cape Verde and the Azores.
  **d.** Haiti and the Dominican Republic.

_____ **20.** The European class that benefited most from the economic expansion of the Commercial Revolution was the
  **a.** peasantry.
  **b.** nobility.
  **c.** merchant class.
  **d.** clergy.

_____ **21.** During the 1400s, advances in shipbuilding were incorporated into the design of
  **a.** astrolabes.
  **b.** caravels.
  **c.** conquistadors.
  **d.** bullions.

_____ **22.** The most valuable products in the Spanish colonies were
  **a.** sugar and tobacco.
  **b.** silver and gold.
  **c.** animal hides and furs.
  **d.** spices and coffee.

_____ **23.** The man honored for suggesting that Columbus had discovered a "New World" was
  **a.** Magellan.
  **b.** Vespucci.
  **c.** Cortés.
  **d.** Hudson.

_____ **24.** An individual risk taker in search of profits is called
  **a.** a mercantilist.
  **b.** a banker.
  **c.** an entrepreneur.
  **d.** a colonist.

_____ **25.** Middle Passage refers to the
  **a.** journey of enslaved persons from Africa to the Americas.
  **b.** shipment of gold and silver from the Americas to Spain.
  **c.** route from Europe to Asia around the tip of South America.
  **d.** northern route from Europe to Asia.

## Essay
_Answer one of the following questions on a separate sheet of paper. (10 points)_

**26a. Critical Thinking** Describe the expedition of Ferdinand Magellan. Who sponsored his voyage? What did it prove?

**26b. Critical Thinking** Describe the triangular trade. Why did the colonists desire enslaved labor?

# Chapter 17 : Form
# Test : B

**Score** _____

## Matching

*Match each item in Column A with an item in Column B by writing the correct letters in the blanks.*
*(3 points each)*

**Column A**

_____ **1.** trade center that lost its power with the onset of transatlantic trade

_____ **2.** pioneered water route from Europe to India

_____ **3.** French missionaries

_____ **4.** Dutch colony at the mouth of the Hudson

_____ **5.** man in whose honor America was named

_____ **6.** Inca emperor who was defeated

_____ **7.** Aztec emperor who was defeated

_____ **8.** discovered by Henry's explorers

_____ **9.** Italian explorer sponsored by Spain

_____ **10.** largest seventeenth-century commercial city

**Column B**

**a.** Jesuits

**b.** Venice

**c.** Columbus

**d.** Vasco da Gama

**e.** Atahualpa

**f.** Amsterdam

**g.** New Amsterdam

**h.** Azores

**i.** Montezuma II

**j.** Vespucci

## Multiple Choice

*In the blank, write the letter of the choice that best completes the statement. (4 points each)*

_____ **11.** The first circumnavigation of the world was completed by the crew of
    **a.** Vasco da Gama.    **c.** Columbus.
    **b.** Pizarro.    **d.** Magellan.

_____ **12.** Advances in European shipbuilding in the 1400s included the use of
    **a.** steam-powered engines.    **c.** triangle-shaped lateen sails.
    **b.** rudders on the sides of ships.    **d.** a single-mast design.

_____ **13.** The first permanent English settlement in the Americas was
    **a.** New Amsterdam.    **c.** Jamestown.
    **b.** Montreal.    **d.** Plymouth.

_____ **14.** Many of the advances of Renaissance cartographers were based on the work of
    **a.** Ptolemy.    **c.** Vasco da Gama.
    **b.** Leonardo da Vinci.    **d.** Aristotle.

_____ **15.** The primary reason for the decrease in the indigenous population on Spanish colonies was
    **a.** the collapse of local agriculture.    **c.** the introduction of European diseases.
    **b.** war casualties during attempts to defeat the Spanish.    **d.** forced labor and capture by slave traders.

_____ **16.** In the West Indies, Columbus believed that he had discovered
    **a.** a "New World."    **c.** the Northwest passage.
    **b.** Asian islands off the coast of India.    **d.** Australia.

# Chapter 17 | Form
# Test | B

_____ **17.** By the mid-1600s, control of the Spice Island trade in Asia had passed to the
   **a.** French.
   **b.** English.
   **c.** Portuguese.
   **d.** Dutch.

_____ **18.** A rebellion of enslaved Africans led to the proclamation in 1804 of an independent
   **a.** Brazil.
   **b.** Bahamas.
   **c.** Haiti.
   **d.** Peru.

_____ **19.** Columbus first set foot in the Americas in what is now
   **a.** the Bahamas.
   **b.** Haiti.
   **c.** Cuba.
   **d.** Florida.

_____ **20.** The greatest increase in trade during the 1600s took place in
   **a.** countries bordering the Atlantic Ocean.
   **b.** countries bordering the Mediterranean Sea.
   **c.** Germany and Italy.
   **d.** countries along the overland trade routes to Asia.

_____ **21.** Cortés's expeditions were motivated primarily by the desire
   **a.** to place Mexico under Portuguese rule.
   **b.** to control the spice trade.
   **c.** for gold.
   **d.** to find sources of slave labor.

_____ **22.** The theory that a state's power depends on its wealth is called
   **a.** joint-stock theory.
   **b.** mercantilism.
   **c.** entrepreneurialism.
   **d.** commercialism.

_____ **23.** The primary components of the triangular trade involved all of the following EXCEPT
   **a.** enslaved people from Africa.
   **b.** manufactured goods from Europe.
   **c.** raw materials from the Americas.
   **d.** porcelain and silk from Asia.

_____ **24.** The first European country to explore the Atlantic in search of a sea route to Asia was
   **a.** England.
   **b.** Spain.
   **c.** Portugal.
   **d.** the Netherlands.

_____ **25.** Through the 1500s, merchants raised the money for overseas ventures primarily from
   **a.** banking families.
   **b.** government-chartered banks.
   **c.** individual entrepreneurs.
   **d.** feudal lords.

## Essay
_Answer one of the following questions on a separate sheet of paper. (10 points)_

**26a. Critical Thinking** Identify the advances in science and technology that allowed Europeans to engage in the exploration of the Atlantic.

**26b. Critical Thinking** Compare and contrast the goals of Spanish and Portuguese overseas expansion. Identify the resulting possessions of each country.

Name ........................................................ Date ........................... Class ....................

# Chapter 18 : *Form*
# Test : Ⓐ

Score _____

## Matching

*Match each item in Column A with an item in Column B by writing the correct letters in the blanks.*
*(3 points each)*

**Column A**

_____ **1.** first leader of the Ottomans

_____ **2.** Islamic rulers of northern India

_____ **3.** Persian-derived language of Pakistan

_____ **4.** the "eyes and ears" of the state

_____ **5.** single braids worn by the Chinese

_____ **6.** local Philippine rulers

_____ **7.** maintained Thai independence

_____ **8.** the sultans' elite officers

_____ **9.** site of present-day Tokyo

_____ **10.** the Ming dynasty navy was made up of these

**Column B**

**a.** janissaries

**b.** junks

**c.** Osman

**d.** queues

**e.** *metsuke*

**f.** Moguls

**g.** Edo

**h.** Urdu

**i.** *datus*

**j.** Mongkut

## Multiple Choice

*In the blank, write the letter of the choice that best completes the statement. (4 points each)*

_____ **11.** Akbar's rule was marked by
   **a.** the establishment of a Mogul capital in Delhi.
   **b.** the construction of the Taj Mahal.
   **c.** religious tolerance between Islam and Hinduism.
   **d.** the destruction of non-Muslim temples.

_____ **12.** The rise of Hong Wu to emperor was unusual because he was
   **a.** a Muslim.
   **b.** a military officer.
   **c.** of Mongol origin.
   **d.** of peasant origin.

_____ **13.** At its height, the Ottoman Empire included parts of all of the following EXCEPT
   **a.** eastern Europe.
   **b.** the Middle East.
   **c.** North Africa.
   **d.** India.

_____ **14.** The elaborate Japanese puppet theater is called
   **a.** Kabuki.   **b.** haiku.   **c.** Bunraku.   **d.** geisha.

_____ **15.** The population of China reached 350 million by
   **a.** 1400.   **b.** 1500.   **c.** 1600.   **d.** 1800.

_____ **16.** During the Ming dynasty, the rulers of China were
   **a.** Manchus.   **b.** Tibetans.   **c.** Mongols.   **d.** Chinese.

_____ **17.** By the late 1700s, most of Indonesia was under the control of the
   **a.** Portuguese.   **b.** Dutch.   **c.** Chinese.   **d.** Arabs.

# Chapter 18 : *Form*
# Test : Ⓐ

_____ **18.** The *sankin-kotai* system ensured

    **a.** the awarding of civil service posts based on merit.

    **b.** the loyalty of daimyos by requiring their service in Edo.

    **c.** the distribution of land to relatives of the shogun.

    **d.** that farmers and peasants could not become warriors.

_____ **19.** During its height, the Ottoman Empire accommodated its diverse population by

    **a.** rescinding the law code of Suleiman.

    **b.** allowing non-Muslims to practice their religions.

    **c.** requiring all citizens to learn Arabic.

    **d.** maintaining a strict separation between government and religion.

_____ **20.** In 1587, Christianity was outlawed in Japan by

    **a.** Oda Nobunaga.   **b.** Nagasaki.   **c.** Hideyoshi.   **d.** Francis Xavier.

_____ **21.** The Forbidden City was built as a home to the rulers of the

    **a.** Qing dynasty.

    **b.** Ming dynasty.

    **c.** Tokugawa shogunate.

    **d.** Mogul Empire.

_____ **22.** The main Spanish settlement on the island of Luzon was

    **a.** Manila.   **b.** Melaka.   **c.** Edo.   **d.** Bangkok.

_____ **23.** During Tokugawa rule, an individual's first loyalty was to the

    **a.** daimyo.   **b.** shogun.   **c.** family.   **d.** father.

_____ **24.** The fifteenth-century transoceanic exploration and trade of the Chinese came to a halt for all of the following reasons EXCEPT

    **a.** Confucian philosophy regarded trade as the lowest of occupations.

    **b.** China faced threats from northern nomads.

    **c.** ocean voyages were expensive.

    **d.** Yong Le became emperor.

_____ **25.** In 1856, Sultan Abdul-Mejid I tried to

    **a.** introduce liberal reforms to the Ottoman Empire.

    **b.** shift the balance of power toward the religious leadership.

    **c.** convert the non-Turkish population to Islam.

    **d.** drive the Young Ottomans out of power and into exile.

## Essay

*Answer one of the following questions on a separate sheet of paper. (10 points)*

**26a. Critical Thinking** Describe the level of religious tolerance in the Islamic empires of the Ottomans and Moguls.

**26b. Critical Thinking** Identify Tokugawa Ieyasu. How did he exert control over the daimyos?

# Chapter 18 : Form
# Test : B

Score _____

## Matching

*Match each item in Column A with an item in Column B by writing the correct letters in the blanks.*
*(3 points each)*

**Column A**

_____ **1.** colonized Vietnam

_____ **2.** form of Japanese theater

_____ **3.** Muslim voyager of the Middle Kingdom

_____ **4.** city renamed Istanbul

_____ **5.** Qing dynasty rulers

_____ **6.** "the Lawgiver"

_____ **7.** first Jesuit in Japan

_____ **8.** kingdom of the Thais

_____ **9.** location of the Taj Mahal

_____ **10.** allowed continued trade, despite Seclusion Act

**Column B**

**a.** Francis Xavier

**b.** French

**c.** Agra

**d.** Dutch

**e.** Zheng He

**f.** Suleiman I

**g.** Ayutthaya

**h.** Constantinople

**i.** Kabuki

**j.** Manchus

## Multiple Choice

*In the blank, write the letter of the choice that best completes the statement. (4 points each)*

_____ **11.** During the Ming dynasty, Chinese persons filled the civil service posts previously held by
    **a.** Mongols.      **b.** Japanese.      **c.** Manchus.      **d.** Koreans.

_____ **12.** The people of Indochina include the
    **a.** Vietnamese.      **b.** Filipinos.      **c.** Koreans.      **d.** Manchus.

_____ **13.** The Hatt-I Humayun decree and subsequent reforms were opposed by
    **a.** Sultan Abdul-Mejid I.      **c.** Muslim, Jewish, and Christian leaders
    **b.** the Young Ottomans and their allies.      afraid of losing power.
     **d.** most merchants and artisans.

_____ **14.** In 1453, the Ottomans conquered the Byzantines and made their capital in
    **a.** Beijing.      **b.** Delhi.      **c.** Constantinople.      **d.** Isfahan.

_____ **15.** The Manchus ruled the Chinese for almost 300 years despite being outnumbered by a ratio of
    **a.** 2 to 1.      **b.** 5 to 1.      **c.** 15 to 1.      **d.** 30 to 1.

_____ **16.** In 1511, the Malay port of Melaka was captured by the
    **a.** Japanese.      **b.** Portuguese.      **c.** Dutch.      **d.** Chinese.

_____ **17.** The victor at Sekigahara and unifier of Japan's warring daimyos was named
    **a.** Oda Nobunaga.      **c.** Tokugawa Ieyasu.
    **b.** Hideyoshi.      **d.** Edo.

# Chapter 18 : Form
# Test : Ⓑ

_____ **18.** Yong Le shifted the capital of the Ming dynasty to
  **a.** Nanjing.
  **b.** Changan.
  **c.** Beijing.
  **d.** Manchuria.

_____ **19.** While welcoming many Western influences, Mongkut maintained the independence of the
  **a.** Vietnamese.
  **b.** Japanese.
  **c.** Malays.
  **d.** Thais.

_____ **20.** All of the following were Mogul rulers EXCEPT
  **a.** Babur.
  **b.** Akbar.
  **c.** Shah Jahan.
  **d.** Shah Abbas.

_____ **21.** For about 200 years from 1636 on, the Japanese maintained a policy of
  **a.** isolation from foreign contact.
  **b.** colonial expansion.
  **c.** state-sponsored Buddhism.
  **d.** toleration of Jesuit missionaries.

_____ **22.** By 1557 the Portuguese had established a trading base in
  **a.** Beijing.
  **b.** Macao.
  **c.** Bangkok.
  **d.** Edo.

_____ **23.** Under Chakkri's rule, the Thai kingdom became known as
  **a.** Indochina.
  **b.** Siam.
  **c.** Chulalongkorn.
  **d.** Java.

_____ **24.** The Shiite form of Islam was practiced by the
  **a.** Safavids.
  **b.** Armenians.
  **c.** Ottomans.
  **d.** Sikhs.

_____ **25.** Under Tokugawa rule, the lowest social class in Japanese society was the
  **a.** samurai.
  **b.** farmers.
  **c.** artisans.
  **d.** merchants.

## Essay
_Answer one of the following questions on a separate sheet of paper. (10 points)_

**26a. Critical Thinking** Summarize the activity of the Portuguese in Southeast Asia, China, and Japan.

**26b. Critical Thinking** Describe some of the factors involved in China's increased food production during the Qing dynasty.

# Chapter 19 : Form
# Test : Ⓐ

Score _____

## Matching

*Match each item in Column A with an item in Column B by writing the correct letters in the blanks.*
*(3 points each)*

**Column A**

_____ **1.** German nobles

_____ **2.** first Tudor monarch

_____ **3.** dynasty that ruled Russia until 1917

_____ **4.** location of Louis XIV's palace

_____ **5.** monarch who refused to marry

_____ **6.** succeeded the Tudor dynasty

_____ **7.** Russia's "window to the West"

_____ **8.** resented Castilian dominance

_____ **9.** Russian nobles

_____ **10.** Prussian rulers and Hapsburg rivals

**Column B**

**a.** Aragon

**b.** Versailles

**c.** Hohenzollerns

**d.** Junkers

**e.** St. Petersburg

**f.** Romanov

**g.** boyars

**h.** Henry VII

**i.** Stuart

**j.** Elizabeth I

## Multiple Choice

*In the blank, write the letter of the choice that best completes the statement. (4 points each)*

_____ **11.** Mary Queen of Scots was executed after
   **a.** marrying the king of Spain.
   **b.** converting to the Protestant faith.
   **c.** losing Calais to the French.
   **d.** being accused of plotting with foreign Catholics.

_____ **12.** The creation of the Holy Synod in Russia placed church leaders under the control of
   **a.** the Eastern Orthodox patriarch.
   **b.** a secular government official.
   **c.** the Roman Catholic hierarchy.
   **d.** the Holy Roman Empire.

_____ **13.** All of the following groups were religious minorities in Spain EXCEPT the
   **a.** Protestants.   **b.** Marranos.   **c.** Moriscos.   **d.** Castilians.

_____ **14.** The theory used to justify absolutist rule in Europe was called
   **a.** divine right.
   **b.** pragmatic sanction.
   **c.** balance of power.
   **d.** regiment of giants.

_____ **15.** During the rule of Frederick William I, Prussia
   **a.** formed an alliance with the Austrian Hapsburgs.
   **b.** developed the most feared and efficient army in Europe.
   **c.** rejected the pragmatic sanction against the division of Hapsburg land.
   **d.** formed an alliance with Hungary.

_____ **16.** After achieving control of government, Cardinal Richelieu set out to
   **a.** increase the power of the nobility.
   **b.** strengthen the power of the Protestant clergy.
   **c.** increase the power of the Huguenots.
   **d.** build an absolute French monarchy.

# Chapter 19 : *Form*
# Test : Ⓐ

_____ **17.** All of the following occurred during the reign of Catherine the Great EXCEPT
  **a.** the release of nobles from government service.
  **b.** the freeing of Russian serfs.
  **c.** the acquisition of previously Polish territory.
  **d.** the defeat of the Ottoman Turks.

_____ **18.** In England, strong opposition was generated by the pro-Catholic policies of
  **a.** Mary I.   **b.** Henry VIII.   **c.** Elizabeth I.   **d.** James VI.

_____ **19.** Maria Theresa encouraged Hapsburg unity by
  **a.** improving Austria's relationship with Prussia.
  **b.** ending unpopular subsidies to glass and textile producers.
  **c.** weakening the control of the central government.
  **d.** eliminating trade barriers.

_____ **20.** The Edict of Nantes decreed that
  **a.** Huguenots must convert to Catholicism.
  **b.** Protestants could worship, but only in areas where they were the majority.
  **c.** only Catholics possessed civil rights.
  **d.** people of all faiths were to be guaranteed complete religious freedom.

_____ **21.** Ivan IV did all of the following EXCEPT
  **a.** execute many advisers and slay his son.
  **b.** increase Russian trade with western Europe.
  **c.** conquer Mongol lands east of Moscow.
  **d.** annex Sweden near the Baltic Sea.

_____ **22.** The long-ruling French monarch known as the Sun King was
  **a.** Louis XIV.   **b.** Henry IV.   **c.** Richelieu.   **d.** Frederick William.

_____ **23.** All of the following occurred during the reign of Elizabeth I EXCEPT
  **a.** lavish spending on court ceremonies.
  **b.** the enactment of the Statute of Apprentices.
  **c.** a long period of economic affluence.
  **d.** enactment of the Poor Laws in 1597 and 1601.

_____ **24.** One factor in Spain's sixteenth-century conflict with England was England's support of the
  **a.** Castilians.
  **b.** Moriscos.
  **c.** Dutch Protestants.
  **d.** Hapsburgs.

_____ **25.** The Thirty Years' War was triggered by
  **a.** the rebellion of Czech Protestants against Ferdinand.
  **b.** Philip of Anjou's ascension to the Spanish throne.
  **c.** Ivan IV's desire to annex Mongol territory.
  **d.** the Prussian attack on Silesia.

## Essay

*Answer one of the following questions on a separate sheet of paper. (10 points)*

**26a.** **Critical Thinking** Why was it important for Russia to gain access to the Baltic and Black Seas? Identify the rulers and conflicts involved in Russia's attempt to achieve this goal.

**26b.** **Critical Thinking** Who were the Huguenots? Describe how they fared under Henry IV, Richelieu, and Louis XIV.

# Chapter 19 : *Form*
# Test : B

**Score** _____

## Matching

*Match each item in Column A with an item in Column B by writing the correct letters in the blanks.*
*(3 points each)*

**Column A**

_____ **1.** birthplace of Russia's Catherine II

_____ **2.** area to which Peter I made China surrender its claims

_____ **3.** Spanish Jews who converted to Christianity

_____ **4.** adviser to Louis XIII

_____ **5.** England's ruling dynasty from 1485 to 1603

_____ **6.** nonnoble representatives of the French Crown

_____ **7.** last English foothold in continental Europe

_____ **8.** form of Spanish spoken in Philip's court

_____ **9.** founder of the Bourbon dynasty

_____ **10.** Spain's most powerful monarch

**Column B**

**a.** Richelieu

**b.** Germany

**c.** Calais

**d.** intendants

**e.** Philip II

**f.** Marranos

**g.** Siberia

**h.** Tudor

**i.** Henry IV

**j.** Castilian

## Multiple Choice

*In the blank, write the letter of the choice that best completes the statement. (4 points each)*

_____ **11.** Frederick the Great and Maria Theresa went to war over Prussia's seizure of
    **a.** Bohemia.                **c.** Westphalia.
    **b.** Silesia.                  **d.** Augsburg.

_____ **12.** During Elizabeth I's reign, England tried to balance the power of the rival nations of
    **a.** Scotland and the Netherlands.    **c.** Spain and France.
    **b.** Scotland and Ireland.            **d.** Spain and Portugal.

_____ **13.** The War of the Spanish Succession was prompted by European fear of a united
    **a.** England and Spain.          **c.** France and Spain.
    **b.** Portugal and Spain.         **d.** Germany and Spain.

_____ **14.** Charles VI convinced European monarchs to accept a pragmatic sanction allowing
    **a.** the division of Hapsburg lands.    **c.** Czechs to practice Calvinism.
    **b.** the Hohenzollerns to rule over Prussia.    **d.** Maria Theresa to inherit the throne of Austria.

_____ **15.** In 1588 the Spanish Armada met defeat at the hands of the
    **a.** Dutch.                   **c.** English.
    **b.** Portuguese.             **d.** Hapsburgs.

_____ **16.** The theory of divine right proposed that
    **a.** the clergy should assume political as well as religious leadership.    **c.** a ruler derived divine authority from his subjects.
    **b.** God alone could rule the people.    **d.** a ruler derived absolute authority to rule from God.

# Chapter 19 : *Form*
# Test : Ⓑ

_____ **17.** Scotland and Ireland became allied with England during the reign of
    **a.** Elizabeth I.
    **c.** Mary Queen of Scots.
    **b.** Henry VII.
    **d.** Henry VIII.

_____ **18.** All of the following groups were exempt from many forms of taxation during the rule of Louis XIV EXCEPT
    **a.** the poor.
    **c.** the nobility.
    **b.** the clergy.
    **d.** government officials.

_____ **19.** The czar who built St. Petersburg and endorsed western European customs was
    **a.** Peter I.
    **c.** Michael Romanov.
    **b.** Ivan IV.
    **d.** Catherine II.

_____ **20.** The lowest social class in England during the 1500s were the
    **a.** gentry.
    **c.** yeomen.
    **b.** merchants.
    **d.** intendants.

_____ **21.** The Russian goal of achieving a Black Sea port was achieved by defeating the
    **a.** Swedes.
    **c.** Lithuanians.
    **b.** Ottoman Turks.
    **d.** Prussians.

_____ **22.** The capital city of Spain during Philip II's rule was
    **a.** Seville.
    **c.** Aragon.
    **b.** Madrid.
    **d.** El Escorial.

_____ **23.** The Time of Troubles refers to a period in Russian history marked by
    **a.** the slaughter of rivals by Ivan the Terrible.
    **c.** noble feuds, peasant revolts, and foreign invasions.
    **b.** Russia's failed effort to gain access to the Baltic Sea.
    **d.** Catherine II's brutal suppression of peasant uprisings.

_____ **24.** The Thirty Years' War ended with the
    **a.** creation of the Peace of Augsburg.
    **c.** issuing of the Edict of Nantes.
    **b.** issuing of the Peace of Westphalia.
    **d.** formation of the Grand Alliance.

_____ **25.** France's minority Protestants were known as
    **a.** Bourbons.
    **c.** Hohenzollerns.
    **b.** Moriscos.
    **d.** Huguenots.

## Essay

*Answer one of the following questions on a separate sheet of paper. (10 points)*

**26a. Critical Thinking** Describe the role that religious differences played in the Thirty Years' War.

**26b. Critical Thinking** Who were the Hapsburgs? The Hohenzollerns? What regions did each control? How did they come into conflict?

# Chapter 20 : *Form*
# Test : Ⓐ

## Matching

*Match each item in Column A with an item in Column B by writing the correct letters in the blanks.*
*(3 points each)*

**Column A**

_____ 1. where Copernicus began his career

_____ 2. believed reason could not explain metaphysics

_____ 3. term for Enlightenment thinkers

_____ 4. found truth in "I think, therefore I am"

_____ 5. advocated by Pennsylvania's founder

_____ 6. home of Galileo

_____ 7. Enlightenment-era French satire

_____ 8. religious philosophy of the 1700s based on natural law

_____ 9. home of the Methodist movement

_____ 10. editor of the *Encyclopédie*

**Column B**

**a.** *Candide*

**b.** Italy

**c.** Kant

**d.** Kraków

**e.** England

**f.** pacifism

**g.** Descartes

**h.** philosophes

**i.** Diderot

**j.** deism

## Multiple Choice

*In the blank, write the letter of the choice that best completes the statement. (4 points each)*

_____ 11. Baron de Montesquieu believed that government power
    **a.** belonged in the hands of an absolute monarch.
    **b.** should never be used to wage war.
    **c.** could be undermined by policies of religious tolerance.
    **d.** was best divided among separate branches.

_____ 12. Calculus was developed by
    **a.** Vesalius.      **b.** Newton.      **c.** Locke.      **d.** Galileo.

_____ 13. Thomas Jefferson based much of the Declaration of Independence on the ideas of
    **a.** John Locke.
    **b.** Thomas Hobbes.
    **c.** William Penn.
    **d.** Immanuel Kant.

_____ 14. Kepler used mathematical formulas to prove that
    **a.** the earth is round.
    **b.** all matter is made up of four elements.
    **c.** the planets move in oval paths.
    **d.** the planets travel at a uniform speed.

_____ 15. Andreas Vesalius achieved his breakthrough discoveries by
    **a.** illegally dissecting human bodies.
    **b.** trying to transform base metals into precious metals.
    **c.** experimenting with the properties of air.
    **d.** carefully observing the moons of Jupiter.

_____ 16. One opponent of the Enlightenment's emphasis on reason was
    **a.** Jean-Jacques Rousseau.
    **b.** Antonio Canova.
    **c.** Frederick II.
    **d.** Voltaire.

_____ **17.** The husband and wife team that contributed to the understanding of oxygen was the
  **a.** Priestleys.    **b.** Kants.    **c.** Lavoisiers.    **d.** Boyles.

_____ **18.** Newton's theories about the law of gravity were published in
  **a.** *Principia.*
  **b.** *Discourse on Method.*
  **c.** *The Skeptical Chymist.*
  **d.** *The Spirit of Laws.*

_____ **19.** Rather than return to the Bastille, Voltaire chose to
  **a.** go into exile in England.
  **b.** face death by the firing squad.
  **c.** recant his theories.
  **d.** immigrate to America and set up a free colony.

_____ **20.** Hugo Grotius became known for proposing that
  **a.** the universe is divided into two realms, physical nature and ultimate reality.
  **b.** an international code based on natural law could reduce disorder.
  **c.** people in a state of nature are reasonable and moral.
  **d.** the earth revolved around the sun.

_____ **21.** William Penn advocated
  **a.** the right of people to rebel violently against unjust government.
  **b.** the abolition of organized religion.
  **c.** an assembly of nations committed to world peace.
  **d.** government by absolute monarchy.

_____ **22.** Until the 1500s, most knowledge of anatomy was based on the work of
  **a.** Ptolemy.    **b.** Claudius Galen.    **c.** Hugo Grotius.    **d.** Aristotle.

_____ **23.** The rule of Leopold II was marked by his attempt to
  **a.** create freedom for the press.
  **b.** equalize land taxes for peasants and nobles.
  **c.** confiscate church property.
  **d.** revoke the reforms of his predecessors.

_____ **24.** Thomas Hobbes argued that the best form of government was
  **a.** a theocracy.
  **b.** an absolute monarchy.
  **c.** a democracy.
  **d.** any type that was chosen by the people.

_____ **25.** The Parisian woman celebrated for running Parisian intellectual gatherings was
  **a.** René Descartes.
  **b.** Maria Theresa.
  **c.** Marie Lavoisier.
  **d.** Madame de Pompadour.

## Essay
*Answer one of the following questions on a separate sheet of paper. (10 points)*

**26a. Critical Thinking** Why were the theories of Copernicus and Galileo a challenge to the authority of the Catholic Church? How was the work of each affected by the Church?

**26b. Critical Thinking** Identify Robert Boyle, and describe his contributions to scientific understanding.

# Chapter 20 : *Form*
# Test : **B**

## Matching
*Match each item in Column A with an item in Column B by writing the correct letters in the blanks.*
*(3 points each)*

**Column A**

_____ **1.** masterwork of Baron de Montesquieu

_____ **2.** Boyle's criticism of alchemy

_____ **3.** site of Madame de Pompadour's salons

_____ **4.** advocated absolute monarchy

_____ **5.** refuted some of Copernicus's hypotheses

_____ **6.** author of *Principia*

_____ **7.** advocate of international law

_____ **8.** influenced Thomas Jefferson

_____ **9.** place over which Maria Theresa ruled

_____ **10.** Voltaire's place of exile

**Column B**

**a.** Grotius

**b.** *The Spirit of Laws*

**c.** Newton

**d.** Paris

**e.** *The Skeptical Chymist*

**f.** Austria

**g.** England

**h.** Kepler

**i.** *Two Treatises of Government*

**j.** *Leviathan*

## Multiple Choice
*In the blank, write the letter of the choice that best completes the statement. (4 points each)*

_____ **11.** Francis Bacon is credited with
   **a.** helping to develop the scientific method.
   **b.** refuting the ideas of Copernicus.
   **c.** originating the idea of natural law.
   **d.** creating the first body of international law.

_____ **12.** According to Hobbes, people
   **a.** do not have the right to rebel against government.
   **b.** can break their contract with the government if it fails to uphold their rights.
   **c.** should never consent to monarchical rule.
   **d.** are peaceful by nature and could be corrupted only by institutions.

_____ **13.** Copernicus proposed that
   **a.** all matter is made up of four elements.
   **b.** the force of gravity prevents objects from flying off the earth.
   **c.** the planets move in oval paths.
   **d.** the sun is at the center of the universe.

_____ **14.** The Enlightenment-influenced ruler who instituted many reforms in Prussia was
   **a.** Leopold II.
   **b.** Maria Theresa.
   **c.** Count von Zinzendorf.
   **d.** Frederick II.

_____ **15.** The period known as the Age of Enlightenment occurred from the late
   **a.** 1400s through the 1600s.
   **b.** 1500s through the 1600s.
   **c.** 1600s through the 1700s.
   **d.** 1700s through the 1900s.

# Chapter 20 : *Form*
# Test : **B**

_____ **16.** Deism was characterized by the belief that

a. violence should never be used to settle disputes.

b. only a monarchy could keep the world orderly and peaceful.

c. religion should be based on reason and natural law.

d. power must be divided equally among separate government branches.

_____ **17.** In *Discourse on Method*, René Descartes begins his search for knowledge by

a. refuting the existence of God.

b. describing the scientific method.

c. describing the movement of the planets.

d. believing only in his own existence.

_____ **18.** Jean-Jacques Rousseau argued that

a. leaders should make decisions based only on reason.

b. people should rely more on emotion and instinct.

c. government inhibited man's natural tendency toward violence.

d. a civilization could be measured only by its level of scientific knowledge.

_____ **19.** Diderot was imprisoned for

a. the publication of *Encyclopédie*.

b. dissecting human corpses.

c. mocking the Church.

d. advocating pacifism.

_____ **20.** The American Constitution was heavily influenced by the writings of

a. Kant.      b. Rousseau.      c. Montesquieu.      d. Pompadour.

_____ **21.** The founder of an American Quaker colony and advocate of pacifism was

a. John Milton.      b. William Penn.      c. Thomas Jefferson.      d. John Wesley.

_____ **22.** Galileo was forced to recant many of his ideas by the

a. English government.

b. Italian government.

c. Catholic Church.

d. Protestant Church.

_____ **23.** All of the following made discoveries in anatomy EXCEPT

a. Andreas Vesalius.      b. Claudius Galen.      c. William Harvey.      d. John Wesley.

_____ **24.** John Locke argued that the natural rights of people

a. exist only in the state of nature.

b. can only be taken away by an absolute monarch.

c. exist apart from any government.

d. are forfeited when they enter into a contract with government.

_____ **25.** The below-average Cambridge student who eventually developed groundbreaking theories in physics was

a. Lavoisier.      b. Copernicus.      c. Galileo.      d. Newton.

## Essay

*Answer one of the following questions on a separate sheet of paper. (10 points)*

**26a. Critical Thinking** To whom did the term *enlightened despots* refer? Identify two people to whom the term applied, and explain why.

**26b. Critical Thinking** Identify two individuals who disagreed with the Enlightenment's emphasis on reason, and explain their views.

Name .................................................................................................... Date ...................... Class ......................

# Chapter 21 : *Form*
# Test : Ⓐ

Score _____

## Matching

*Match each item in Column A with an item in Column B by writing the correct letters in the blanks.*
*(3 points each)*

**Column A**

_____ **1.** site of First Continental Congress

_____ **2.** pamphlet advocating colonial independence

_____ **3.** supporter of Parliament and Puritans

_____ **4.** supporter of Charles I

_____ **5.** made the Church of England the state religion

_____ **6.** site of 1770 massacre

_____ **7.** the Merry Monarch

_____ **8.** aimed at keeping James II from the throne

_____ **9.** received the Olive Branch Petition

_____ **10.** Paul Revere's partner

**Column B**

**a.** Cavalier

**b.** Boston

**c.** Philadelphia

**d.** *Common Sense*

**e.** Roundhead

**f.** George III

**g.** Clarendon Code

**h.** William Dawes

**i.** Charles II

**j.** Exclusion Bill

## Multiple Choice

*In the blank, write the letter of the choice that best completes the statement. (4 points each)*

_____ **11.** Patrick Henry was a congressional delegate from
   **a.** New York.    **b.** Virginia.    **c.** Massachusetts.    **d.** Pennsylvania.

_____ **12.** Before assuming the English throne, James I was king of
   **a.** Ireland.    **b.** France.    **c.** Scotland.    **d.** the Netherlands.

_____ **13.** The agreement that bound the American states together from 1781 to 1787 was called the
   **a.** Constitution.
   **b.** Declaration of Independence.
   **c.** Bill of Rights.
   **d.** Articles of Confederation.

_____ **14.** According to the principle of habeas corpus,
   **a.** a person cannot be held in prison without just cause.
   **b.** only a king could impose martial law.
   **c.** only Anglicans could attend English universities.
   **d.** a monarch rules under the authority of God.

_____ **15.** The leader of Parliament's forces during the English Civil War was
   **a.** William Laud.
   **b.** Oliver Cromwell.
   **c.** Sir Robert Walpole.
   **d.** John Adams.

_____ **16.** The birth of a son to James II prompted fear in the English Parliament of continued
   **a.** Anglican rule.    **b.** Puritan rule.    **c.** Calvinist rule.    **d.** Catholic rule.

_____ **17.** The Act of Union in 1707 united
   **a.** England and Ireland.
   **b.** the House of Stuart with the House of Hanover.
   **c.** England and Scotland.
   **d.** France and Scotland.

# Chapter 21 *Form*
# Test : Ⓐ

_____ 18. In return for approving additional taxes, Parliament demanded that Charles I sign the
  **a.** Petition of Right.
  **b.** National Covenant.
  **c.** Exclusion Bill.
  **d.** Bill of Rights.

_____ 19. The British responded to the Boston Tea Party by
  **a.** passing repressive measures known as the Intolerable Acts.
  **b.** repealing the Stamp and Declaratory Acts.
  **c.** refusing to accept shipments from any American port.
  **d.** sending 700 troops to Concord.

_____ 20. The Great Migration refers to the
  **a.** postrevolutionary departure of royalists from the American colonies.
  **b.** exodus of Puritans to the American colonies.
  **c.** departure of the royal family from England after the civil war.
  **d.** exodus of Methodists to England.

_____ 21. In 1779, the American side in the Revolutionary War was joined by a new ally, which was
  **a.** France.
  **b.** Canada.
  **c.** Spain.
  **d.** Germany.

_____ 22. The principal author of the Declaration of Independence was
  **a.** Benjamin Franklin.
  **b.** Thomas Paine.
  **c.** John Locke.
  **d.** Thomas Jefferson.

_____ 23. The period known as the Restoration began when
  **a.** Charles I was executed.
  **b.** Charles II ascended to the throne.
  **c.** James II returned from exile.
  **d.** the Puritans took control of Parliament.

_____ 24. The British Parliament reasserted its right to pass laws governing the colonies with the
  **a.** Stamp Act.
  **b.** Navigation Acts.
  **c.** Declaratory Act.
  **d.** Act of Union.

_____ 25. By 1640, the Scots had gone to war rather than accept Charles I's attempt to influence
  **a.** the Short Parliament.
  **b.** the Long Parliament.
  **c.** Catholic religious practice.
  **d.** Calvinist religious practice.

## Essay
*Answer one of the following questions on a separate sheet of paper. (10 points)*

**26a. Critical Thinking** Describe the influence of European theorists on the Declaration of Independence and the Constitution of the United States.

**26b. Critical Thinking** Identify Oliver Cromwell, and describe his achievements.

# Chapter 21 : Form
# Test : B

## Matching
*Match each item in Column A with an item in Column B by writing the correct letters in the blanks.*
*(3 points each)*

**Column A**

_____ **1.** brought William III to power

_____ **2.** Scottish agreement to preserve religious rights

_____ **3.** site of British army surrender

_____ **4.** married the daughter of James II

_____ **5.** archbishop of Canterbury

_____ **6.** Whig leader, adviser to George I

_____ **7.** British march to Concord interrupted here

_____ **8.** created to limit power of Charles I

_____ **9.** angered colonists by enforcing Navigation Acts

_____ **10.** attempt at peaceful compromise with Great Britain

**Column B**

**a.** William Laud

**b.** Lexington

**c.** Petition of Right

**d.** Yorktown

**e.** William of Orange

**f.** George Grenville

**g.** National Covenant

**h.** Olive Branch Petition

**i.** Glorious Revolution

**j.** Sir Robert Walpole

## Multiple Choice
*In the blank, write the letter of the choice that best completes the statement. (4 points each)*

_____ **11.** During the reign of Charles II,
   **a.** England was under continual martial law.
   **b.** Puritan rules of behavior were strictly enforced.
   **c.** the arts and sciences received royal support.
   **d.** Parliament was controlled by supporters of Cromwell.

_____ **12.** One factor motivating Ireland's rebellion against England in 1641 was anger at the
   **a.** execution of the archbishop of Canterbury.
   **b.** practice of seizing Irish land for English settlers.
   **c.** attempt to introduce the Calvinist prayer book in the Irish Church.
   **d.** attempt to introduce the Catholic prayer book in the Irish Church.

_____ **13.** Great Britain recognized the American colonies as an independent nation in
   **a.** 1776.          **b.** 1781.          **c.** 1783.          **d.** 1789.

_____ **14.** England was declared a commonwealth after the defeat of
   **a.** Oliver Cromwell.    **b.** Charles I.          **c.** Charles II.          **d.** George II.

_____ **15.** The Stamp Act of 1765 required
   **a.** the payment of duty on all imports.
   **b.** the payment of a direct tax on all printed materials.
   **c.** colonists to house British troops.
   **d.** all non-British manufactured goods to be identified by a stamp.

_____ **16.** The group in English Parliament that tried to prevent James II from becoming king was the
   **a.** Tories.          **b.** Whigs.          **c.** Cavaliers.          **d.** Roundheads.

# Chapter 21 : *Form*
## Test : Ⓑ

_____ **17.** On April 19, 1775, British troops were sent to Concord in order to
  **a.** arrest the leaders of the Continental Congress.
  **b.** defeat the French allies of the colonists.
  **c.** protect the assets of the British East India Company.
  **d.** confiscate the colonists' military supplies.

_____ **18.** James I's belief in divine right brought him into conflict with
  **a.** the English Parliament.
  **b.** the Cavaliers.
  **c.** Oliver Cromwell.
  **d.** the king of Scotland.

_____ **19.** The Restoration gave England
  **a.** a commonwealth government.
  **b.** an absolute monarchy.
  **c.** a constitutional monarchy.
  **d.** a dictatorship.

_____ **20.** The First Continental Congress met in
  **a.** Philadelphia.
  **b.** Boston.
  **c.** New York.
  **d.** Concord.

_____ **21.** The Declaration of Independence was greatly influenced by John Locke's concept of
  **a.** the social contract.
  **b.** divine right.
  **c.** checks and balances.
  **d.** federalism.

_____ **22.** Supporters of Parliament during the English Civil War were called the
  **a.** Royalists.
  **b.** Cavaliers.
  **c.** Roundheads.
  **d.** Tories.

_____ **23.** The French and Indian War involved disputes over
  **a.** land claims and fur-trading rights.
  **b.** smuggling and shipbuilding in colonial ports.
  **c.** French adherence to the Navigation Acts.
  **d.** the right to tax Canadian colonists.

_____ **24.** Many Puritans left England because of
  **a.** England's adoption of Calvinism as the state religion.
  **b.** Charles I's marriage to a Spanish Catholic.
  **c.** the persecution of their leader, William Laud.
  **d.** the oppressive policies of James I and Charles I.

_____ **25.** The Intolerable Acts were the British response to the
  **a.** Quebec Act.
  **b.** First Continental Congress.
  **c.** Boston Massacre.
  **d.** Boston Tea Party.

## Essay
*Answer one of the following questions on a separate sheet of paper. (10 points)*

**26a. Critical Thinking** Describe the evolution of American government in the decade after the achievement of independence.

**26b. Critical Thinking** Describe the English Bill of Rights. When was it passed? What provisions did it contain?

# Chapter 22 : Form
# Test : A

**Score** _____

## Matching

*Match each item in Column A with an item in Column B by writing the correct letters in the blanks.*
*(3 points each)*

**Column A**

_____ **1.** included bishops and abbots

_____ **2.** the unified French legal system

_____ **3.** Paris prison stormed by a mob

_____ **4.** type of French government before the revolution

_____ **5.** group of extreme radicals

_____ **6.** formed by those locked out of Estates-General

_____ **7.** plan that forbade trade with Britain

_____ **8.** repressive measures designed to stifle dissent

_____ **9.** comprised 97 percent of the French population

_____ **10.** those who continued to support the king

**Column B**

**a.** the Bastille

**b.** the Third Estate

**c.** monarchy

**d.** royalists

**e.** Carlsbad Decrees

**f.** Jacobins

**g.** National Assembly

**h.** Continental System

**i.** Napoleonic Code

**j.** the higher clergy

## Multiple Choice

*In the blank, write the letter of the choice that best completes the statement. (4 points each)*

_____ **11.** In 1789, King Louis XVI summoned the Estates-General primarily to
   **a.** eliminate feudal dues.
   **b.** increase the influence of the peasants.
   **c.** raise taxes to pay off growing debt.
   **d.** protect the privileges of the First and Second Estates.

_____ **12.** Robespierre's execution marked the end of
   **a.** the Reign of Terror.
   **b.** the Directory.
   **c.** the Enlightenment.
   **d.** the Napoleonic Code.

_____ **13.** The largest social group included in the Third Estate was
   **a.** the bourgeoisie.    **b.** the artisans.    **c.** the peasants.    **d.** the nobility.

_____ **14.** Napoleon undertook all of the following actions EXCEPT
   **a.** placing education under government control.
   **b.** requiring all citizens to pay taxes.
   **c.** restructuring the French legal system.
   **d.** prohibiting state censorship.

_____ **15.** The policy of summoning civilian men into military service is
   **a.** conscription.
   **b.** scorched-earth.
   **c.** coup d'état.
   **d.** feudalism.

_____ **16.** The Tennis Court Oath was made by
   **a.** a group of moderates known as Girondists.
   **b.** King Louis XVI.
   **c.** Napoleon.
   **d.** representatives of the Third Estate.

# Chapter 22 *Form*
## Test : Ⓐ

_____ **17.** The old European monarchies were reestablished by the
    **a.** Concert of Europe.
    **b.** National Assembly.
    **c.** Carlsbad Decrees.
    **d.** Congress of Vienna.

_____ **18.** The resentment of foreign rule and the desire to restore local customs are characteristics of
    **a.** dictatorship.
    **b.** nationalism.
    **c.** liberalism.
    **d.** imperialism.

_____ **19.** Louis XVI was executed after being accused of
    **a.** supporting universal suffrage.
    **b.** conspiring with foreign monarchs.
    **c.** sabotaging the reactionaries.
    **d.** aiding the Jacobins.

_____ **20.** Prerevolutionary French society was marked by great social
    **a.** inequality.
    **b.** harmony.
    **c.** mobility.
    **d.** apathy.

_____ **21.** Napoleon seized power by overthrowing the
    **a.** First Estate.
    **b.** consulate.
    **c.** Directory.
    **d.** monarchy.

_____ **22.** Metternich's principle advocating the restoration of royal authority was called
    **a.** legitimacy.
    **b.** balance of power.
    **c.** compensation.
    **d.** indemnity.

_____ **23.** The Declaration of the Rights of Man guaranteed all of the following EXCEPT
    **a.** freedom of speech.
    **b.** equal rights for women.
    **c.** freedom of religion.
    **d.** protection against arbitrary arrest.

_____ **24.** Napoleon's invasion of Russia was motivated by
    **a.** the creation of a French-British alliance.
    **b.** the defeat of the French fleet at Trafalgar.
    **c.** the Russian scorched-earth policy.
    **d.** Czar Alexander's decision to resume trade with England.

_____ **25.** The fall of the Bastille led quickly to the formation of
    **a.** a revolutionary government in Paris.
    **b.** the National Assembly.
    **c.** the Committee of Public Safety.
    **d.** an alliance between the peasants and the nobles.

## Essay
*Answer one of the following questions on a separate sheet of paper. (10 points)*

**26a. Critical Thinking** Describe three factors that led to military conflict between France and its neighbors during the revolutionary period.

**26b. Critical Thinking** Describe the ways European leaders tried to reestablish the prerevolutionary order after the defeat of Napoleon.

# Chapter 22 : Form
# Test : **B**

## Matching
*Match each item in Column A with an item in Column B by writing the correct letters in the blanks.*
*(3 points each)*

**Column A**

_____ **1.** doctors, lawyers, merchants

_____ **2.** rivals of the Jacobins

_____ **3.** ruled France during the Reign of Terror

_____ **4.** income tax placed on church members

_____ **5.** decision by popular vote

_____ **6.** rarely called meeting of the three social classes

_____ **7.** regular meetings of the European powers

_____ **8.** wanted to imprison royals and abolish monarchy

_____ **9.** a one-house assembly

_____ **10.** money paid by France for war damages

**Column B**

**a** the Estates-General

**b.** the radicals

**c.** indemnity

**d.** Girondists

**e.** unicameral legislature

**f.** plebiscite

**g.** Concert of Europe

**h.** bourgeoisie

**i.** Committee of Public Safety

**j.** tithe

## Multiple Choice
*In the blank, write the letter of the choice that best completes the statement. (4 points each)*

_____ **11.** Napoleon's agreement with the Catholic Church
    **a.** restored the authority of the lower clergy.
    **b.** acknowledged Catholicism while maintaining religious tolerance.
    **c.** returned confiscated land to the Church.
    **d.** allowed Pope Pius to name all bishops.

_____ **12.** The nobility's main source of income was
    **a.** feudal dues collected from peasants.
    **b.** tithes collected from church members.
    **c.** taxes on the income of artisans and merchants.
    **d.** government salaries.

_____ **13.** Members of the political faction favoring extreme change were called
    **a.** Girondists.
    **b.** royalists.
    **c.** Jacobins.
    **d.** "The Marseillaise."

_____ **14.** The neutral areas set up to surround France were called
    **a.** *sans-culottes.*
    **b.** buffer states.
    **c.** natural frontiers.
    **d.** the four powers.

_____ **15.** King Louis XVI left Versailles for Paris when his palace was surrounded by
    **a.** nobles demanding greater privileges.
    **b.** peasants demanding voting rights.
    **c.** soldiers demanding higher wages.
    **d.** women demanding bread.

_____ **16.** By 1812, Napoleon had conquered most of Europe EXCEPT
    **a.** Austria.
    **b.** England.
    **c.** Holland.
    **d.** Spain.

# Chapter 22 : *Form*
## Test : **B**

_____ **17.** All of the following French leaders died by execution EXCEPT
   **a.** Robespierre.  **c.** Danton.
   **b.** Napoleon.  **d.** Louis XVI.

_____ **18.** One of the National Assembly's most important reforms was to
   **a.** lower taxes on the nobility.  **c.** restore absolute monarchy.
   **b.** abolish feudal dues.  **d.** raise taxes on the artisans.

_____ **19.** A major goal of the Quadruple Alliance was to
   **a.** encourage the spread of liberalism.  **c.** prevent democratic revolutions.
   **b.** abolish absolute monarchy.  **d.** support Napoleon's heirs.

_____ **20.** Before the revolution, members of the Third Estate had
   **a.** a smaller tax burden than the other estates.  **c.** greater political influence than the clergy.
   **b.** a voice in government equal to that of the First and Second Estates.  **d.** a high tax burden and little political power.

_____ **21.** The Austrian chief minister who presided over the Congress of Vienna was
   **a.** Prince Klemens von Metternich.  **c.** the Duke of Wellington.
   **b.** Frederick William III.  **d.** Marie Antoinette.

_____ **22.** A major factor in Napoleon's failure to defeat Russia was
   **a.** the harsh Russian winter.  **c.** the opposition of the Catholic Church.
   **b.** Russian naval supremacy.  **d.** the Continental System.

_____ **23.** The attack on a Paris prison by enraged citizens was called
   **a.** the storming of the Bastille.  **c.** the Reign of Terror.
   **b.** the Great Fear.  **d.** the Long March.

_____ **24.** The Constitution of 1791 provided voting rights for
   **a.** all male citizens.  **c.** nobles and clergy only.
   **b.** all male and female citizens.  **d.** male citizens who paid a minimum tax.

_____ **25.** All of the following contributed to the French financial crisis EXCEPT
   **a.** lavish spending by Louis XV.  **c.** cost-cutting measures of Louis XVI.
   **b.** French support for the American Revolution.  **d.** unwillingness of the nobility and clergy to pay taxes.

## Essay
*Answer one of the following questions on a separate sheet of paper. (10 points)*

**26a. Critical Thinking** Describe the class structure of prerevolutionary French society.

**26b. Critical Thinking** Identify and describe four ways the French Revolution had a lasting influence outside of France.

# Chapter 23 : Form
# Test : Ⓐ

Score _____

## Matching

*Match each item in Column A with an item in Column B by writing the correct letters in the blanks.*
*(3 points each)*

**Column A**

_____ **1.** produced thread to be used for high-quality muslin

_____ **2.** forbade British union activity

_____ **3.** inventor of the power loom

_____ **4.** encouraged by Frederick Taylor

_____ **5.** Faraday's discoveries helped its creation

_____ **6.** forced many farmers to move to towns to find work

_____ **7.** American mill town

_____ **8.** rose from barber to textile tycoon

_____ **9.** inventor of the first practical steamboat

_____ **10.** involves shared business management and liability

**Column B**

**a.** enclosure movement

**b.** Arkwright

**c.** Fulton

**d.** spinning mule

**e.** partnership

**f.** Fall River

**g.** Cartwright

**h.** electric motor

**i.** Combination Acts

**j.** division of labor

## Multiple Choice

*In the blank, write the letter of the choice that best completes the statement. (4 points each)*

_____ **11.** Factors that contributed to Great Britain's industrial success included all of the following EXCEPT
  **a.** a labor pool comprised of displaced farmers.
  **b.** an abundance of capital.
  **c.** rich natural resources and a river network that provided transport.
  **d.** political stability provided by an absolute monarchy.

_____ **12.** The system in which profits are used to expand factories and invest in new businesses is called
  **a.** the factory system.
  **b.** mass production.
  **c.** industrial capitalism.
  **d.** collective bargaining.

_____ **13.** During the 1700s, the percentage of Europeans living in towns or cities was about
  **a.** 10 percent.
  **b.** 25 percent.
  **c.** 50 percent.
  **d.** 80 percent.

_____ **14.** The inventor of the wireless telegraph was
  **a.** Alexander Graham Bell.
  **b.** James Clerk Maxwell.
  **c.** Samuel Morse.
  **d.** Guglielmo Marconi.

_____ **15.** People involved in the domestic system earned money by working
  **a.** in unionized factories.
  **b.** on the estates of large rural landlords.
  **c.** in textile mills.
  **d.** at home.

# Chapter 23 : Form
# Test : Ⓐ

_____ **16.** Working conditions in nineteenth-century industry led to the growth of
  **a.** partnerships.　　**b.** the factory system.　　**c.** the middle class.　　**d.** labor unions.

_____ **17.** Most rural villagers in preindustrial times were
  **a.** farmers.　　**b.** merchants.　　**c.** artisans.　　**d.** servants.

_____ **18.** Collective bargaining refers to
  **a.** workers forming an association called a labor union.
  **b.** a government decreeing improved conditions for a group of workers.
  **c.** union leaders and an employer meeting together to reach an agreement.
  **d.** stockholders voting to determine workers' wages and products' prices.

_____ **19.** The country nicknamed "the workshop of the world" because of the success of its industrialists was
  **a.** Great Britain.　　**b.** the United States.　　**c.** Germany.　　**d.** France.

_____ **20.** Most of the earliest factories were located near major
  **a.** cities.　　**b.** natural harbors.　　**c.** waterways.　　**d.** railways.

_____ **21.** A business organization controlled by stockholders is called a
  **a.** partnership.　　**b.** corporation.　　**c.** union.　　**d.** collective.

_____ **22.** Textile workers in the mid-nineteenth century often
  **a.** worked long hours with dangerous machinery.
  **b.** worked in crudely constructed tenements.
  **c.** had much better working conditions than their counterparts in agriculture.
  **d.** hired domestic servants to perform their housework.

_____ **23.** All of the following inventions helped to revolutionize the textile industry EXCEPT
  **a.** the flying shuttle.
  **b.** the spinning jenny.
  **c.** the water frame.
  **d.** the dirigible.

_____ **24.** The nineteenth-century workers in the best position to exert bargaining pressure on their employers were
  **a.** employees of large-scale farmers.
  **b.** skilled workers who practiced a specific craft.
  **c.** workers in the textile industry.
  **d.** workers who operated machines.

_____ **25.** Major advances in metal production were made by William Kelly and
  **a.** Henry Bessemer.
  **b.** Eli Whitney.
  **c.** Richard Arkwright.
  **d.** James Hargreaves.

## Essay
*Answer one of the following questions on a separate sheet of paper. (10 points)*

**26a. Critical Thinking** Describe the mass-production process and the work of two innovators who contributed to its development.

**26b. Critical Thinking** Describe some of the changes the Industrial Revolution brought about in the lives of middle-class and working-class women.

# Chapter 23 : Form
# Test : **B**

Score _____

## Matching

Match each item in Column A with an item in Column B by writing the correct letters in the blanks.
(3 points each)

**Column A**

_____ **1.** business organization of two or more entrepreneurs

_____ **2.** early textile center

_____ **3.** inventor of the spinning jenny

_____ **4.** developed the oil-burning engine

_____ **5.** site of an early canal leading to coal fields

_____ **6.** money to invest in labor, materials, and machines

_____ **7.** assembly-line innovator

_____ **8.** inventor of cotton-cleaning machine

_____ **9.** meeting between union leaders and an employer

_____ **10.** inventor of the incandescent lightbulb and phonograph

**Column B**

**a.** James Hargreaves

**b.** Lowell, Massachusetts

**c.** capital

**d.** Thomas Edison

**e.** Rudolf Diesel

**f.** partnership

**g.** Eli Whitney

**h.** Manchester, England

**i.** collective bargaining

**j.** Henry Ford

## Multiple Choice

In the blank, write the letter of the choice that best completes the statement. (4 points each)

_____ **11.** Europe's largest city in the eighteenth century was
   **a.** Manchester.　　**b.** Paris.　　　　**c.** Rome.　　　　**d.** London.

_____ **12.** Someone who takes the risk of setting up a new business is called
   **a.** an aristocrat.　　**b.** a specialist.　　**c.** a partner.　　**d.** an entrepreneur.

_____ **13.** Early attempts by British workers to form labor unions were met with
   **a.** encouragement by factor owners.　　**c.** opposition from the worker associations.
   **b.** opposition from skilled laborers.　　**d.** opposition from the British Parliament.

_____ **14.** The average life expectancy in the preindustrial period was about
   **a.** age 20.　　**b.** age 40.　　　　**c.** age 60.　　　　**d.** age 70.

_____ **15.** The British tradition of planting crops and grazing on village lands was ended by the
   **a.** depression.　　　　　　　　　**c.** enclosure movement.
   **b.** factory system.　　　　　　　**d.** domestic system.

_____ **16.** The concept of interchangeable parts involved
   **a.** using assembly lines to decrease the cost of production.
   **b.** having workers perform identical specialized tasks.
   **c.** using machines to create uniform, exchangeable goods.
   **d.** allowing business costs to be shared equally among several partners.

# Chapter 23 : Form
# Test : B

_____ **17.** During the early industrial period, small industries often coordinated work schedules with
  **a.** rural festivals.     **b.** religious rituals.     **c.** agricultural cycles.   **d.** business cycles.

_____ **18.** James Watt helped set the Industrial Revolution in motion by developing
  **a.** the flying shuttle.
  **b.** a steam engine.
  **c.** a power loom.
  **d.** the water frame.

_____ **19.** Frederick Taylor is known for encouraging manufacturers to
  **a.** reinvest profits into new businesses.
  **b.** divide production work into specialized tasks.
  **c.** keep their industrial technology secret.
  **d.** fund railroad construction.

_____ **20.** In general, the Industrial Revolution led to increased
  **a.** flexibility in the European social structure.
  **b.** reliance in the textile industry on home-based labor.
  **c.** demand for skilled agricultural labor.
  **d.** skepticism in the value of education.

_____ **21.** The industry that spurred the introduction of the factory system was
  **a.** textile production.
  **b.** glassblowing.
  **c.** coal mining.
  **d.** automobile production.

_____ **22.** Rural villages had to be largely self-sufficient primarily because of
  **a.** feudal laws and obligations.
  **b.** the expense and difficulty of transportation.
  **c.** high taxes on commerce and trade.
  **d.** inequalities in the distribution of land.

_____ **23.** The early nineteenth-century textile industry was characterized by all of the following EXCEPT
  **a.** the extensive use of child labor.
  **b.** dangerous and unsanitary working conditions.
  **c.** an exclusively male workforce.
  **d.** the building of tenement housing for workers by mill owners.

_____ **24.** By 1870, the two countries that most closely ranked alongside Great Britain as industrial powers were the United States and
  **a.** France.     **b.** Italy.     **c.** Germany.     **d.** Japan.

_____ **25.** An engineer who contributed to advances in engine development was
  **a.** Ferdinand von Zeppelin.
  **b.** Gottlieb Daimler.
  **c.** Guglielmo Marconi.
  **d.** James Clerk Maxwell.

## Essay
_Answer one of the following questions on a separate sheet of paper. (10 points)_

**26a. Critical Thinking** Provide several reasons why Great Britain was able to achieve early industrial success.

**26b. Critical Thinking** Describe the working conditions of eighteenth- and nineteenth-century factory workers. How did these conditions contribute to the growth of labor unions?

# Chapter 24 : *Form*
# Test : **A**

Score _____

## Matching

*Match each item in Column A with an item in Column B by writing the correct letters in the blanks.*
*(3 points each)*

**Column A**

_____ **1.** economic activities controlled by the government

_____ **2.** gave women greater educational opportunity

_____ **3.** attempt at model Socialist community

_____ **4.** Courbet's characteristic style

_____ **5.** proposed that elements are composed of atoms

_____ **6.** nineteenth-century opera house

_____ **7.** the means of production should be owned by society

_____ **8.** British romantic poet

_____ **9.** formulated by Schleiden and Schwann

_____ **10.** critic of laissez-faire economics; free speech advocate

**Column B**

**a.** socialism

**b.** cell theory

**c.** Royal Albert Hall

**d.** mercantilism

**e.** John Stuart Mill

**f.** Robert Burns

**g.** realism

**h.** Mount Holyoke

**i.** New Harmony

**j.** John Dalton

## Multiple Choice

*In the blank, write the letter of the choice that best completes the statement. (4 points each)*

_____ **11.** According to Adam Smith, an economy works best when it is driven by
    **a.** government policy.
    **b.** foreign trade.
    **c.** competition.
    **d.** capital investment.

_____ **12.** All of the following were social scientists EXCEPT
    **a.** Sigmund Freud.
    **b.** Auguste Comte.
    **c.** Ivan Pavlov.
    **d.** Joseph Lister.

_____ **13.** The exploits of three dashing musketeers were recounted in a novel by
    **a.** Johann Wolfgang von Goethe.
    **b.** Leo Tolstoy.
    **c.** Sir Walter Scott.
    **d.** Alexandre Dumas.

_____ **14.** Between 1870 and 1900, unprecedented numbers of Europeans
    **a.** died of plague.
    **b.** died of malnutrition.
    **c.** immigrated to other countries.
    **d.** moved from urban to rural areas.

_____ **15.** The world's first vaccination was given by
    **a.** Edward Jenner.    **b.** Louis Pasteur.    **c.** Gregor Mendel.    **d.** John Dalton.

_____ **16.** Claude Monet became known as a master of
    **a.** naturalist literature.
    **b.** romantic composition.
    **c.** impressionist painting.
    **d.** symbolic poetry.

# Chapter 24 Form
# Test A

_____ **17.** Nineteenth-century surgical patients were less prone to dangerous infection because of the use of
   **a.** carbolic acid.   **b.** chloroform.   **c.** ether.   **d.** X rays.

_____ **18.** Supporters of laissez-faire policies favored
   **a.** the prohibition of child labor.
   **b.** reduced government interference in the economy.
   **c.** the formation of state-run labor unions.
   **d.** the improvement of working conditions in textile factories.

_____ **19.** The theorist who attempted to provide a scientific basis for socialism was
   **a.** Charles Darwin.   **b.** G. W. F. Hegel.   **c.** Karl Marx.   **d.** Robert Owen.

_____ **20.** The novels of Charles Dickens often
   **a.** depicted the deplorable conditions of the poor.
   **b.** illustrated his compassion for the Russian peasantry.
   **c.** focused on the glory and valor of legendary heroes.
   **d.** demonstrated a rejection of realist styles.

_____ **21.** The philosophy of utilitarianism stressed
   **a.** the repeal of laws that constrained industry.
   **b.** the utility of a free trade policy.
   **c.** public control of the means of production.
   **d.** measuring any law by its usefulness.

_____ **22.** Frederick Law Olmsted and his partners designed
   **a.** the Moulin Rouge.
   **b.** Central Park.
   **c.** the Louvre Museum.
   **d.** the Royal Albert Hall.

_____ **23.** The first women's college in America was opened by
   **a.** Mary Antin.   **b.** Sigmund Freud.   **c.** Mary Lyon.   **d.** George Sand.

_____ **24.** According to Charles Darwin, animal groups must struggle to survive because
   **a.** all living things desire to adapt.
   **b.** population tends to increase faster than the food supply.
   **c.** extinction is inevitable for most species.
   **d.** plant groups are better adapted for survival.

_____ **25.** William Wilberforce and Lord Shaftesbury favored
   **a.** government involvement in social concerns.
   **b.** laissez-faire economic policies.
   **c.** abolition of mercantilist controls on trade.
   **d.** seizure of power by the proletariat.

## Essay

_Answer one of the following questions on a separate sheet of paper. (10 points)_

**26a. Critical Thinking** Describe and explain the rapid urbanization that occurred in the industrialized countries. What problems resulted from this phenomenon?

**26b. Critical Thinking** Discuss Karl Marx's view of class struggle. How did this struggle emerge? What did Marx predict as its natural outcome?

# Chapter 24 : Form
# Test : B

Score _____

## Matching
*Match each item in Column A with an item in Column B by writing the correct letters in the blanks.*
*(3 points each)*

**Column A**

_____ **1.** anesthetic developed in nineteenth century

_____ **2.** Parisian art museum

_____ **3.** author of *The Wealth of Nations*

_____ **4.** author of *The Descent of Man*

_____ **5.** pioneered by Sigmund Freud

_____ **6.** the working class

_____ **7.** impressionist

_____ **8.** no government interference

_____ **9.** symbolist

_____ **10.** wrote classic study of English working class

**Column B**

**a.** psychoanalysis

**b.** laissez-faire

**c.** Friedrich Engels

**d.** Claude Monet

**e.** Adam Smith

**f.** chloroform

**g.** Charles Darwin

**h.** Stéphane Mallarmé

**i.** Louvre

**j.** proletariat

## Multiple Choice
*In the blank, write the letter of the choice that best completes the statement. (4 points each)*

_____ **11.** Karl Marx argued that history was advanced by the conflict between

    **a.** classes.    **b.** ideas.    **c.** nations.    **d.** capitalists.

_____ **12.** According to David Ricardo's "iron law of wages,"

    **a.** wages would increase only during a "boom" period.

    **b.** employers should be forced by the government to increase wages.

    **c.** wages would increase naturally over time.

    **d.** workers were condemned to falling wages and continual poverty.

_____ **13.** During the 1800s, all of the following contributed to improved health and population growth EXCEPT

    **a.** the development of new methods of preserving food.

    **b.** migration out of the crowded cities.

    **c.** advances in the prevention and treatment of disease.

    **d.** the availability of a greater variety of food products.

_____ **14.** All of the following scientists contributed to our understanding of radioactivity EXCEPT

    **a.** Marie Sklodowska Curie.

    **b.** Wilhelm K. Roentgen.

    **c.** Max Planck.

    **d.** Edward Jenner.

_____ **15.** By 1914 the percentage of British people living in cities had reached

    **a.** 10 percent.    **b.** 35 percent.    **c.** 50 percent.    **d.** 80 percent.

_____ **16.** Adam Smith criticized mercantilism because he disapproved of

    **a.** competition between national and foreign industries.

    **b.** competition between local merchants.

    **c.** the regulation of commerce and industry by the government.

    **d.** the pursuit of wealth.

# Chapter 24 : Form
# Test : B

_____ **17.** The emphasis on emotion and imagination over reason was characteristic of
    **a.** socialism.      **b.** romanticism.      **c.** realism.      **d.** symbolism.

_____ **18.** Jean-Baptiste de Lamarck's theory, which was eventually disproved, suggested that living things
    **a.** are made up of tiny units of matter called cells.
    **b.** adapt to their environment and pass the changes on to the next generation.
    **c.** increase in number faster than their food supply increases.
    **d.** reproduce only if they are well adapted to their environment.

_____ **19.** During the 1830s and 1840s, the British Parliament passed legislation
    **a.** outlawing all use of child labor.
    **b.** regulating working conditions for women and children.
    **c.** establishing a minimum wage.
    **d.** banning the publication of _The Communist Manifesto_.

_____ **20.** The compositions of Ludwig van Beethoven and Peter Tchaikovsky
    **a.** emphasized reason, form, and order.
    **b.** were intended to stir the emotions.
    **c.** rejected romantic sentimentality.
    **d.** were influenced by the symbolist movement.

_____ **21.** Louis Pasteur discovered that bacteria
    **a.** did not cause smallpox.
    **b.** can appear spontaneously.
    **c.** reproduce like other living things.
    **d.** cannot adapt to a change in environment.

_____ **22.** Balzac's collection of novels and stories is called
    **a.** _The American Tragedy._
    **b.** _War and Peace._
    **c.** _Songs of Experience._
    **d.** _The Human Comedy._

_____ **23.** Gregor Mendel's experiments with pea plants provided the basis for the study of
    **a.** cells.      **b.** genes.      **c.** bacteria.      **d.** atoms.

_____ **24.** The Welsh socialist who tried to set up a model community in Indiana was
    **a.** Friedrich Engels.      **b.** Karl Marx.      **c.** Robert Owen.      **d.** Jeremy Bentham.

_____ **25.** The movement of people from rural areas to cities is referred to as
    **a.** urbanization.      **b.** emigration.      **c.** immigration.      **d.** city planning.

## Essay
_Answer one of the following questions on a separate sheet of paper. (10 points)_

**26a. Critical Thinking** Discuss the factors that contributed to increased emigration from Europe in the late nineteenth century.

**26b. Critical Thinking** Describe two artistic movements of the 1800s, and explain how each movement influenced the work of one artist.

# Chapter 25 : *Form*
# Test : Ⓐ

**Score** _____

## Matching

*Match each item in Column A with an item in Column B by writing the correct letters in the blanks.*
*(3 points each)*

**Column A**

_____ **1.** favored apportionment of electoral districts

_____ **2.** first Canadian prime minister

_____ **3.** leader of the WSPU

_____ **4.** French reactionaries who wanted to restore absolute monarchy

_____ **5.** petitioned Parliament for political change

_____ **6.** led the Haitian revolt

_____ **7.** sold the Louisiana Territory

_____ **8.** helped Chile achieve independence

_____ **9.** army officer whose case deeply split France

_____ **10.** asked Congress to pass the Nineteenth Amendment

**Column B**

**a.** John A. Macdonald

**b.** Napoleon I

**c.** Whigs

**d.** Toussaint-Louverture

**e.** Emmeline Pankhurst

**f.** Woodrow Wilson

**g.** ultraroyalists

**h.** Chartists

**i.** Bernardo O'Higgins

**j.** Alfred Dreyfus

## Multiple Choice

*In the blank, write the letter of the choice that best completes the statement. (4 points each)*

_____ **11.** The country originally founded as a British prisoners' colony is
   **a.** New Zealand.
   **b.** Prince Edward Island.
   **c.** British Honduras.
   **d.** Australia.

_____ **12.** The Constitutional Act of 1791 divided Quebec into
   **a.** English-ruled and French-ruled colonies.
   **b.** English-speaking and French-speaking colonies.
   **c.** English and Native American territories.
   **d.** English and American territories.

_____ **13.** William Gladstone directed all of the following reforms EXCEPT
   **a.** making civil services posts dependent on competitive exams.
   **b.** implementing the secret ballot.
   **c.** dividing Britain into equal electoral districts.
   **d.** allowing women to vote in national elections.

_____ **14.** The number of Americans who died in the Civil War was around
   **a.** 50,000.    **b.** 100,000.    **c.** 300,000.    **d.** 600,000.

_____ **15.** A quick seizure of political power is referred to as
   **a.** a plebiscite.    **b.** a coup d'état.    **c.** an apportion.    **d.** a suffragette.

_____ **16.** In the early 1800s, the greatest political power in Britain was wielded by the
   **a.** working class.
   **b.** middle class.
   **c.** landed aristocracy.
   **d.** clergy.

# Chapter 25 : *Form*
# Test : Ⓐ

_____ **17.** The colonial leaders of Latin America who had been born in Europe were called
     **a.** mestizos.
     **b.** creoles.
     **c.** Fabians.
     **d.** *peninsulares.*

_____ **18.** After achieving power, Charles X sought to restore
     **a.** the directory.
     **b.** absolute monarchy.
     **c.** constitutional monarchy.
     **d.** constitutional democracy.

_____ **19.** The Venezuelan-born creole who led the liberation of South America was
     **a.** Simón Bolívar.
     **b.** King João.
     **c.** Dom Pedro.
     **d.** Miguel Hidalgo.

_____ **20.** Florida was ceded to the United States
     **a.** as part of the Louisiana Purchase.
     **b.** as part of the Gadsden Purchase.
     **c.** because of Spain's internal conflicts.
     **d.** after the Mexican-American War.

_____ **21.** One Latin American colony that achieved independence with little bloodshed was
     **a.** Haiti.
     **b.** Brazil.
     **c.** Mexico.
     **d.** Peru.

_____ **22.** France's presidential elections in 1848 resulted in the victory of
     **a.** François Toussaint-Louverture.
     **b.** Louis Philippe.
     **c.** Louis-Napoleon Bonaparte.
     **d.** Napoleon Bonaparte.

_____ **23.** American women first achieved the right to vote at the state level in
     **a.** Wyoming, Colorado, and Utah.
     **b.** North and South Carolina.
     **c.** Kansas.
     **d.** Michigan and New York.

_____ **24.** Irish hatred of British rule was generated by all of the following EXCEPT
     **a.** a law requiring Catholics to pay taxes to the Anglican Church.
     **b.** the British refusal to allow the export of Irish grain.
     **c.** the control of Irish land by the English and the Scots.
     **d.** the British response to the potato famine.

_____ **25.** The Dominion of Canada originally included all of the following EXCEPT
     **a.** New Brunswick.
     **b.** Nova Scotia.
     **c.** Upper Canada.
     **d.** Manitoba.

## Essay
*Answer one of the following questions on a separate sheet of paper. (10 points)*

**26a.** **Critical Thinking** Describe the relationship between church and state in the Latin American colonies of Spain and Portugal.

**26b.** **Critical Thinking** Summarize the efforts of women to achieve greater legal and political rights in England and the United States. Identify the leaders of these efforts.

# Chapter 25 : Form
# Test : Ⓑ

**Score** _____

## Matching

*Match each item in Column A with an item in Column B by writing the correct letters in the blanks.*
*(3 points each)*

**Column A**

_____ **1.** woman fighting for the right to vote

_____ **2.** "Citizen-King"

_____ **3.** ruled Paris briefly

_____ **4.** organizer of the NWSA

_____ **5.** head of the British cabinet

_____ **6.** colonial-born white aristocrats

_____ **7.** evolved into the Conservative party

_____ **8.** urged self-rule for Canada

_____ **9.** urged home rule for Ireland

_____ **10.** hoped to install socialism through
parliamentary action

**Column B**

**a.** Louis Philippe

**b.** creoles

**c.** Commune

**d.** Elizabeth Cady Stanton

**e.** prime minister

**f.** Charles Stewart Parnell

**g.** Fabians

**h.** Lord Durham

**i.** suffragette

**j.** Tories

## Multiple Choice

*In the blank, write the letter of the choice that best completes the statement. (4 points each)*

_____ **11.** The self-governing territories established by Britain in the 1800s were called
    **a.** colonies.
    **b.** dominions.
    **c.** provinces.
    **d.** communes.

_____ **12.** Prussia won the provinces of Alsace and Lorraine from
    **a.** Russia.
    **b.** France.
    **c.** Crimea.
    **d.** Sardinia.

_____ **13.** Miguel Hidalgo led Native Americans and mestizos in a revolt against
    **a.** Spanish rule.
    **b.** French rule.
    **c.** American rule.
    **d.** Portuguese rule.

_____ **14.** Married British women achieved property rights through the efforts of
    **a.** suffragists.
    **b.** socialists.
    **c.** activists.
    **d.** trade unionists.

_____ **15.** After Napoleon's invasion, King João transferred his monarchy to
    **a.** Brazil.
    **b.** Portugal.
    **c.** Spain.
    **d.** Mexico.

_____ **16.** The Reform Act of 1832 reduced
    **a.** the property qualifications necessary to vote.
    **b.** the parliamentary representation of urban areas.
    **c.** the ability of worker associations to form trade unions.
    **d.** the male dominance of parliament.

# Chapter 25 : *Form*
# Test : B

_____ **17.** The first successful uprising in the Latin American colonies was staged by enslaved Africans in
   **a.** Brazil.
   **b.** Haiti.
   **c.** Peru.
   **d.** Chile.

_____ **18.** The greatest crisis of the Third Republic involved the
   **a.** fall of the Commune.
   **b.** case of Alfred Dreyfus.
   **c.** Prussian siege of Paris.
   **d.** conflict over the Crimean Peninsula.

_____ **19.** Great Britain gained control of Quebec in the
   **a.** Maori Wars.
   **b.** French and Indian War.
   **c.** Revolutionary War.
   **d.** Franco-Prussian War.

_____ **20.** Between 1870 and 1900, the population of the United States increased by
   **a.** 20 percent.
   **b.** 35 percent.
   **c.** 60 percent.
   **d.** 100 percent.

_____ **21.** The President who acquired the Louisiana Territory from France was
   **a.** Abraham Lincoln.
   **b.** Woodrow Wilson.
   **c.** Thomas Jefferson.
   **d.** George Washington.

_____ **22.** The rush of new immigrants into Australia was sparked by the
   **a.** defeat of the Maori.
   **b.** defeat of the Aborigines.
   **c.** completion of the Pacific Railway.
   **d.** discovery of gold.

_____ **23.** All of the following are true of the 1845 Irish potato famine EXCEPT that
   **a.** many Irish fled the country for the United States.
   **b.** at least a million Irish died of starvation or disease.
   **c.** the British government responded with immediate and generous aid.
   **d.** a deadly fungus destroyed much of the potato crop.

_____ **24.** The first Southern state to secede from the Union was
   **a.** South Carolina.
   **b.** North Carolina.
   **c.** Georgia.
   **d.** Alabama.

_____ **25.** After *Les Trois Glorieuses*, Parisians forced Charles X to
   **a.** abdicate the throne.
   **b.** restore Catholicism as the state religion.
   **c.** issue the July Ordinances.
   **d.** repay aristocrats for property lost during the revolution.

## Essay
*Answer one of the following questions on a separate sheet of paper. (10 points)*

**26a. Critical Thinking** Describe the roles of Simón Bolívar and José de San Martín in liberating Latin America from Spanish rule.

**26b. Critical Thinking** Provide a summary of New Zealand's political history.

# Chapter 26 : Form
# Test : Ⓐ

**Score** _____

## Matching
*Match each item in Column A with an item in Column B by writing the correct letters in the blanks.*
*(3 points each)*

**Column A**

_____ **1.** treaty ending Russo-Turkish War

_____ **2.** first ruler of a united Italy

_____ **3.** anarchist leader

_____ **4.** economic union

_____ **5.** champion of German working class

_____ **6.** the Italian unity movement

_____ **7.** accepted Bismarck's resignation

_____ **8.** massacre of a minority group

_____ **9.** a local Russian assembly

_____ **10.** to achieve objectives by any means necessary

**Column B**

**a.** zemstvo

**b.** *Risorgimento*

**c.** Michael Bakunin

**d.** San Stefano

**e.** realpolitik

**f.** pogrom

**g.** Victor Emmanuel II

**h.** *Zollverein*

**i.** William II

**j.** Lassalle

## Multiple Choice
*In the blank, write the letter of the choice that best completes the statement. (4 points each)*

_____ **11.** William I's title as ruler of a united Germany was
  **a.** chancellor.
  **b.** prime minister.
  **c.** Junker.
  **d.** kaiser.

_____ **12.** Bismarck tried to claim that he protected worker interests by directing passage of the
  **a.** anti-Socialist bill.
  **b.** Sickness Insurance Law.
  **c.** May Laws.
  **d.** October Manifesto.

_____ **13.** In 1815 the Italian provinces of Lombardy and Venetia were controlled by
  **a.** the national government of Italy.
  **b.** Austria.
  **c.** the Bourbon monarchy.
  **d.** the pope.

_____ **14.** In October 1905, Nicholas II was forced to issue a manifesto that
  **a.** abolished the secret police.
  **b.** granted emancipation to the serfs.
  **c.** prohibited the persecution of the Jews.
  **d.** granted lawmaking power to the duma.

_____ **15.** During the mid-1800s, Bohemia and Moravia became the industrial centers of
  **a.** Germany.
  **b.** the Russian Empire.
  **c.** the Ottoman Empire.
  **d.** the Austro-Hungarian Empire.

_____ **16.** To gain control of Schleswig, Bismarck began a war with
  **a.** Prussia.
  **b.** Bavaria.
  **c.** Denmark.
  **d.** France.

_____ **17.** Pope Pius IX broke diplomatic ties with Germany because of
  **a.** passage of the May Laws.
  **b.** establishment of the *Zollverein*.
  **c.** the popularity of the Center party.
  **d.** the end of the Kulturkampf.

# Chapter 26 : Form
# Test : Ⓐ

_____ **18.** The decline of the Ottoman Empire made European powers fear
  **a.** Russian expansion.
  **b.** Turkish expansion.
  **c.** Hungarian expansion.
  **d.** Serbian expansion.

_____ **19.** The reign of Nicholas I was marked by his attempts to
  **a.** emancipate the serfs.
  **b.** hasten Russian industrialization.
  **c.** suppress all opposition to the autocracy.
  **d.** end Japanese control of Manchuria.

_____ **20.** The Universal German Workingmen's Association became a major political force after its merger with the
  **a.** Mensheviks.
  **b.** Bolsheviks.
  **c.** Social Democratic party.
  **d.** Conservative party.

_____ **21.** The Genoan-born nationalist leader who founded Young Italy was
  **a.** Charles Albert.
  **b.** Camillo di Cavour.
  **c.** Giuseppe Mazzini.
  **d.** Giuseppe Garibaldi.

_____ **22.** The Magyars are the people of
  **a.** Bohemia.
  **b.** Hungary.
  **c.** Montenegro.
  **d.** Bulgaria.

_____ **23.** A major reason for Russia's late industrialization was
  **a.** the Mensheviks' distaste for industrial development.
  **b.** the relative prosperity of its peasantry.
  **c.** a continued conflict between Eastern Orthodoxy and Catholicism.
  **d.** its serf-based agricultural system.

_____ **24.** The Seven Weeks' War began soon after Prussian troops entered
  **a.** Holstein.
  **b.** Austria.
  **c.** Schleswig.
  **d.** Bulgaria.

_____ **25.** Sardinia gained foreign support by
  **a.** aiding Austria during the Crimean War.
  **b.** aiding France and Great Britain during the Crimean War.
  **c.** opposing the Balkan League.
  **d.** signing a treaty with Emperor Francis Joseph.

## Essay
_Answer one of the following questions on a separate sheet of paper. (10 points)_

**26a. Critical Thinking** Describe the role played by Camillo di Cavour in furthering the goal of Italian unification.

**26b. Critical Thinking** Describe and compare two Russian radical political groups.

# Chapter 26 *Form*
# Test B

## Matching
*Match each item in Column A with an item in Column B by writing the correct letters in the blanks.*
*(3 points each)*

**Column A**

_____ **1.** Czar Liberator

_____ **2.** aimed at weakening German Catholics

_____ **3.** in theory, made Russia a constitutional monarchy

_____ **4.** clever adviser to the Sardinian king

_____ **5.** first ruler of a united Germany

_____ **6.** called "the powder keg of Europe"

_____ **7.** object of Russian-Japanese conflict

_____ **8.** German chancellor

_____ **9.** divided Bulgaria into three parts

_____ **10.** Hungarian leader

**Column B**

**a.** May Laws

**b.** Alexander II

**c.** Francis Deak

**d.** Manchuria

**e.** Otto von Bismarck

**f.** October Manifesto

**g.** Camillo di Cavour

**h.** Congress of Berlin

**i.** the Balkans

**j.** William I

## Multiple Choice
*In the blank, write the letter of the choice that best completes the statement. (4 points each)*

_____ **11.** The struggle between the Catholic Church and the German state was referred to as the
  **a.** *Risorgimento.*
  **b.** Kulturkampf.
  **c.** Metternich.
  **d.** dual monarchy.

_____ **12.** In 1860 the entire Italian Peninsula came under unified rule with the exception of
  **a.** the Two Sicilies.
  **b.** Rome and Venetia.
  **c.** Lombardy and Venetia.
  **d.** Sardinia.

_____ **13.** The German Conservative party was controlled by
  **a.** workers.
  **b.** Catholics.
  **c.** serfs.
  **d.** Junkers.

_____ **14.** Two-thirds of the population of the Russian Empire was composed of
  **a.** Slavs.
  **b.** Magyars.
  **c.** Serbs.
  **d.** Slovaks.

_____ **15.** Smaller German states opposed unification, fearing that a united Germany would be dominated by
  **a.** Frankfurt.
  **b.** Prussia.
  **c.** Austria.
  **d.** Schleswig.

_____ **16.** In 1848 the effort of the united Italian forces to drive the Austrians out of Italy failed when
  **a.** Pope Pius IX withdrew his troops.
  **b.** Charles Albert gained control of Lombardy and Venetia.
  **c.** the Sardinians joined the Austrian side.
  **d.** angry mobs forced Mazzini to flee Rome.

# Chapter 26 : *Form*
# Test : **B**

_____ **17.** The achievement of independence by the Greeks illustrated the weakening of the
    **a.** Austro-Hungarian Empire.
    **b.** Ottoman Empire.
    **c.** Russian Empire.
    **d.** Slavic Empire.

_____ **18.** The Balkan League included all of the following countries EXCEPT
    **a.** Serbia.
    **b.** Montenegro.
    **c.** Romania.
    **d.** Bulgaria.

_____ **19.** German states formed a *Zollverein* to
    **a.** facilitate commerce between German states.
    **b.** raise tariffs on trans-Germanic trade.
    **c.** unite the German states under the rule of the kaiser.
    **d.** prevent Danish annexation of Schleswig.

_____ **20.** After the *Ausgleich*, or Compromise, Francis Joseph remained ruler of both
    **a.** Schleswig and Holstein.
    **b.** Austria and Hungary.
    **c.** Serbia and Bosnia.
    **d.** Russia and Manchuria.

_____ **21.** The government of the Kingdom of the Two Sicilies was overthrown by
    **a.** Giuseppe Garibaldi.
    **b.** Victor Emmanuel II.
    **c.** Camillo di Cavour.
    **d.** Charles Albert.

_____ **22.** Jews were often victims of persecution under Alexander III's policy of
    **a.** realpolitik.
    **b.** nihilism.
    **c.** militarism.
    **d.** Russification.

_____ **23.** Ferdinand Lassalle fought against the low wages and harsh working conditions of
    **a.** Italian workers.
    **b.** Hungarian workers.
    **c.** German workers.
    **d.** Russian workers.

_____ **24.** The Decembrist Revolt was an attempt to seize power by
    **a.** Bakunin-led nihilists.
    **b.** Bolsheviks.
    **c.** Russian military officers.
    **d.** the zemstvos.

_____ **25.** In preparation for war against Austria, Bismarck did all of the following EXCEPT
    **a.** offer Russia aid against Polish rebels.
    **b.** offer France compensation for remaining neutral.
    **c.** make an alliance with King Christian IX.
    **d.** make an alliance with Italy by supporting its territorial claims.

## Essay

*Answer one of the following questions on a separate sheet of paper. (10 points)*

**26a. Critical Thinking** Explain how and why nationalism threatened the stability of the Austro-Hungarian Empire.

**26b. Critical Thinking** Explain how Russia's agricultural system contributed to its late industrialization.

# Chapter 27 : Form

# Test : Ⓐ

Score _____

## Matching
*Match each item in Column A with an item in Column B by writing the correct letters in the blanks.*
*(3 points each)*

**Column A**

_____ **1.** opposed Qing dynasty

_____ **2.** New York journalist turned African explorer

_____ **3.** remained independent despite French invasion

_____ **4.** Spanish were blamed for its sinking

_____ **5.** territory having its own government, but guided by a foreign power

_____ **6.** subject of British-Venezuelan dispute

_____ **7.** object of Japanese attack

_____ **8.** present-day Zimbabwe

_____ **9.** present-day Libya

_____ **10.** territory ruled directly by an imperial power

**Column B**

**a.** protectorate

**b.** Stanley

**c.** *Maine*

**d.** Port Arthur

**e.** Rhodesia

**f.** United League

**g.** Siam

**h.** colony

**i.** Guiana

**j.** Tripoli

## Multiple Choice
*In the blank, write the letter of the choice that best completes the statement. (4 points each)*

_____ **11.** Mohandas K. Gandhi fought for the rights of Indians in
  **a.** Korea.
  **b.** Japan.
  **c.** Libya.
  **d.** South Africa.

_____ **12.** Cecil Rhodes made his African fortune by
  **a.** mining gold and diamonds.
  **b.** planting bananas, melons, and other exotic fruit.
  **c.** planting cotton and jute.
  **d.** cultivating and processing rubber.

_____ **13.** British merchants earned huge profits in China by smuggling in
  **a.** textiles.
  **b.** silk.
  **c.** gold.
  **d.** opium.

_____ **14.** In 1885, 14 nations met in Berlin to discuss the partition of
  **a.** Southeast Asia.
  **b.** South America.
  **c.** China.
  **d.** Africa.

_____ **15.** Much of Europe's knowledge of Africa was gained from missionaries such as
  **a.** Matthew C. Perry.
  **b.** David Livingstone.
  **c.** Rudyard Kipling.
  **d.** Samory Touré.

_____ **16.** The Spanish-American War occurred during the presidency of
  **a.** Theodore Roosevelt.
  **b.** William McKinley.
  **c.** James Monroe.
  **d.** Woodrow Wilson.

# Chapter 27 : Form
# Test : Ⓐ

_____ **17.** The West African state of Liberia avoided European colonization primarily because of
    **a.** the determination of Emperor Menelik II.  **c.** its support from the United States.
    **b.** its status as a British protectorate.  **d.** its lack of arable land and other exploitable resources.

_____ **18.** Indian soldiers in the service of the British were called
    **a.** Boers.  **c.** viceroys.
    **b.** sepoys.  **d.** Boxers.

_____ **19.** Afrikaners is the name given to the South African settlers from
    **a.** the Netherlands.  **c.** Great Britain.
    **b.** Belgium.  **d.** France.

_____ **20.** In 1853 Matthew Perry used naval power to force Japan to
    **a.** begin trading with the United States.  **c.** end the opium trade.
    **b.** cut off trade with Europe.  **d.** end its colonization of Korea.

_____ **21.** The Roosevelt Corollary implied that the United States would
    **a.** not tolerate European interference in the Americas.  **c.** not accept third-party arbitration of territorial disputes.
    **b.** not accept Spanish influence in Cuba.  **d.** intervene in Latin America to force repayment of foreign debts.

_____ **22.** One powerful African king who battled the Europeans in South Africa was
    **a.** Muhammad Ali.  **c.** Menelik II.
    **b.** Abd al-Qadir.  **d.** Shaka.

_____ **23.** In 1882 an Egyptian revolt was defeated and the country was ruled as a British
    **a.** colony.  **c.** protectorate.
    **b.** sphere of influence.  **d.** dominion.

_____ **24.** Japan became an industrial power during the rule of the
    **a.** British viceroy.  **c.** Meiji leaders.
    **b.** Qing dynasty.  **d.** shogun.

_____ **25.** Colonial officials often discouraged native peoples from
    **a.** learning European languages.  **c.** converting to Christianity.
    **b.** adopting Western lifestyles.  **d.** practicing traditional customs and rituals.

## Essay
_Answer one of the following questions on a separate sheet of paper. (10 points)_

**26a. Critical Thinking** Provide a summary of the political history of South Africa.

**26b. Critical Thinking** Describe the events leading to the construction of the Panama Canal. What was the role of the United States? Why was the canal's construction important?

# Chapter 27 : *Form*
# Test : B

Score _____

## Matching
*Match each item in Column A with an item in Column B by writing the correct letters in the blanks. (3 points each)*

**Column A**

_____ **1.** discouraged European interference in the Americas

_____ **2.** founded colony in present-day Zimbabwe

_____ **3.** led by Cetywayo, initially defeated the British

_____ **4.** British called them Boers

_____ **5.** demanded that Japan open up for trade

_____ **6.** domination of one country by another

_____ **7.** was used as proof of Europeans' superiority

_____ **8.** resisted British colonialists in the Gold Coast

_____ **9.** encouraged Chinese opium use

_____ **10.** repelled Italian invasion

**Column B**

**a.** imperialism

**b.** Great Britain

**c.** Monroe Doctrine

**d.** Cecil Rhodes

**e.** Afrikaners

**f.** Ethiopia

**g.** Zulu

**h.** Matthew C. Perry

**i.** social Darwinism

**j.** Ashanti

## Multiple Choice
*In the blank, write the letter of the choice that best completes the statement. (4 points each)*

_____ **11.** The Suez Canal connected the
   **a.** Malay and Indochinese Peninsulas.
   **b.** Nile River to the Persian Gulf.
   **c.** Pacific and Atlantic Oceans.
   **d.** Red Sea to the Mediterranean Sea.

_____ **12.** By 1860 colonial control of most of India had been achieved by the
   **a.** Germans.
   **b.** Belgians.
   **c.** British.
   **d.** French.

_____ **13.** The region King Leopold II made into his private plantation was
   **a.** Sierra Leone.
   **b.** Togo.
   **c.** Congo.
   **d.** Angola.

_____ **14.** Samory Touré led his armies against French invaders in
   **a.** North Africa.
   **b.** West Africa.
   **c.** South Africa.
   **d.** Indochina.

_____ **15.** Non-Western nationalist leaders were inspired by the outcome of the
   **a.** Indian Revolt of 1857.
   **b.** Boxer Uprising.
   **c.** Opium War.
   **d.** Russo-Japanese War.

_____ **16.** During the 1840s, thousands of French citizens migrated to the colony of
   **a.** Libya.
   **b.** Algeria.
   **c.** New Zealand.
   **d.** Zimbabwe.

_____ **17.** In 1910 Korea became a colony of the
   **a.** Japanese.
   **b.** Chinese.
   **c.** British.
   **d.** Americans.

# Chapter 27 : *Form*
# Test : **B**

_____ **18.** Woodrow Wilson sent U.S. soldiers to capture Pancho Villa for
  **a.** killing American citizens.
  **b.** assassinating a president of Mexico.
  **c.** invading Cuba.
  **d.** overthrowing the government of Porfirio Díaz.

_____ **19.** A region where an imperialist power possesses exclusive trading rights but does not govern is referred to as a
  **a.** colony.
  **b.** protectorate.
  **c.** sphere of influence.
  **d.** partition.

_____ **20.** In 1898 the Philippines became a colony again after the
  **a.** defeat of its rebels by the Spanish.
  **b.** failure of the Japanese to help it defeat the Americans.
  **c.** defeat of its rebels by the Dutch.
  **d.** failure of the United States to keep its promise of independence.

_____ **21.** The essence of the imperialist attitude is captured in the poem "The White Man's Burden" written by
  **a.** Charles Darwin.
  **b.** Rudyard Kipling.
  **c.** Henry M. Stanley.
  **d.** Benito Juárez.

_____ **22.** The Qing dynasty fell, and Sun Yat-sen became president after the
  **a.** Revolution of 1911.
  **b.** Boxer Uprising.
  **c.** Opium War.
  **d.** Sino-Japanese War.

_____ **23.** The construction of the Panama Canal was made possible by the
  **a.** success of the Mexican Revolution.
  **b.** British acceptance of arbitration with Venezuela.
  **c.** Spanish defeat in Cuba.
  **d.** American intervention in Colombia.

_____ **24.** The last European colony established in North Africa and Italy's only African possession was the territory then called
  **a.** Tripoli.
  **b.** Tunis.
  **c.** the Sudan.
  **d.** Dahomey.

_____ **25.** All of the following territories became part of the Union of South Africa EXCEPT
  **a.** the Transvaal.
  **b.** the Cape Colony.
  **c.** Natal.
  **d.** the Congo.

## Essay
*Answer one of the following questions on a separate sheet of paper. (10 points)*

**26a. Critical Thinking** Describe the role of the Industrial Revolution in triggering European imperialism in the nineteenth century.

**26a. Critical Thinking** Identify two African countries that avoided colonization during the 1800s. How did they manage to remain independent?

# Chapter 28 : *Form*
# Test : Ⓐ

**Score** _____

## Matching

*Match each item in Column A with an item in Column B by writing the correct letters in the blanks.*
*(3 points each)*

**Column A**

_____ **1.** part of Germany after Franco-Prussian War

_____ **2.** site of Russian Revolution

_____ **3.** introduced by Admiral Sims

_____ **4.** battle at which tank warfare was introduced

_____ **5.** passenger liner sunk by the Germans

_____ **6.** the glorification of war

_____ **7.** the preparation for war

_____ **8.** led the French at Verdun

_____ **9.** leader of the unified command in the west

_____ **10.** ship whose guns Bolsheviks aimed at the Winter Palace

**Column B**

**a.** Henri Pétain

**b.** mobilization

**c.** *Lusitania*

**d.** the Somme

**e.** Alsace-Lorraine

**f.** *Aurora*

**g.** Ferdinand Foch

**h.** convoy system

**i.** militarism

**j.** Petrograd

## Multiple Choice

*In the blank, write the letter of the choice that best completes the statement. (4 points each)*

_____ **11.** Germany ignored an 1839 treaty that guaranteed the neutrality of
    **a.** Serbia.
    **b.** Belgium.
    **c.** England.
    **d.** Luxembourg.

_____ **12.** The term for an understanding—but not an alliance—between two nations is
    **a.** entente.
    **b.** cordon sanitaire.
    **c.** contraband.
    **d.** armistice.

_____ **13.** Rasputin was a mystical healer and adviser to
    **a.** Nicholas II.
    **b.** Winston Churchill.
    **c.** Woodrow Wilson.
    **d.** Otto von Bismarck.

_____ **14.** The Slavic territories annexed by Austria-Hungary in 1908 were
    **a.** Alsace-Lorraine.
    **b.** Bosnia-Herzegovina.
    **c.** Serbia and Albania.
    **d.** Serbia and Montenegro.

_____ **15.** The Bolsheviks believed that a socialist society
    **a.** could be achieved through parliamentary action.
    **b.** must be the work of the masses.
    **c.** could be achieved through a peasant-led revolution.
    **d.** could be introduced by a small group of dedicated revolutionaries.

_____ **16.** In 1917 the Germans resumed a policy of unrestricted submarine warfare in order to
    **a.** discourage American entry into the war.
    **b.** break American control of the seas.
    **c.** break British control of the seas.
    **d.** win "the race to the sea."

# Chapter 28 : *Form*
# **Test : Ⓐ**

_____ **17.** The number of soldiers killed or wounded in World War I was about
  **a.** 2 million.
  **b.** 9 million.
  **c.** 30 million.
  **d.** 100 million.

_____ **18.** Austria-Hungary's ultimatum to Serbia was triggered by
  **a.** Germany's invasion of Belgium.
  **b.** the assassination of Archduke Francis Ferdinand.
  **c.** the sinking of the *Lusitania*.
  **d.** the delivery of the Zimmermann telegram.

_____ **19.** The members of the Triple Entente were France, Russia, and
  **a.** Germany.
  **b.** Great Britain.
  **c.** Serbia.
  **d.** Austria-Hungary.

_____ **20.** Disagreeing with Woodrow Wilson, France demanded that any peace settlement must include
  **a.** the payment of reparations.
  **b.** the guarantee of freedom of the seas.
  **c.** the guarantee of freedom of trade.
  **d.** the establishment of a "general assembly of nations."

_____ **21.** During the long stalemate on the Western Front, many soldiers
  **a.** returned home for rest and recovery.
  **b.** returned home to work in weapons production.
  **c.** lived in trenches for weeks at a time.
  **d.** deserted to the opposing side.

_____ **22.** At the beginning of the war, Italy
  **a.** sided with the Allies.
  **b.** sided with the Central Powers.
  **c.** sided with the Ottoman Empire.
  **d.** remained neutral.

_____ **23.** Bringing Russia back into the war against the Central Powers was one objective of Allied support for the
  **a.** Reds.
  **b.** Whites.
  **c.** Bolsheviks.
  **d.** Petrograd Soviet.

_____ **24.** The failure of the Schlieffen Plan was finally made apparent by
  **a.** United States entrance into the war.
  **b.** continued British control of the seas.
  **c.** Russian defeat in Tannenberg.
  **d.** German defeat at the Battle of the Marne.

_____ **25.** Russia felt compelled to aid Serbia in order to maintain
  **a.** its position as defender of Slavic interests.
  **b.** its membership in the Triple Entente.
  **c.** its relationship with France.
  **d.** the principle of Serbian neutrality.

## Essay
*Answer one of the following questions on a separate sheet of paper. (10 points)*

**26a.** **Critical Thinking** Describe the loss of territory suffered by the Central Powers as a result of the agreements made at the end of World War I.

**26b.** **Critical Thinking** Describe the use of new military technology and methods that characterized World War I.

# Chapter 28 : *Form*
# Test : **B**

## Matching

*Match each item in Column A with an item in Column B by writing the correct letters in the blanks.*
*(3 points each)*

**Column A**

_____ **1.** site of Francis Ferdinand's assassination

_____ **2.** leader of the Red Army

_____ **3.** threatened by Pan-Slavism

_____ **4.** aided the British fight against the Ottomans

_____ **5.** place through which Russia desired naval access

_____ **6.** ignored German demand to cancel mobilization

_____ **7.** meaning "warring"

_____ **8.** prohibited goods

_____ **9.** agreement to end hostilities

_____ **10.** site of early German defeat

**Column B**

**a.** the Dardanelles

**b.** contraband

**c.** Sarajevo

**d.** the Marne

**e.** Leon Trotsky

**f.** Austria-Hungary

**g.** Arabs

**h.** belligerent

**i.** armistice

**j.** Nicholas II

## Multiple Choice

*In the blank, write the letter of the choice that best completes the statement. (4 points each)*

_____ **11.** Italy joined the Triple Alliance largely because it
   **a.** feared the expansion of Slavic nationalism.
   **b.** desired allies against Austria-Hungary.
   **c.** feared the expansion of Serbian nationalism.
   **d.** desired allies against France.

_____ **12.** As the war settled into a stalemate, countries tried to maintain citizens' morale by
   **a.** agreeing to halt the use of dreaded poison gas weapons.
   **b.** keeping civilians out of the war effort.
   **c.** focusing factory production on consumer goods.
   **d.** spreading propaganda.

_____ **13.** Great Britain put aside its reluctance and entered the war when Germany
   **a.** marched into Luxembourg.
   **b.** issued its ultimatum to Russia.
   **c.** declared war on France.
   **d.** refused to withdraw from Belgium.

_____ **14.** The prime minister of Russia's provisional government and a leader in the Petrograd Soviet was
   **a.** Kerensky.     **b.** Rasputin.     **c.** Lenin.     **d.** Trotsky.

_____ **15.** The Balkan Wars of 1912–1913 ended with Serbia's unhappiness over
   **a.** its inability to acquire Albania.
   **b.** Russia's alliance with the Slavs.
   **c.** Russia's support of the French.
   **d.** the annexation of Bosnia-Herzegovina.

_____ **16.** The policy of requiring civilians to serve in the military is called
   **a.** militarism.     **b.** entente.     **c.** conscription.     **d.** mobilization.

# Chapter 28 : *Form*
## Test : **B**

_____ **17.** German authorities helped Lenin return to Russia because they
   **a.** shared his belief in revolutionary socialism.
   **b.** supported the Reds in Russia's civil war.
   **c.** hoped he could increase Russia's involvement in World War I.
   **d.** hoped he could promote Russia's withdrawal from World War I.

_____ **18.** The convoy system helped the Allies counteract
   **a.** the German U-boat campaign.
   **b.** the German use of poison gas.
   **c.** the withdrawal of Russia from the war.
   **d.** Turkish control of the Mediterranean.

_____ **19.** The war strategy of Alfred von Schlieffen called for the quick defeat of
   **a.** the French followed by an offensive on the Eastern Front.
   **b.** the British followed by an offensive on the Eastern Front.
   **c.** the Germans followed by an offensive on the Western Front.
   **d.** the Russians followed by an offensive against France.

_____ **20.** The March revolution, which led to the czar's abdication, was largely the result of
   **a.** Bolshevik planning and leadership.
   **b.** a spontaneous citizens' uprising.
   **c.** Menshevik planning and leadership.
   **d.** American agitation.

_____ **21.** The Treaty of Versailles resulted in all of the following EXCEPT
   **a.** German payment of reparations.
   **b.** Italy's loss of German-speaking areas in the Alps.
   **c.** the return of Alsace-Lorraine to France.
   **d.** Germany's loss of its overseas possessions.

_____ **22.** The major factor in the decision of the United States to enter the war was
   **a.** the sinking of the *Lusitania*.
   **b.** the sinking of American ships by German submarines.
   **c.** Mexico's decision to support Germany.
   **d.** German-American agitation in favor of the Allies.

_____ **23.** Despite having received a conciliatory reply to its ultimatum, on July 28, 1914, Austria-Hungary declared war on
   **a.** Italy.    **b.** Russia.    **c.** Germany.    **d.** Serbia.

_____ **24.** Armenian civilians were the victims of mass killings conducted by the
   **a.** Germans.    **b.** English.    **c.** Ottoman Turks.    **d.** Russians.

_____ **25.** The Allied offensive on the Dardanelles was halted by the Turkish victory at
   **a.** Verdun.    **b.** Gallipoli.    **c.** Petrograd.    **d.** Constantinople.

## Essay
*Answer one of the following questions on a separate sheet of paper. (10 points)*

**26a.** **Critical Thinking** Identify the Fourteen Points plan, and describe some of its major elements. To what extent was the plan adopted?

**26b.** **Critical Thinking** Explain the relationship between World War I and the end of czarist rule in Russia.

# Chapter 29 : *Form*
# Test : **A**

**Score** _____

## Matching
*Match each item in Column A with an item in Column B by writing the correct letters in the blanks.*
*(3 points each)*

**Column A**

_____ **1.** 1920s women's style seen as uninhibited

_____ **2.** 1920s architectural style merging beauty and practicality

_____ **3.** Irish nationalist leader

_____ **4.** pact renouncing war as means of settling disputes

_____ **5.** prosperous Russian farmer

_____ **6.** in theory, controlled Soviet government

_____ **7.** Nazi attack on Jewish homes, businesses, and synagogues

_____ **8.** *der Führer*

_____ **9.** *Il Duce*

_____ **10.** Germany's post-World War I republic

**Column B**

**a.** proletariat

**b.** Kellogg-Briand

**c.** *Kristallnacht*

**d.** Benito Mussolini

**e.** flapper

**f.** kulak

**g.** Weimar

**h.** Bauhaus

**i.** Eamon De Valera

**j.** Adolf Hitler

## Multiple Choice
*In the blank, write the letter of the choice that best completes the statement. (4 points each)*

_____ **11.** The 1935 Nuremberg Laws deprived German
    **a.** workers of the right to strike.
    **b.** Communists of the right to hold public office.
    **c.** Jews of their citizenship.
    **d.** citizens of freedom of speech.

_____ **12.** The atmosphere and excesses of the Roaring Twenties were captured in F. Scott Fitzgerald's novel
    **a.** *The Great Gatsby.*
    **b.** *Ulysses.*
    **c.** *The Sun Also Rises.*
    **d.** *The Waste Land.*

_____ **13.** New Deal legislation was introduced by President
    **a.** Harding.
    **b.** Coolidge.
    **c.** Wilson.
    **d.** Roosevelt.

_____ **14.** The theory of "permanent revolution" stressed the
    **a.** importance of building a strong Soviet military.
    **b.** importance of building a strong Soviet economy.
    **c.** role of the peasants in leading popular uprisings.
    **d.** need to encourage communism all over the world.

_____ **15.** One technique used by Stalin to strengthen his control of the Soviet Union was
    **a.** methodically purging potential rivals and enemies.
    **b.** placing supporters of Trotsky in leadership positions.
    **c.** making alliances with the powerful kulaks.
    **d.** granting Communist party members immunity from arrest.

# Chapter 29 : Form
# Test : Ⓐ

_____ **16.** In the period after World War I, France was governed predominantly by
   **a.** Labour governments.                    **c.** Communist governments.
   **b.** Conservative governments.              **d.** coalition governments.

_____ **17.** Hitler's expansion of the German military violated the terms established in 1919 by the
   **a.** NEP.                                    **c.** Comintern.
   **b.** Treaty of Versailles.                   **d.** Locarno Treaties.

_____ **18.** The increased mobility of Americans during the 1920s was primarily due to
   **a.** greater use of automobiles and the      **c.** the completion of a transcontinental
       spread of highways.                            railway system.
   **b.** the growth of aviation as a means of     **d.** economic prosperity generated by
       mass transportation.                           New Deal reforms.

_____ **19.** Until World War I, the world's leading economic power was
   **a.** the United States.   **b.** Great Britain.   **c.** Germany.   **d.** Russia.

_____ **20.** Arnold Schoenberg is best known for
   **a.** his involvement in the creation of       **c.** his harsh, dissonant, musical
       modern dance.                                  compositions.
   **b.** his advances in the field of             **d.** the broad social criticism expressed in his
       psychoanalysis.                                novels.

_____ **21.** By 1933 the percentage of the American workforce that was unemployed had reached
   **a.** 5 percent.        **b.** 10 percent.        **c.** 25 percent.        **d.** 55 percent.

_____ **22.** *Mein Kampf* expresses the political views of
   **a.** Adolf Hitler.                            **c.** Benito Mussolini
   **b.** Arnold Schoenberg.                        **d.** Joseph Stalin.

_____ **23.** Zora Neale Hurston is associated with the movement known as
   **a.** cubism.                                  **c.** the Harlem Renaissance.
   **b.** Bauhaus.                                 **d.** surrealism.

_____ **24.** The former Red Army general who was assassinated in Mexico was
   **a.** Leon Trotsky.     **b.** Léon Blum.     **c.** Joseph Stalin.     **d.** Maksim Gorky.

_____ **25.** All of the following people were part of the music or film industries of the 1920s and 1930s
       EXCEPT
   **a.** Al Jolson.        **b.** Walter Gropius.        **c.** Tommy Dorsey.        **d.** Bessie Smith.

## Essay
*Answer one of the following questions on a separate sheet of paper. (10 points)*

**26a. Critical Thinking** Why did the United States emerge from World War I in a stronger economic
condition than European nations?

**26b. Critical Thinking** Describe the effects of 1930s totalitarian rule on artistic and intellectual
freedom in Germany and Russia.

# Chapter 29 : *Form*
# Test : **B**

Score _____

## Matching
*Match each item in Column A with an item in Column B by writing the correct letters in the blanks.*
*(3 points each)*

**Column A**

_____ **1.** organization established by Lenin

_____ **2.** site of Soviet labor camps

_____ **3.** transformed art of dance

_____ **4.** writer associated with Harlem Renaissance

_____ **5.** part of the United Kingdom

_____ **6.** surrealist artist

_____ **7.** treaties meant to ensure European peace

_____ **8.** name Hitler gave his government

_____ **9.** built to prevent German invasion

_____ **10.** Russian economic program

**Column B**

**a.** Northern Ireland

**b.** Siberia

**c.** Locarno

**d.** Salvador Dali

**e.** NEP

**f.** Claude McKay

**g.** Third Reich

**h.** Isadora Duncan

**i.** Comintern

**j.** Maginot Line

## Multiple Choice
*In the blank, write the letter of the choice that best completes the statement. (4 points each)*

_____ **11.** The leader of France's Popular Front government was
  **a.** Léon Blum.
  **b.** Ramsay MacDonald.
  **c.** Maksim Gorky.
  **d.** Eamon De Valera.

_____ **12.** All of the following were athletic heroes of the post-World War I era EXCEPT
  **a.** Babe Ruth.
  **b.** Helen Wills Moody.
  **c.** Bill Tilden.
  **d.** Arnold Schoenberg.

_____ **13.** The followers of Mussolini were known as
  **a.** Brownshirts.
  **b.** Blackshirts.
  **c.** kulaks.
  **d.** Gestapo.

_____ **14.** The 1932 Ukrainian famine brought about by Stalin's grain seizures caused the death of
  **a.** 80,000 people.
  **b.** 150,000 people.
  **c.** 1,000,000 people.
  **d.** millions of people.

_____ **15.** Fascists, like Communists, advocated
  **a.** the abolition of private property.
  **b.** the abolition of the existing class structure.
  **c.** totalitarian government.
  **d.** coalition government.

_____ **16.** The United States did not join the League of Nations because of the opposition of
  **a.** Great Britain.
  **b.** Russia.
  **c.** Woodrow Wilson.
  **d.** the U.S. Congress.

Name ................................ Date .............. Class .................

# Chapter 29 : *Form*
# Test : **B**

_____ **17.** Adolf Hitler and the Nazis achieved control of the German government
    **a.** in a 1932 coup d'état.
    **b.** after an armed uprising led by factory workers.
    **c.** by a vote of the German people.
    **d.** after a popular uprising outside the parliament building.

_____ **18.** The necessity of "building socialism in a single country" was emphasized by
    **a.** Lenin.
    **b.** Stalin.
    **c.** Trotsky.
    **d.** Prokofiev.

_____ **19.** All of the following contributed to Italy's postwar economic problems EXCEPT
    **a.** factory takeovers.
    **b.** land seizures.
    **c.** huge territorial gains.
    **d.** workers unemployment.

_____ **20.** The country to emerge from World War I with the most dynamic industrial economy was
    **a.** England.
    **b.** France.
    **c.** Germany.
    **d.** the United States.

_____ **21.** *Ulysses*, James Joyce's 1922 novel, is viewed as a landmark for its
    **a.** realistic portrayal of horror and suffering caused by war.
    **b.** depiction of two young Americans roaming through postwar Europe.
    **c.** use of "stream of consciousness" to present the characters' inner thoughts.
    **d.** depiction of the plight of Oklahoma farmers in the midst of severe drought.

_____ **22.** Under the Soviet collectivization plan, farmland was to be owned by
    **a.** individual peasants.
    **b.** peasant syndicates.
    **c.** proletariat-run corporations.
    **d.** the Soviet government.

_____ **23.** Many Germans claimed that Weimar leaders had betrayed the nation by
    **a.** joining the League of Nations.
    **b.** joining the Commonwealth of Nations.
    **c.** accepting the Treaty of Versailles.
    **d.** granting Hitler emergency powers.

_____ **24.** Britain's Trade Disputes Act of 1927 prohibited
    **a.** general strikes.
    **b.** membership in the Labour party.
    **c.** membership in Irish nationalist groups.
    **d.** trade with Germany.

_____ **25.** The founder of the Bauhaus school of architecture was
    **a.** Walter Gropius.
    **b.** Frank Lloyd Wright.
    **c.** Igor Stravinsky.
    **d.** Martha Graham.

## Essay
*Answer one of the following questions on a separate sheet of paper. (10 points)*

**26a. Critical Thinking** Identify the political figures involved in the struggle to succeed Lenin as Soviet leader. Describe their political views and the outcome of their competition.

**26b. Critical Thinking** Describe two ways technology impacted American popular culture in the post-World War I era.

# Chapter 30 : Form
# Test : Ⓐ

Score _____

## Matching

*Match each item in Column A with an item in Column B by writing the correct letters in the blanks.*
*(3 points each)*

**Column A**

_____ **1.** advocate of civil disobedience

_____ **2.** policy for China favored by the West

_____ **3.** ruling family of Nicaragua supported by the United States

_____ **4.** leader of the Young Turks

_____ **5.** founded by Sun Yat-sen

_____ **6.** increased Japan's influence over China

_____ **7.** Roosevelt's policy regarding Latin America

_____ **8.** overthrew shah, then became one

_____ **9.** Brazilian dictator

_____ **10.** demanded separate state for Indian Muslims

**Column B**

**a.** Mohammed Ali Jinnah

**b.** Twenty-One Demands

**c.** Reza Khan

**d.** Somoza

**e.** Guomindang

**f.** Mohandas K. Gandhi

**g.** Getúlio Vargas

**h.** Open Door

**i.** Good Neighbor

**j.** Mustafa Kemal

## Multiple Choice

*In the blank, write the letter of the choice that best completes the statement. (4 points each)*

_____ **11.** Indians were outraged when the British opened fire on an unarmed gathering in
   **a.** Ankara.       **b.** Amritsar.       **c.** London.       **d.** Ahmadabad.

_____ **12.** The Chinese were angered by a Treaty of Versailles provision that
   **a.** placed the country under British rule.
   **b.** divided control of the country between the British and the French.
   **c.** placed the country under French rule.
   **d.** granted Japan economic control of the Shandong Peninsula.

_____ **13.** After negotiations failed to solve the oil workers' strike, Lázaro Cárdenas
   **a.** imprisoned Mexican union leaders.
   **b.** gave in to oil company demands.
   **c.** nationalized foreign-owned oil wells.
   **d.** refused to sell oil to the United States and Great Britain.

_____ **14.** After World War I, all that remained of the Ottoman Empire was the area of present-day
   **a.** Bulgaria.       **b.** Turkey.       **c.** Greece.       **d.** Iran.

_____ **15.** At the Pan American conference of 1933, the United States agreed
   **a.** to strictly enforce the Roosevelt Corollary.
   **b.** to strictly enforce the Monroe Doctrine.
   **c.** not to intervene in Latin American affairs.
   **d.** not to invest in Latin American economies.

_____ **16.** In the 1920s, capital used to expand heavy industry in Japan was provided mainly by
   **a.** government-controlled banks.
   **b.** wealthy peasants.
   **c.** Western governments.
   **d.** Chinese merchants.

# Chapter 30 : *Form*
# Test : Ⓐ

_____ **17.** Mexican government in the early twentieth century is best characterized as a
  **a.** one-party system.
  **c.** constitutional monarchy.
  **b.** multiparty democracy.
  **d.** dictatorship.

_____ **18.** After many Kenyans died fighting the Germans in World War I, the British
  **a.** granted Kenya full independence.
  **c.** allowed Harry Thuku to govern Kenya.
  **b.** allowed European settlers to seize the land of native Kenyans.
  **d.** asked Jomo Kenyatta to help spur Kenyan nationalism.

_____ **19.** Conflict between the Red Army and the Guomindang allowed Japan to seize control of
  **a.** Korea.
  **c.** Nanjing.
  **b.** Manchuria.
  **d.** the Shandong Peninsula.

_____ **20.** One factor motivating Japan's attempt to industrialize rapidly was
  **a.** the loss of its colonies as a result of World War I.
  **c.** the need to provide employment for its growing population.
  **b.** its ample supply of natural resources.
  **d.** the collapse of its silk and mineral industries.

_____ **21.** As leader of Persia, Reza Khan encouraged
  **a.** the spread of Western political influence.
  **c.** the use of the Arabic language.
  **b.** greater freedom for women.
  **d.** his country's alignment with Germany during World War I.

_____ **22.** During the 1930s, Japanese life was increasingly influenced by
  **a.** Zionism.    **b.** communism.    **c.** militarism.    **d.** pacifism.

_____ **23.** The Guomindang defeated the warlords and established a government in Nanjing under the leadership of
  **a.** Chiang Kai-shek.    **b.** Mao Zedong.    **c.** Sun Yat-sen.    **d.** Hirohito.

_____ **24.** To protest the British salt tax in India, Gandhi led
  **a.** a boycott of British manufactured goods.
  **c.** a delegation to the British Parliament.
  **b.** a march from Ahmadabad to the sea.
  **d.** an attack on British warehouses.

_____ **25.** Jewish immigration to Palestine from Europe was stimulated by all of the following EXCEPT
  **a.** anti-Jewish pogroms in Russia.
  **c.** persecution of Jews in Nazi Germany.
  **b.** the desire to reestablish a Jewish homeland.
  **d.** Reza Shah Pahlavi's alignment with Hitler.

## Essay
*Answer one of the following questions on a separate sheet of paper. (10 points)*

**26a. Critical Thinking** Summarize the changes that occurred in Turkey during the rule of Kemal Atatürk.

**26b. Critical Thinking** Provide examples of the support given by African, Asian, and Middle Eastern peoples to the British in World War I. Were they rewarded for their efforts?

# Chapter 30 : *Form*
# Test : **B**

**Score** _____

## Matching
*Match each item in Column A with an item in Column B by writing the correct letters in the blanks. (3 points each)*

**Column A**

_____ **1.** country in which Harry Thuku was a nationalist leader

_____ **2.** philosophy of Mao Zedong

_____ **3.** post-World War I invader of Turkey

_____ **4.** country where Gandhi first led protests

_____ **5.** Japan's large private businesses

_____ **6.** movement for a Jewish homeland

_____ **7.** leader who some hoped could check military extremists

_____ **8.** through World War I, Great Britain's most important colony

_____ **9.** opposed American troops in Nicaragua

_____ **10.** victor in first open Argentinean presidential election

**Column B**

**a.** South Africa

**b.** Greece

**c.** *zaibatsu*

**d.** Hipólito Irigoyen

**e.** Augusto César Sandino

**f.** Kenya

**g.** Zionism

**h.** Hirohito

**i.** communism

**j.** India

## Multiple Choice
*In the blank, write the letter of the choice that best completes the statement. (4 points each)*

_____ **11.** Gandhi chose the spinning wheel as the symbol of the National Congress to represent the ideal of
    **a.** nonviolence.
    **b.** equality before the law.
    **c.** religious freedom.
    **d.** self-sufficiency.

_____ **12.** After his ouster as head of the Chinese republic, Sun Yat-sen formed
    **a.** an alliance with Yuan Shigai.
    **b.** an alliance with Mao Zedong.
    **c.** the Guomindang party.
    **d.** the Chinese Communist party.

_____ **13.** Many colonial peoples were encouraged by Woodrow Wilson's endorsement of
    **a.** the right to self-determination.
    **b.** civil disobedience.
    **c.** pacifism.
    **d.** nationalization.

_____ **14.** As first president of Turkey, Mustafa Kemal did all of the following EXCEPT
    **a.** create a separation between government and religion.
    **b.** reform the legal code and Westernize the government.
    **c.** encourage the use of the metric system and the Western calendar.
    **d.** encourage the use of the Arabic language and script.

_____ **15.** In the 1930s, the Argentinean government had come under the control of
    **a.** foreign oil companies.
    **b.** the Socialist party.
    **c.** Getúlio Vargas.
    **d.** the military.

# Chapter 30 : Form
# Test : B

_____ **16.** To increase Mexican agricultural production, Lázaro Cárdenas endorsed
  **a.** the creation of a single, nationalized agricultural corporation.
  **b.** foreign ownership of all farmland.
  **c.** foreign investment in government-owned farms.
  **d.** the creation of peasant-operated cooperative farms.

_____ **17.** After World War I, a League of Nations mandate to govern Palestine was granted to
  **a.** France.    **b.** Great Britain.    **c.** the United States.    **d.** Egypt.

_____ **18.** All of the following contributed to Japanese unhappiness with the West EXCEPT
  **a.** the League of Nations' refusal to adopt a statement of racial equality.
  **b.** the 1924 changes in U.S. immigration policy.
  **c.** the postwar distribution of Germany's northern Pacific territories.
  **d.** Western insistence on an Open Door policy in China.

_____ **19.** The Long March was led by
  **a.** Mohandas Gandhi. **b.** César Sandino.    **c.** Mao Zedong.    **d.** Jomo Kenyatta.

_____ **20.** Gandhi's term to describe his methods of nonviolent protest was
  **a.** satyagraha.    **b.** Mahatma.    **c.** _zaibatsu._    **d.** fez.

_____ **21.** Venezuelan demonstrations against the domination of foreign oil companies led to
  **a.** government nationalization of the oil industry.
  **b.** more equal distribution of oil profits.
  **c.** suppression of the protests by the Venezuelan army.
  **d.** intervention by the United States Army.

_____ **22.** Mao Zedong built the Red Army by focusing on the recruitment of
  **a.** Guomindang soldiers.
  **b.** rural peasants.
  **c.** urban workers.
  **d.** urban intellectuals.

_____ **23.** Arab nationalists were angered by the
  **a.** Amritsar Massacre.
  **b.** Balfour Declaration.
  **c.** Twenty-One Demands.
  **d.** Good Neighbor policy.

_____ **24.** The 1937 elections in India heightened tension between
  **a.** Arabs and Jews.
  **b.** Arabs and Hindus.
  **c.** Muslims and Hindus.
  **d.** Muslims and Christians.

_____ **25.** Iran is located
  **a.** on the Mediterranean Sea's eastern coast.
  **b.** on the Arabian Peninsula.
  **c.** in North Africa.
  **d.** between Turkey and Pakistan.

## Essay
_Answer one of the following questions on a separate sheet of paper. (10 points)_

**26a. Critical Thinking** Describe two factors that led to the growth of nationalist militarism in Japan during the 1930s.

**26b. Critical Thinking** How did United States policy toward Latin America change in the period beginning in the late 1920s?

# Chapter 31 : *Form*
# Test : Ⓐ

Score _____

## Matching

*Match each item in Column A with an item in Column B by writing the correct letters in the blanks.*
*(3 points each)*

**Column A**

_____ **1.** resigned after Norway and Denmark fell

_____ **2.** site of first Japanese attack on United States

_____ **3.** the Nazi-run puppet government of France

_____ **4.** site of German concentration camp

_____ **5.** defense of the common interests of countries against attack

_____ **6.** ordered use of the atomic bomb

_____ **7.** directed Operation Overlord

_____ **8.** policy of granting concessions to Hitler

_____ **9.** signified America's shift from isolationism

_____ **10.** bound Germany, Italy, and Japan

**Column B**

**a.** Atlantic Charter

**b.** collective security

**c.** Tripartite Pact

**d.** Neville Chamberlain

**e.** Dwight D. Eisenhower

**f.** Vichy

**g.** appeasement

**h.** Harry S Truman

**i.** Pearl Harbor

**j.** Dachau

## Multiple Choice

*In the blank, write the letter of the choice that best completes the statement. (4 points each)*

_____ **11.** By occupying Norway and Denmark, Germany achieved
    **a.** access to the Atlantic Ocean.
    **b.** access to the Baltic Sea.
    **c.** control of the Baltic states.
    **d.** control of the Mediterranean.

_____ **12.** During the war's early phases, the U.S. Congress generally favored
    **a.** supporting Germany.
    **b.** supporting Russia.
    **c.** supporting England and France.
    **d.** remaining neutral.

_____ **13.** The second atomic bomb ever used in warfare was dropped on
    **a.** Hiroshima.
    **b.** Nagasaki.
    **c.** Pearl Harbor.
    **d.** Okinawa.

_____ **14.** German losses at Stalingrad were made greater by
    **a.** Hitler's refusal to retreat.
    **b.** Russia's use of U-boats.
    **c.** Russia's use of kamikaze pilots.
    **d.** the sustained Allied air offensive.

_____ **15.** During the Spanish Civil War, Hitler gave German support to the
    **a.** Republicans.
    **b.** International Brigade.
    **c.** Nationalists.
    **d.** Loyalists.

_____ **16.** The collapse of France paved the way for Japan to achieve control of
    **a.** Hong Kong.
    **b.** Indochina.
    **c.** Belgium.
    **d.** the Netherlands.

# Chapter 31 : *Form*
## Test : Ⓐ

_____ **17.** The League of Nations took action against Italy's aggression in Africa by
   **a.** sending League troops into Italy.
   **b.** sending League troops into Ethiopia.
   **c.** prohibiting the sale of weapons to Italy.
   **d.** prohibiting the sale of iron, coal, and oil to Italy.

_____ **18.** The last Axis power to surrender was
   **a.** Italy.
   **b.** Germany.
   **c.** Japan.
   **d.** Austria.

_____ **19.** The Ardennes gap in the Maginot Line aided the
   **a.** Germans in their invasion of France.
   **b.** Russians in their defense of Petrograd.
   **c.** Allies in their evacuation from Dunkirk.
   **d.** Japanese in their attack on Pearl Harbor.

_____ **20.** Mussolini was killed by
   **a.** American troops.
   **b.** Russian troops.
   **c.** the French Resistance.
   **d.** Italian partisans.

_____ **21.** Groups chosen for extermination by the Nazis on racial grounds included all of the following EXCEPT
   **a.** Jews.
   **b.** Slavs.
   **c.** Gypsies.
   **d.** Austrians.

_____ **22.** One factor in Germany's inability to take Moscow was
   **a.** the airlift of American troops to Moscow.
   **b.** the airlift of American troops to Leningrad.
   **c.** the harsh Russian winter.
   **d.** the leadership of Erwin Rommel.

_____ **23.** Nuremberg was the site of
   **a.** the first meeting of the United Nations.
   **b.** war crimes trials of Nazi leaders.
   **c.** war crimes trials of Japanese leaders.
   **d.** Hitler's suicide.

_____ **24.** After his calls for unity against Hitler were rejected, Stalin signed the
   **a.** Munich Pact.
   **b.** Nazi-Soviet Nonaggression Pact.
   **c.** Anti-Comintern Pact.
   **d.** Neutrality Acts.

_____ **25.** After Hitler invaded western Poland, Russia quickly moved to occupy
   **a.** the Baltic republics.
   **b.** the Balkan republics.
   **c.** Czechoslovakia.
   **d.** Serbia.

## Essay
*Answer one of the following questions on a separate sheet of paper. (10 points)*

**26a. Critical Thinking** Write a summary of the war in the Pacific.

**26b. Critical Thinking** Describe Hitler's plan for a "New Order" and the Nazis' treatment of conquered peoples and ethnic minorities.

# Chapter 31 : *Form*
# Test : **B**

**Score** _____

## Matching

*Match each item in Column A with an item in Column B by writing the correct letters in the blanks.*
*(3 points each)*

**Column A**

_____ **1.** valiantly resisted Soviet expansionism

_____ **2.** divided into four zones at war's end

_____ **3.** day of Japan's surrender

_____ **4.** country that suffered most casualties in World War II

_____ **5.** victorious general in Spanish Civil War

_____ **6.** site of Japanese naval defeat

_____ **7.** pilot on suicide mission

_____ **8.** Nazi murder of the Jews, for example

_____ **9.** condemned Italian aggression in his country

_____ **10.** site of war crimes trials

**Column B**

**a.** Francisco Franco

**b.** Russia

**c.** genocide

**d.** kamikaze

**e.** Midway

**f.** Haile Selassie

**g.** V-J

**h.** Berlin

**i.** Nuremberg

**j.** Finland

## Multiple Choice

*In the blank, write the letter of the choice that best completes the statement. (4 points each)*

_____ **11.** World War II began with Germany's invasion of
    **a.** Czechoslovakia.
    **b.** Austria.
    **c.** Poland.
    **d.** France.

_____ **12.** In 1940 a new British government was formed by
    **a.** Neville Chamberlain.
    **b.** Bernard Montgomery.
    **c.** Winston Churchill.
    **d.** Erwin Rommel.

_____ **13.** All of the following countries were generally satisfied with the World War I peace settlements EXCEPT
    **a.** the United States.
    **b.** France.
    **c.** Italy.
    **d.** Great Britain.

_____ **14.** More than 1 million residents died during Germany's two-year siege of
    **a.** Paris.
    **b.** Moscow.
    **c.** Warsaw.
    **d.** Leningrad.

_____ **15.** After the armistice with Vichy officials and the surrender of General von Arnim, the Allies controlled all of
    **a.** France.
    **b.** North Africa.
    **c.** Scandinavia.
    **d.** Italy.

_____ **16.** Despite heavy losses, the RAF was able to maintain
    **a.** air supremacy over the Pacific.
    **b.** air supremacy over Great Britain.
    **c.** naval supremacy in the Mediterranean.
    **d.** control of the Libyan desert.

# Chapter 31 : *Form*
# Test : **B**

_____ **17.** Stalin's "scorched-earth" policy was aimed at
    **a.** forcing the Finns to surrender quickly.
    **b.** destroying anything of use to the Germans.
    **c.** forcing the Latvians to surrender quickly.
    **d.** destroying anything of use to the Japanese.

_____ **18.** The 1936 German occupation of the Rhineland was met by
    **a.** an immediate French counterattack.
    **b.** an immediate British counterattack.
    **c.** no military opposition.
    **d.** the joint military response of France and Britain.

_____ **19.** The entrance of the United States into the war was prompted by
    **a.** a Japanese attack on the United States.
    **b.** a German attack on the United States.
    **c.** an Italian attack on the United States.
    **d.** an Italian attack on the British.

_____ **20.** D-Day refers to the day on which
    **a.** the United States dropped an atomic bomb on Hiroshima.
    **b.** the United States entered the war.
    **c.** the Allies staged a massive landing in France.
    **d.** the Germans surrendered.

_____ **21.** Volunteers from the United States and around the world joined the International Brigade to fight
    **a.** communism in Russia.
    **b.** the Italians in Ethiopia.
    **c.** the Japanese in China.
    **d.** fascism in Spain.

_____ **22.** Harry Truman represented the United States at the Allied conference at
    **a.** Potsdam.
    **b.** Yalta.
    **c.** Kuril Island.
    **d.** Okinawa.

_____ **23.** The French Resistance opposed collaboration with
    **a.** the Vichy government.
    **b.** the Allies.
    **c.** Charles de Gaulle.
    **d.** Pietro Badoglio.

_____ **24.** The sinking of the *Bismarck* was a key Allied victory in the battle for control of the
    **a.** Baltic.
    **b.** Atlantic.
    **c.** Pacific.
    **d.** Mediterranean.

_____ **25.** The policy of "appeasing" Hitler was advocated by
    **a.** Soviet dictator Joseph Stalin.
    **b.** British Prime Minister Neville Chamberlain.
    **c.** American President Franklin Roosevelt.
    **d.** Japanese Admiral Isoroku Yamamoto.

## Essay
*Answer one of the following questions on a separate sheet of paper. (10 points)*

**26a. Critical Thinking** Describe the response of the League of Nations to Japanese and Italian aggression. How effective was this response?

**26b. Critical Thinking** How did Hitler use the cause of German unity as justification for territorial expansion?

# Chapter 32 : Form
# Test : A

**Score** _____

## Matching

*Match each item in Column A with an item in Column B by writing the correct letters in the blanks.*
*(3 points each)*

**Column A**

_____ **1.** capital of Federal Republic of West Germany

_____ **2.** Soviet counterpart to Marshall Plan

_____ **3.** conflict here caused downfall of Fourth Republic

_____ **4.** used courts to protect African American rights

_____ **5.** first man on the moon

_____ **6.** city divided by concrete wall in 1961

_____ **7.** headed Senate Committee on Investigation

_____ **8.** site of the United Nations

_____ **9.** early recipient of Truman Doctrine assistance

_____ **10.** warned of "military-industrial complex"

**Column B**

**a.** New York

**b.** Bonn

**c.** Neil Armstrong

**d.** Greece

**e.** Joseph McCarthy

**f.** NAACP

**g.** COMECON

**h.** Berlin

**i.** Dwight D. Eisenhower

**j.** Algeria

## Multiple Choice

*In the blank, write the letter of the choice that best completes the statement. (4 points each)*

_____ **11.** Economic problems worsened by military spending made Brezhnev cultivate a policy of
    **a.** containment.
    **b.** mutual assured destruction.
    **c.** detente.
    **d.** stagflation.

_____ **12.** In 1949, alarmed by the Berlin and Czechoslovak crises, the Western Allies formed
    **a.** the OAS.
    **b.** SEATO.
    **c.** CENTO.
    **d.** NATO.

_____ **13.** The Soviet de-Stalinization program took place from
    **a.** 1947 to 1956.
    **b.** 1956 to 1964.
    **c.** 1964 to 1972.
    **d.** 1972 to 1981.

_____ **14.** Canada's Parti Quebecois urged the formation of an independent country created from
    **a.** Native American majority territory.
    **b.** the western Canadian provinces.
    **c.** the English-speaking majority provinces.
    **d.** the French-speaking majority provinces.

_____ **15.** The political leader who threatened to force the Allies out of West Berlin in 1961 was
    **a.** John F. Kennedy.
    **b.** Konrad Adenauer.
    **c.** Nikita Khrushchev.
    **d.** Joseph Stalin.

_____ **16.** Ten million refugees from Eastern Europe settled in
    **a.** West Germany.
    **b.** France.
    **c.** Great Britain.
    **d.** Luxembourg.

# Chapter 32 : Form
## Test : Ⓐ

_____ **17.** *Sputnik I* was the name of the
  **a.** Soviet Union's first ICBM.
  **b.** world's first space satellite.
  **c.** Soviet Union's first atomic bomb.
  **d.** American spy plane shot down by the Soviets.

_____ **18.** European economic cooperation was greatly strengthened by the creation of the
  **a.** Common Market.
  **b.** Economic and Social Council.
  **c.** Commonwealth of Nations.
  **d.** General Assembly.

_____ **19.** The Communist country that Tito helped to avoid Soviet domination was
  **a.** East Germany.
  **b.** Czechoslovakia.
  **c.** Poland.
  **d.** Yugoslavia.

_____ **20.** The American civil rights movement suffered a setback when Martin Luther King was assassinated in
  **a.** 1954.
  **b.** 1960.
  **c.** 1968.
  **d.** 1975.

_____ **21.** The American role in Vietnam was expanded into full-scale participation in combat by
  **a.** Richard Nixon.
  **b.** Lyndon Johnson.
  **c.** Gerald Ford.
  **d.** Jimmy Carter.

_____ **22.** The permanent members of the UN Security Council include all of the following EXCEPT
  **a.** China.
  **b.** France.
  **c.** the Soviet Union.
  **d.** Germany.

_____ **23.** Postwar West German politics was dominated by the Social Democrats and the
  **a.** Christian Democrats.
  **b.** Gaullist Union.
  **c.** Conservatives.
  **d.** Labour party.

_____ **24.** The Cuban missile crisis arose after the Soviets began
  **a.** an invasion of Cuba.
  **b.** a blockade of Cuba.
  **c.** installing nuclear missiles in Cuba.
  **d.** aiming ICBMs at Cuba.

_____ **25.** The European aid program begun by the United States in the late 1940s became known as
  **a.** the Marshall Plan.
  **b.** SALT.
  **c.** the Warsaw Pact.
  **d.** the Truman Doctrine.

## Essay
*Answer one of the following questions on a separate sheet of paper. (10 points)*

**26a. Critical Thinking** Describe some of the problems faced by the American economy in the 1970s.

**26b. Critical Thinking** Identify and describe the origins and purposes of two international organizations that emerged after World War II.

# Chapter 32 : *Form*
# Test : **B**

## Matching
*Match each item in Column A with an item in Column B by writing the correct letters in the blanks.*
*(3 points each)*

**Column A**

_____ **1.** United States took over French anti-Communist drive here

_____ **2.** Lyndon Johnson urged its creation

_____ **3.** aimed at reducing Soviet bloc-West German tension

_____ **4.** term for Soviet control of Eastern Europe

_____ **5.** policy of resisting spread of communism

_____ **6.** leader whose resolve was tested by Cuba

_____ **7.** 80 percent French-speaking

_____ **8.** technique used increasingly by American industry in the 1950s and 1960s

_____ **9.** successor to Franklin D. Roosevelt

_____ **10.** 1970s relaxation of superpower relations

**Column B**

**a.** iron curtain

**b.** Great Society

**c.** John F. Kennedy

**d.** Harry S Truman

**e.** detente

**f.** automation

**g.** containment

**h.** Vietnam

**i.** *Ostpolitik*

**j.** Quebec

## Multiple Choice
*In the blank, write the letter of the choice that best completes the statement or answers the question.*
*(4 points each)*

_____ **11.** The Western Allies responded to the Soviet blockade of Berlin
  **a.** with little action.
  **b.** by building a wall.
  **c.** with their own blockade of Cuba.
  **d.** by staging a massive airlift of supplies.

_____ **12.** During de Gaulle's presidency, France
  **a.** gave up its attempt to develop nuclear weapons.
  **b.** became a member of NATO.
  **c.** granted its African colonies independence.
  **d.** developed closer ties with Britain.

_____ **13.** During the 1970s, the American economy experienced stagflation, a mixture of
  **a.** high unemployment and low inflation.
  **b.** high unemployment and high inflation.
  **c.** low unemployment and low inflation.
  **d.** low unemployment and high inflation.

_____ **14.** The international assembly that replaced the League of Nations after World War I is
  **a.** COMECON.
  **b.** the Security Council.
  **c.** the United Nations.
  **d.** NATO.

_____ **15.** The controversial 1956 speech that denounced the policies of Stalin was given by
  **a.** János Kádár.
  **b.** Leonid Brezhnev.
  **c.** Alexander Dubček.
  **d.** Nikita Khrushchev.

_____ **16.** The Soviet Union exploded its first atomic bomb in
  **a.** 1949.
  **b.** 1959.
  **c.** 1961.
  **d.** 1969.

# Chapter 32 : *Form*
# Test : B

_____ **17.** The postwar European welfare states were characterized by
- **a.** the rule of weak presidents and coalition governments.
- **b.** stringent postwar restrictions on labor union activity.
- **c.** the inability to compete economically with East Asia.
- **d.** their provision of free education, health care, and other benefits for their citizens.

_____ **18.** The Watergate scandal began
- **a.** when Vice President Spiro Agnew was accused of taking bribes.
- **b.** when President Nixon vetoed the War Powers Limitation Act.
- **c.** after the shooting of antiwar protesters by National Guardsmen.
- **d.** after a break-in at the offices of the Democratic National Committee.

_____ **19.** Where was the most rapid growth of the American population during the postwar era?
- **a.** urban centers
- **b.** suburban areas
- **c.** small rural towns
- **d.** farms

_____ **20.** By 1947 all of the following countries were considered Soviet satellites EXCEPT
- **a.** Poland.
- **b.** Romania.
- **c.** Bulgaria.
- **d.** Greece.

_____ **21.** In 1960 gradual improvement in United States-Soviet relations came to a halt after the
- **a.** launch of *Sputnik I.*
- **b.** downing of an American U-2 spy plane.
- **c.** Brezhnev-Nixon summit.
- **d.** Soviets invaded Hungary.

_____ **22.** The careers of many Americans were ruined by the anti-Communist campaign led by
- **a.** Neil Armstrong.
- **b.** Richard Nixon.
- **c.** John F. Kennedy.
- **d.** Joseph McCarthy.

_____ **23.** The Supreme Court ruled in *Brown* v. *Board of Education of Topeka, Kansas* that
- **a.** federal agencies could not be used to enforce desegregation orders.
- **b.** racial segregation in public schools was illegal.
- **c.** teachers with Communist beliefs could be dismissed.
- **d.** the NAACP could use the court system to challenge civil rights violations.

_____ **24.** The Treaty of Rome resulted in the creation of
- **a.** the International Court of Justice.
- **b.** the United Nations.
- **c.** the European Economic Community.
- **d.** NATO.

_____ **25.** When the Soviet army invaded Hungary, the Western Allies
- **a.** took no concrete action in support of the Hungarians.
- **b.** succeeded in expelling Russia from the Security Council.
- **c.** prevented Hungarian refugees from settling in the West.
- **d.** supported the government of Antonin Novotny.

## Essay
*Answer one of the following questions on a separate sheet of paper. (10 points)*

**26a. Critical Thinking** Describe the emergence of Canada's national identity after World War II. What factors complicated its process of nation building?

**26b. Critical Thinking** Summarize the changes in Soviet leadership and Soviet policy toward the West during the postwar period.

# Chapter 33 : *Form*
# Test : Ⓐ

**Score** _____

## Matching

*Match each item in Column A with an item in Column B by writing the correct letters in the blanks.*
*(3 points each)*

**Column A**

_____ **1.** Chiang Kai-shek set up his new capital here

_____ **2.** Indian prime minister assassinated in 1991

_____ **3.** Philippine rebels

_____ **4.** governed by Supreme Command of the Allied Powers

_____ **5.** China assumed its control in 1997

_____ **6.** first directly elected South Korean president

_____ **7.** leader of the brutal Khmer Rouge

_____ **8.** site of Chinese crackdown against student demonstrators

_____ **9.** withstood the U.S. Army

_____ **10.** Kampuchea

**Column B**

**a.** Japan

**b.** Roh Tae Woo

**c.** Tiananmen Square

**d.** Viet Cong

**e.** Huks

**f.** Pol Pot

**g.** Taipei

**h.** Rajiv Gandhi

**i.** Cambodia

**j.** Hong Kong

## Multiple Choice

*In the blank, write the letter of the choice that best completes the statement. (4 points each)*

_____ **11.** In 1992 the Japanese government broke with long-standing policy by
    **a.** allowing industrial development near Tokyo.
    **b.** contributing troops as part of a UN peacekeeping mission.
    **c.** imposing trade quotas on U.S. automotive imports.
    **d.** normalizing relations with China.

_____ **12.** The country bombed by the United States despite its government's neutrality in the Vietnam War was
    **a.** Singapore.
    **b.** China.
    **c.** Thailand.
    **d.** Cambodia.

_____ **13.** Pragmatists in the Chinese Communist party were accused of betrayal during the
    **a.** Korean War.
    **b.** Cultural Revolution.
    **c.** Four Modernizations.
    **d.** Great Leap Forward.

_____ **14.** In recent years, Sri Lanka has experienced conflict between Tamil Hindus and Sinhalese
    **a.** Muslims.
    **b.** Christians.
    **c.** Buddhists.
    **d.** Jains.

_____ **15.** The Japanese ruled Korea as a colony until
    **a.** the end of World War I.
    **b.** the end of World War II.
    **c.** 1958.
    **d.** 1973.

_____ **16.** From 1955 to 1993, Japanese leadership was dominated by
    **a.** Emperor Hirohito.
    **b.** the U.S. occupation government.
    **c.** a series of Socialist coalitions.
    **d.** a single political party, the LDP.

# Chapter 33 : *Form*
# Test : Ⓐ

_____ **17.** The ANZUS treaty links the United States, Australia, and
    **a.** Indonesia.
    **b.** Great Britain.
    **c.** France.
    **d.** New Zealand.

_____ **18.** The largely Muslim country formed in 1947 by the partition of India was
    **a.** Kashmir.
    **b.** Pakistan.
    **c.** Sri Lanka.
    **d.** Bangladesh.

_____ **19.** While encouraging market reforms during the 1980s, China's pragmatic leaders continued to oppose
    **a.** economic ties with the West.
    **b.** economic ties with the United States.
    **c.** investment in military production.
    **d.** the granting of greater political freedoms to its citizens.

_____ **20.** One reason for the rupture in Soviet-Chinese relations was
    **a.** differing views about Marxism.
    **b.** differing views about the United States.
    **c.** Russian support for Chiang Kai-shek.
    **d.** Chinese support for the de-Stalinization campaign.

_____ **21.** Until 1948 the country now called Myanmar was
    **a.** part of British India.
    **b.** part of Indonesia.
    **c.** ruled by the French.
    **d.** ruled by the Chinese.

_____ **22.** The prohibition on Japanese military development had the side effect of
    **a.** helping the country concentrate its resources on producing consumer goods.
    **b.** increasing the country's dependence on imported consumer goods.
    **c.** increasing the country's dependence on Chinese military protection.
    **d.** making North Korea the dominant military power in the Pacific.

_____ **23.** Democratic elections meant to unify Vietnam in 1956 were prevented by
    **a.** Communist leader Ho Chi Minh.
    **b.** South Vietnamese leader Ngo Dinh Diem.
    **c.** the Japanese.
    **d.** the Chinese.

_____ **24.** Of the troops representing the UN during the Korean War, 90 percent of the soldiers came from
    **a.** China.
    **b.** the Soviet Union.
    **c.** Vietnam.
    **d.** the United States.

_____ **25.** Since 1950 the Tibetan people have suffered under
    **a.** Japanese rule.
    **b.** Korean rule.
    **c.** Chinese rule.
    **d.** Vietnamese rule.

## Essay
*Answer one of the following questions on a separate sheet of paper. (10 points)*

**26a. Critical Thinking** Summarize the history of the relationship between China and Taiwan.

**26b. Critical Thinking** Describe the role of the United States in Japan's postwar reconstruction.

Name .................................................. Date .................. Class ..................

# Chapter 33 : *Form*
# Test : Ⓑ

**Score** _____

## Matching
*Match each item in Column A with an item in Column B by writing the correct letters in the blanks.*
*(3 points each)*

**Column A**

_____ **1.** its nuclear tests stirred Pacific protests

_____ **2.** Burma

_____ **3.** directed American activity in occupied Japan

_____ **4.** nation that includes the island of Borneo

_____ **5.** Pacific island country

_____ **6.** city devastated by 1995 earthquake

_____ **7.** gained power after the death of Mao

_____ **8.** campaigner against Chinese control of Tibet

_____ **9.** capital of North Korea

_____ **10.** leader of Vietnamese Communists

**Column B**

**a.** Papua New Guinea

**b.** Dalai Lama

**c.** Kobe

**d.** Pyongyang

**e.** Ho Chi Minh

**f.** Malaysia

**g.** Myanmar

**h.** Douglas MacArthur

**i.** France

**j.** Deng Xiaoping

## Multiple Choice
*In the blank, write the letter of the choice that best completes the statement. (4 points each)*

_____ **11.** While nominally democratic, until the 1980s South Korea was essentially ruled by a
  **a.** king.
  **b.** Communist dictatorship.
  **c.** military dictatorship.
  **d.** Chinese-run puppet regime.

_____ **12.** After his defeat by the Communists, Chiang Kai-shek led his followers to
  **a.** South Korea.
  **b.** Beijing.
  **c.** Taiwan.
  **d.** Hong Kong.

_____ **13.** After he fled the Philippines, Ferdinand Marcos was succeeded as president by
  **a.** Corazon Aquino.
  **b.** Benazir Ali Bhutto.
  **c.** Indira Gandhi.
  **d.** Fidel Ramos.

_____ **14.** The postwar Japanese constitution barred
  **a.** the country from trading with the Soviet Union.
  **b.** Hirohito from becoming emperor.
  **c.** the country from maintaining military forces.
  **d.** Hirohito from remaining as emperor.

_____ **15.** Nearly one-third of the Cambodian population died during the rule of
  **a.** the Khmer Rouge.
  **b.** the Viet Cong.
  **c.** King Norodom Sihanouk.
  **d.** General Suharto.

_____ **16.** Many inhabitants of East Timor have been killed since the former Portuguese colony was seized by
  **a.** Indonesia.
  **b.** France.
  **c.** Britain.
  **d.** Malaysia.

# Chapter 33 : *Form*
# Test : **B**

_____ **17.** North Korean economic growth over the past four decades has been hindered by
   **a.** frequent changes in political leadership.
   **b.** the repressive policies of Zhou Enlai and Deng Xiaoping.
   **c.** huge military expenditures.
   **d.** insufficient focus on heavy industrial development.

_____ **18.** President Lyndon Johnson used the Gulf of Tonkin incident as justification for
   **a.** breaking diplomatic ties with China.
   **b.** seeking greater U.S. involvement in Vietnam.
   **c.** ending U.S. involvement in Taiwan.
   **d.** seeking greater U.S. involvement in Korea.

_____ **19.** The Tiananmen Square crackdown stirred fears in Hong Kong about the
   **a.** transfer of power to the Chinese.
   **b.** transfer of power to the British.
   **c.** city-state's relationship with Thailand.
   **d.** city-state's relationship with the United States.

_____ **20.** All of the following occurred while Japan was under SCAP rule EXCEPT
   **a.** the consolidation of agriculture into efficient large-scale farms.
   **b.** the creation of a British-style governing cabinet.
   **c.** the elimination of the political authority of the emperor.
   **d.** the provision by the United States of a massive aid package.

_____ **21.** The Korean leader known as the "Great Leader" who created a cult of personality around himself was
   **a.** Kim Jong Il.
   **b.** Kim Young Sam.
   **c.** Roh Tae Woo.
   **d.** Kim Il Sung.

_____ **22.** After being partitioned India received millions of
   **a.** Sikh migrants from Sri Lanka.
   **b.** Hindu migrants from Pakistan.
   **c.** Muslim migrants from Pakistan.
   **d.** Muslim migrants from Kashmir.

_____ **23.** The disastrous economic plan launched by the Chinese in 1958 was known as the
   **a.** domino theory.
   **b.** Great Leap Forward.
   **c.** Cultural Revolution.
   **d.** Four Modernizations.

_____ **24.** Pakistan was used by the United States as a base for assisting anti-Soviet rebels in
   **a.** Vietnam.    **b.** North Korea.    **c.** Laos.    **d.** Afghanistan.

_____ **25.** A continuing cause of tension between Japan and many countries is
   **a.** Japan's naval control of the Pacific.
   **b.** Japan's export of government-subsidized raw materials.
   **c.** Japan's nuclear weapons program.
   **d.** the difficulty foreign companies face trying to sell goods in Japan.

## Essay
*Answer one of the following questions on a separate sheet of paper. (10 points)*

**26a. Critical Thinking** Describe the effects of the Vietnam War on neighboring Cambodia.

**26b. Critical Thinking** Explain the events that led to the creation of Bangladesh.

# Chapter 34 : Form
# Test : Ⓐ

## Matching

*Match each item in Column A with an item in Column B by writing the correct letters in the blanks.*
*(3 points each)*

**Column A**

_____ **1.** oil-rich state that gained independence from Italy

_____ **2.** involved in Rwandan conflict

_____ **3.** movement for cooperation by African nations

_____ **4.** the former Gold Coast

_____ **5.** declared Rhodesia independent

_____ **6.** former president of Tanzania

_____ **7.** African literary movement

_____ **8.** Africa's most populous nation

_____ **9.** leaders in war against Ethiopian dictatorship

_____ **10.** negotiated with Nelson Mandela

**Column B**

**a.** Ghana

**b.** Eritreans

**c.** Ian Smith

**d.** F. W. de Klerk

**e.** Libya

**f.** Julius Nyerere

**g.** negritude

**h.** Hutu

**i.** Pan-Africanism

**j.** Nigeria

## Multiple Choice

*In the blank, write the letter of the choice that best completes the statement. (4 points each)*

_____ **11.** Nobel Prize winner Wole Soyinka was charged with treason by
    **a.** South Africa.
    **b.** France.
    **c.** Nigeria.
    **d.** Ghana.

_____ **12.** Angola and Mozambique did not achieve independence until the
    **a.** death of Cecil Rhodes.
    **b.** death of Charles de Gaulle.
    **c.** collapse of the Fourth Republic.
    **d.** overthrow of the Portuguese dictatorship.

_____ **13.** In the United Nations General Assembly, African nations hold
    **a.** no voting rights.
    **b.** one-tenth of the votes.
    **c.** one-third of the votes.
    **d.** two-thirds of the votes.

_____ **14.** The policy of apartheid in South Africa was legalized and strengthened by
    **a.** Great Britain.
    **b.** the Afrikaners.
    **c.** the African National Congress.
    **d.** the Rhodesian Front.

_____ **15.** Ethnic conflict in Nigeria led to the short-lived creation of the Republic of Biafra by the
    **a.** Muslims.
    **b.** Kikuyu.
    **c.** Sudanese.
    **d.** Ibo.

_____ **16.** In 1974 Ethiopian military leaders ousted the monarchy of
    **a.** Joseph D. Mobutu.
    **b.** Mobutu Sese Seko.
    **c.** Kwame Nkrumah.
    **d.** Haile Selassie.

# Chapter 34 Form
# Test A

_____ **17.** All of the following factors have contributed to famine in Africa EXCEPT
   **a.** an overdependence on cash crops.  **c.** soaring population growth.
   **b.** an overabundance of capital.  **d.** the transformation of fertile land into desert.

_____ **18.** Civil war broke out among ethnic groups in Rwanda and
   **a.** Uganda.  **b.** Burundi.  **c.** Kenya.  **d.** Ghana.

_____ **19.** The worst desertification has occurred in
   **a.** Gambia.  **c.** Malawi.
   **b.** the Sahel.  **d.** South Africa.

_____ **20.** Despite opposition from the colons, Charles de Gaulle's negotiations with the rebels led to independence in
   **a.** Ghana.  **c.** Somalia.
   **b.** Nigeria.  **d.** Algeria.

_____ **21.** Crops that are grown for profit and exported are referred to as
   **a.** market prices.  **c.** subsistence crops.
   **b.** key resources.  **d.** cash crops.

_____ **22.** In the early 1990s, starvation in Somalia was worsened by
   **a.** fierce fighting between the Tutsi and the Tigreans.  **c.** the arrival of the UN-sponsored military force.
   **b.** fierce fighting among rival clans.  **d.** the withdrawal of the UN-sponsored military force.

_____ **23.** The earliest postwar independence movements to succeed in Africa were those of
   **a.** East Africa.  **c.** North Africa.
   **b.** South Africa.  **d.** West Africa.

_____ **24.** Nigeria's prospering economy was crippled in the 1980s by
   **a.** surpluses in the world supply of oil.  **c.** the exodus of white settlers.
   **b.** the damaging effects of the Biafran war.  **d.** economic sanctions aimed at ending apartheid.

_____ **25.** After a military takeover in 1969, a socialist government was established in Libya by
   **a.** Muammar al-Qaddafi.  **c.** Jomo Kenyatta.
   **b.** Ahmed Sékou Touré.  **d.** Theo Ayoola.

## Essay
*Answer one of the following questions on a separate sheet of paper. (10 points)*

**26a. Critical Thinking** Describe South Africa's policy of apartheid. How did it originate? When was it abandoned?

**26b. Critical Thinking** Summarize the history of Kenya's struggle for independence. Describe the role of Jomo Kenyatta.

# Chapter 34 : *Form*
# Test : **B**

Score _____

## Matching
*Match each item in Column A with an item in Column B by writing the correct letters in the blanks.*
*(3 points each)*

**Column A**

_____ **1.** region bordering on the Sahara

_____ **2.** sponsor of 1992 mission in Somalia

_____ **3.** genocide victims in Rwanda

_____ **4.** surrendered to Nigeria in 1970

_____ **5.** formerly Rhodesia

_____ **6.** formerly Nyasaland

_____ **7.** led fight for independence of Ghana

_____ **8.** name given to Kenyan freedom movement

_____ **9.** founded in Addis Ababa

_____ **10.** exiled writer critical of Nigeria's military government

**Column B**

**a.** Organization of African Unity

**b.** Kwame Nkrumah

**c.** Wole Soyinka

**d.** Mau Mau

**e.** Tutsi

**f.** United Nations

**g.** Sahel

**h.** Biafra

**i.** Zimbabwe

**j.** Malawi

## Multiple Choice
*In the blank, write the letter of the choice that best completes the statement. (4 points each)*

_____ **11.** The countries of Africa with predominantly Arab cultures are located in the continent's
   **a.** south.
   **b.** east.
   **c.** west.
   **d.** north.

_____ **12.** During the 1980s, Western countries accused Muammar al-Qaddafi of
   **a.** bombing military installations in Libya.
   **b.** sabotaging their economic ties with Libya.
   **c.** aiding international terrorists.
   **d.** supporting apartheid in South Africa.

_____ **13.** The Ethiopian military tried to crush the independence movement in
   **a.** Burundi.
   **b.** Mozambique.
   **c.** Tigre.
   **d.** Soweto.

_____ **14.** The president of Senegal who helped found the literary movement of negritude was
   **a.** Léopold Sédar Senghor.
   **b.** Dei-Anang.
   **c.** Julius Nyerere.
   **d.** Yoweri Museveni.

_____ **15.** At the end of World War II, all of the following states were independent EXCEPT
   **a.** Liberia.
   **b.** Egypt.
   **c.** Ethiopia.
   **d.** Ghana.

_____ **16.** In 1947 Jomo Kenyatta assumed the presidency of
   **a.** a newly independent Kenya.
   **b.** the African National Congress.
   **c.** the Kenya African Union.
   **d.** the Organization of African Unity.

# Chapter 34 : *Form*
# Test : Ⓑ

_____ **17.** During the period of colonial rule, most Africans lived by
  **a.** cash crop farming.
  **b.** working on European-owned plantations.
  **c.** subsistence farming.
  **d.** working on government-owned plantations.

_____ **18.** Member nations in the Economic Community of West African States help preserve scarce cash by
  **a.** developing one-product economies.
  **b.** increasing tariffs on regional trade.
  **c.** increasing taxes on oil revenue.
  **d.** engaging in a barter system.

_____ **19.** During the 1970s and 1980s, the Organization of African Unity tried to
  **a.** halt the spread of Pan-Africanist ideals.
  **b.** support the beleaguered South African government.
  **c.** remain neutral in cold war politics.
  **d.** lend financial support to the Rhodesian Front.

_____ **20.** Ahmed Sékou Touré turned down Charles de Gaulle's offer to provide Guinea
  **a.** full independence.
  **b.** membership in the Commonwealth of Nations.
  **c.** membership in the French Community.
  **d.** control of its own foreign policy while maintaining economic links with France.

_____ **21.** In the 1990s, Tanzania finally abandoned its
  **a.** economic relationship with France.
  **b.** socialist economic policies.
  **c.** policy of apartheid.
  **d.** policy of support for international terrorism.

_____ **22.** In the early 1970s, the economy of Zaire was strengthened by
  **a.** an increase in the price of copper.
  **b.** an increase in the price of oil.
  **c.** a decrease in the price of oil.
  **d.** Mobutu's seizure of foreign businesses.

_____ **23.** Nelson Mandela was jailed for treason by the South African government in
  **a.** 1932.
  **b.** 1962.
  **c.** 1976.
  **d.** 1989.

_____ **24.** In the early 1990s, armed conflict broke out in Algeria between the government and the
  **a.** anticolonial opposition.
  **b.** Islamic opposition.
  **c.** French.
  **d.** Kikuyu.

_____ **25.** Great Britain's wealthiest colony in Africa was
  **a.** Tunisia.
  **b.** the Gold Coast.
  **c.** Libya.
  **d.** Kenya.

## Essay
*Answer one of the following questions on a separate sheet of paper. (10 points)*

**26a. Critical Thinking** Describe how ethnic division has led to conflict in two African nations.

**26b. Critical Thinking** Identify and describe two economic or social problems faced by African countries in the 1990s.

# Chapter 35 : Form
# Test : Ⓐ

**Score** _____

## Matching

*Match each item in Column A with an item in Column B by writing the correct letters in the blanks.*
*(3 points each)*

**Column A**

_____ **1.** imposed embargo on sale of oil

_____ **2.** seized by Israel during Six-Day War

_____ **3.** provides irrigation in Turkey

_____ **4.** first prime minister of Israel

_____ **5.** leader of Iran's Shiite

_____ **6.** capital of Lebanon

_____ **7.** Iranian shah

_____ **8.** returned to Egypt by Israel

_____ **9.** PLO leader

_____ **10.** Jordanian leader

**Column B**

**a.** Mohammad Reza Pahlavi

**b.** OPEC

**c.** Sinai Peninsula

**d.** Yasir Arafat

**e.** Euphrates

**f.** Ayatollah Khomeini

**g.** King Hussein

**h.** West Bank

**i.** Beirut

**j.** David Ben-Gurion

## Multiple Choice

*In the blank, write the letter of the choice that best completes the statement. (4 points each)*

_____ **11.** In 1947 Great Britain relinquished control of Palestine to the
  **a.** United Nations.
  **b.** PLO.
  **c.** Jews.
  **d.** Arabs.

_____ **12.** Many Arab states broke ties with Egypt over its
  **a.** rejection of the Camp David Accords.
  **b.** refusal to join the Arab League.
  **c.** signing of a peace agreement with Israel.
  **d.** signing of a peace agreement with the United States.

_____ **13.** The term *intifada* refers to the uprising of
  **a.** Kurds in Iraq.
  **b.** Palestinians in the West Bank and Gaza Strip.
  **c.** Shiite in Iraq.
  **d.** Palestinians in Jordan.

_____ **14.** Many of Palestine's Jews lived on collective farms called
  **a.** cartels.
  **b.** Zionists.
  **c.** Haganah.
  **d.** kibbutzim.

_____ **15.** Desalination could help Israel, Jordan, and Syria solve their problems with
  **a.** territorial disputes.
  **b.** urban overcrowding.
  **c.** underemployment.
  **d.** water shortages.

_____ **16.** Two Middle Eastern leaders who became victims of assassination were
  **a.** Anwar el-Sadat and Menachim Begin.
  **b.** Anwar el-Sadat and Yitzhak Rabin.
  **c.** Hosni Mubarak and King Faisal II.
  **d.** Hosni Mubarak and Ayatollah Ruhollah Khomeini.

# Chapter 35 : *Form*
# Test : Ⓐ

_____ **17.** In 1975 civil war broke out in Lebanon over the presence of
  **a.** PLO troops in the country.
  **b.** Syrian troops in the country.
  **c.** Egyptian troops in the country.
  **d.** Israeli troops in the country.

_____ **18.** Nasser's standing in the Arab world was boosted by his handling of the
  **a.** Suez Canal crisis.
  **b.** 1948–1949 war.
  **c.** Six-Day War.
  **d.** *intifada.*

_____ **19.** The first Arab leader to set foot in peace on Israeli soil was
  **a.** Anwar el-Sadat.
  **b.** Yasir Arafat.
  **c.** Hosni Mubarak.
  **d.** King Farouk.

_____ **20.** In 1991 a coalition of forces led by the United States forced an Iraqi retreat from
  **a.** Lebanon.
  **b.** Kuwait.
  **c.** Iran.
  **d.** Turkey.

_____ **21.** The first female prime minister to govern a Middle Eastern Muslim country was
  **a.** Golda Meir.
  **b.** Tansu Çiller.
  **c.** Haffez al-Assad.
  **d.** Gamel Abdel Nasser.

_____ **22.** The largest city in the Middle East is
  **a.** Jerusalem.
  **b.** Cairo.
  **c.** Beirut.
  **d.** Baghdad.

_____ **23.** The United Arab Republic was a short-lived union between
  **a.** Palestinian Christians and Muslims.
  **b.** Egypt and Palestine.
  **c.** Egypt and Syria.
  **d.** Iran and Iraq.

_____ **24.** In 1993 Israel signed a historic agreement with
  **a.** the PLO.
  **b.** Syria.
  **c.** Iraq.
  **d.** Egypt.

_____ **25.** The 1948–1949 war between Israel and the Arab states ended with a
  **a.** resounding victory for Israel.
  **b.** resounding victory for the Arabs.
  **c.** return to British rule in Palestine.
  **d.** stalemate with little change in territorial control.

## Essay
*Answer one of the following questions on a separate sheet of paper. (10 points)*

**26a. Critical Thinking** Describe the Suez Crisis. What was the role of the United States?

**26b. Critical Thinking** Summarize the events leading to the creation of the State of Israel. What was the reaction of neighboring Arab states to its creation?

# Chapter 35 : Form
# Test : **B**

**Score** _____

## Matching

*Match each item in Column A with an item in Column B by writing the correct letters in the blanks.*
*(3 points each)*

**Column A**

_____ **1.** Jewish self-defense force

_____ **2.** where American hostages were held

_____ **3.** primary goal had been elimination of Israel

_____ **4.** first female head of a Middle Eastern state

_____ **5.** brief union of Egypt and Syria

_____ **6.** Sadat's successor

_____ **7.** NATO member

_____ **8.** invaded by Iraq in 1990

_____ **9.** organization founded in 1945

_____ **10.** became Turkish prime minister in 1993

**Column B**

**a.** Tansu Çiller

**b.** PLO

**c.** Haganah

**d.** Hosni Mubarak

**e.** Tehran

**f.** Golda Meir

**g.** UAR

**h.** Turkey

**i.** Kuwait

**j.** Arab League

## Multiple Choice

*In the blank, write the letter of the choice that best completes the statement. (4 points each)*

_____ **11.** After the Six-Day War, the amount of territory controlled by Israel
    **a.** had tripled.
    **b.** had been cut in half.
    **c.** remained what it was before the conflict.
    **d.** decreased slightly.

_____ **12.** By 1947 the only major European-ruled territory in the Middle East was
    **a.** Transjordan.
    **b.** Egypt.
    **c.** Syria.
    **d.** Palestine.

_____ **13.** As of 1997, foreign troops still controlled much of
    **a.** Egypt.
    **b.** Turkey.
    **c.** Lebanon.
    **d.** Jordan.

_____ **14.** The terms of a withdrawal from the Golan Heights remained an obstacle to peace between
    **a.** Kuwait and Iraq.
    **b.** Iran and Iraq.
    **c.** Syria and Egypt.
    **d.** Syria and Israel.

_____ **15.** OPEC imposed an oil embargo in response to U.S. support for Israel during the
    **a.** Camp David meetings.
    **b.** Six-Day War.
    **c.** 1973 war.
    **d.** *intifada.*

_____ **16.** Prime Minister Mossadeg's plan to use Iranian oil revenue for social reform came to a halt when
    **a.** he was deposed in a Iraq-backed coup.
    **b.** he was deposed in a United States-backed coup.
    **c.** his country was invaded by Iraq.
    **d.** the Iranian oil industry was nationalized by Great Britain.

# Chapter 35 : Form
# Test : B

_____ **17.** The United States withdrew its offer to aid Egypt's Aswan Dam project because of Nasser's
   **a.** nationalization of the Suez Canal.
   **b.** annexation of the Gaza Strip.
   **c.** growing ties with the Soviet Union.
   **d.** invasion of Israel.

_____ **18.** An adherence to traditional religious values and practices is referred to as
   **a.** Zionism.
   **b.** desalination.
   **c.** fundamentalism.
   **d.** Pan-Arabism.

_____ **19.** At Jimmy Carter's invitation, Menachem Begin met at Camp David with
   **a.** David Ben-Gurion.
   **b.** Anwar el-Sadat.
   **c.** Yasir Arafat.
   **d.** Shimon Peres.

_____ **20.** The Islamic religion was founded in present-day
   **a.** Yemen.
   **b.** Palestine.
   **c.** Egypt.
   **d.** Saudi Arabia.

_____ **21.** In 1952 army officers unhappy with the rule of the corrupt King Farouk seized control of the
   **a.** Israeli government.
   **b.** Egyptian government.
   **c.** Syrian government.
   **d.** Lebanese government.

_____ **22.** Ayatollah Khomeini was succeeded by
   **a.** Hashemi Rafsanjani.
   **b.** Mohammed Reza Pahlavi.
   **c.** Shimon Peres.
   **d.** Saddam Hussein.

_____ **23.** In 1979 diplomats were taken hostage when a United States embassy was stormed by
   **a.** Iranians.
   **b.** Iraqis.
   **c.** Lebanese.
   **d.** Palestinians.

_____ **24.** The United Nations plan to partition Palestine was rejected by
   **a.** Jewish leaders.
   **b.** Arab leaders.
   **c.** the British.
   **d.** the Americans.

_____ **25.** From 1949 to 1967, Palestinians on the West Bank were governed by
   **a.** Israel.
   **b.** Egypt.
   **c.** the PLO.
   **d.** Jordan.

## Essay
*Answer one of the following questions on a separate sheet of paper. (10 points)*

**26a. Critical Thinking** Identify and describe two major peace agreements made between Israeli and Arab parties.

**26b. Critical Thinking** Describe the importance of oil and water resources to the Middle Eastern countries.

# Chapter 36 : *Form*
# Test : Ⓐ
**Score** _____

## Matching

*Match each item in Column A with an item in Column B by writing the correct letters in the blanks.*
*(3 points each)*

**Column A**

_____ **1.** free trade agreement

_____ **2.** Haiti's longtime dictator

_____ **3.** initially popular president of Argentina

_____ **4.** dominant Mexican political party

_____ **5.** until the 1930s, one of world's wealthiest nations

_____ **6.** Costa Rican leader, peacemaker in Nicaragua

_____ **7.** Kennedy's Latin American aid program

_____ **8.** base of Shining Path guerrillas

_____ **9.** includes Haiti and Dominican Republic

_____ **10.** priest who became Haiti's president

**Column B**

**a.** Alliance for Progress

**b.** Argentina

**c.** Hispaniola

**d.** NAFTA

**e.** Jean Bertrand Aristide

**f.** Juan Perón

**g.** Peru

**h.** PRI

**i.** Oscar Arias

**j.** François Duvalier

## Multiple Choice

*In the blank, write the letter of the choice that best completes the statement. (4 points each)*

_____ **11.** During the 1970s, Mexico's increased prosperity resulted primarily from
   **a.** rising oil prices.
   **b.** the overthrow of the military government.
   **c.** greater agricultural production.
   **d.** the overthrow of the Communist government.

_____ **12.** After seizing power from Batista, Castro introduced reforms that
   **a.** improved health care and education.
   **b.** increased freedom of the press and other civil liberties.
   **c.** privatized the major industries.
   **d.** privatized the large landholdings.

_____ **13.** Roman Catholic archbishop Oscar Romero was slain by
   **a.** Zapatista rebels.
   **b.** Sandinista rebels.
   **c.** El Salvadoran death squads.
   **d.** Cuban exiles.

_____ **14.** By 1967 almost one-quarter of Nicaragua's land was owned by the
   **a.** drug dealers.
   **b.** Fujimori family.
   **c.** Somoza family.
   **d.** Castro family.

_____ **15.** The first woman president in the Western Hemisphere was
   **a.** João Goulart.
   **b.** Violeta Chamorro.
   **c.** Eva Perón.
   **d.** Isabel Perón.

_____ **16.** The growth rate of Latin America's population is about
   **a.** one-quarter that of the United States.
   **b.** half that of the United States.
   **c.** the same as that of the United States.
   **d.** three times that of the United States.

# Chapter 36 *Form*
# Test Ⓐ

_____ **17.** In 1995 the OAS intervened to stop a war between Ecuador and
    **a.** Brazil.
    **b.** Colombia.
    **c.** Peru.
    **d.** Bolivia.

_____ **18.** Since the late 1980s, Brazil has been ruled by
    **a.** Socialist dictatorships.
    **b.** right-wing military dictatorships.
    **c.** a series of democratic governments.
    **d.** Fernando Collor de Mello.

_____ **19.** Latin American ability to repay loans from foreign banks was hindered by
    **a.** a worldwide recession in the 1980s.
    **b.** American bank failures during the 1980s.
    **c.** the allocation of farmland for cash crops.
    **d.** increased Latin American investment by multinational corporations.

_____ **20.** During Pinochet's rule in Chile,
    **a.** most American copper-mining companies were nationalized.
    **b.** the country experienced long periods of hyperinflation.
    **c.** many Chileans were killed or imprisoned by the military.
    **d.** the government discouraged foreign investment.

_____ **21.** _____ signed an agreement giving his country control of the Panama Canal in 1999.
    **a.** Manuel Noriega
    **b.** Omar Torrijos
    **c.** Oscar Arias
    **d.** Ernesto Pérez Balladares

_____ **22.** The Falkland Islands became the object of a 1982 war between Great Britain and
    **a.** Chile.
    **b.** Brazil.
    **c.** Peru.
    **d.** Argentina.

_____ **23.** In 1994 international confidence in Zedillo's government was shaken by
    **a.** the economic embargo imposed by the United States.
    **b.** the devaluation of the Mexican peso.
    **c.** Brazil's suspension of its debt repayment.
    **d.** the death of Salvador Allende.

_____ **24.** A major factor in the recent growth of many Latin American cities is the arrival of
    **a.** poor farmers from the countryside.
    **b.** landowners from the countryside.
    **c.** anti-Castro exiles from Cuba.
    **d.** immigrants from western Europe.

_____ **25.** During the 1980s the Nicaraguan government received aid from the governments of many western European countries and
    **a.** the United States.
    **b.** the Soviet Union.
    **c.** El Salvador.
    **d.** Honduras.

## Essay

*Answer one of the following questions on a separate sheet of paper. (10 points)*

**26a. Critical Thinking** Describe the relationship between the United States and Cuba under Castro's leadership.

**26b. Critical Thinking** Identify the origins of the conflict in El Salvador. Which side did the United States support in the country's civil war?

# Chapter 36 : Form
# Test : B

**Score** _____

## Matching
*Match each item in Column A with an item in Column B by writing the correct letters in the blanks.*
*(3 points each)*

**Column A**

_____ **1.** Peruvian diplomat, UN secretary general

_____ **2.** experienced by Argentina in the late 1980s

_____ **3.** shift from public ownership of businesses

_____ **4.** 1947 mutual defense pact

_____ **5.** controller of Panama Canal until 1999

_____ **6.** country of Medellin-based drug cartels

_____ **7.** Chile's longtime dictator

_____ **8.** non-Haitian half of Hispaniola

_____ **9.** invaded by the United States in 1989

_____ **10.** Nicaraguan election winner in 1990

**Column B**

**a.** Rio Treaty

**b.** Augusto Pinochet

**c.** Dominican Republic

**d.** Javier Pérez de Cuéllar

**e.** hyperinflation

**f.** United States

**g.** Violeta Chamorro

**h.** privatization

**i.** Colombia

**j.** Panama

## Multiple Choice
*In the blank, write the letter of the choice that best completes the statement or answers the question.*
*(4 points each)*

_____ **11.** The social structure of Latin America is characterized by
    **a.** the domination of its middle-class majority.
    **b.** great social and economic equality.
    **c.** disparity between the impoverished masses and the wealthy elite.
    **d.** disparity between the wealthy rural inhabitants and the urban poor.

_____ **12.** Socialist Salvador Allende achieved power in Chile
    **a.** after the overthrow of dictator Eduardo Frei Ruiz-Tagle.
    **b.** in a U.S.-backed military coup.
    **c.** by winning democratic elections for the presidency.
    **d.** in a Soviet-backed military coup.

_____ **13.** The Iran-Contra scandal in the 1980s involved the illegal diversion of funds to rebels in
    **a.** Cuba.
    **b.** Panama.
    **c.** Haiti.
    **d.** Nicaragua.

_____ **14.** During the cold war, the United States often tried to undermine
    **a.** conservative Latin American governments.
    **b.** left-wing Latin American governments.
    **c.** the efforts of the Organization of American States.
    **d.** the governments of Mercosur members.

_____ **15.** With the help of the United States and the United Nations, Jean Bertrand Aristide was restored as the leader of a democratic
    **a.** Nicaragua.
    **b.** Brazil.
    **c.** Haiti.
    **d.** Panama.

# Chapter 36 : *Form*
# Test : **B**

_____ **16.** Alberto Fujimori succeeded in
  **a.** defeating the Shining Path guerrillas.
  **b.** reducing hyperinflation in Argentina.
  **c.** crushing the Medellin drug cartel.
  **d.** helping most Peruvians rise out of poverty.

_____ **17.** Latin America's poor farmers are known as
  **a.** campesinos.  **b.** porteños.  **c.** Zapatistas.  **d.** contras.

_____ **18.** Defeat in the Falklands discredited the Argentine
  **a.** military government.
  **b.** government of Juan Perón.
  **c.** government of Isabel Perón.
  **d.** government of Carlos Menem.

_____ **19.** The 1993 NAFTA agreement removed quotas and other barriers to trade among Mexico, the United States, and
  **a.** Cuba.  **b.** Canada.  **c.** Brazil.  **d.** Panama.

_____ **20.** El Salvador's wealth has been almost completely controlled by
  **a.** its Socialist government.
  **b.** American copper-mining companies.
  **c.** a tiny group of elite families.
  **d.** drug barons.

_____ **21.** The U.S.-backed exiles who staged the Bay of Pigs invasion failed to topple the government of
  **a.** Guatemala.  **b.** El Salvador.  **c.** Chile.  **d.** Cuba.

_____ **22.** The broad alliance that overthrew Somoza in Nicaragua was led by the
  **a.** National Guard.
  **b.** Farabundo Martí National Liberation Front.
  **c.** Sandinista National Liberation Front.
  **d.** Institutionalized Revolutionary Party.

_____ **23.** During the rule of Fulgencio Batista, the Cuban economy was dominated by
  **a.** state-owned corporations.
  **b.** Russian companies.
  **c.** Mexican companies.
  **d.** American companies.

_____ **24.** A Latin American leader seized by the United States and convicted for drug smuggling was
  **a.** Fernando Henrique Cardoso.
  **b.** Manuel Noriega.
  **c.** Fidel Castro.
  **d.** Augusto Pinochet.

_____ **25.** Liberation theology marked a change in the Catholic Church's historically close relationship with Latin America's
  **a.** campesinos.
  **b.** Communists.
  **c.** ruling elites.
  **d.** liberals.

## Essay
*Answer one of the following questions on a separate sheet of paper. (10 points)*

**26a. Critical Thinking** Describe the problem of Latin American debt. How is it being resolved? Why does it affect the United States?

**26b. Critical Thinking** Summarize Haiti's political history over the last four decades.

# Chapter 37 : Form
# Test : Ⓐ

## Matching

*Match each item in Column A with an item in Column B by writing the correct letters in the blanks.*
*(3 points each)*

**Column A**

_____ **1.** opposed British presence in Ireland

_____ **2.** post-Soviet Union federation

_____ **3.** Czech playwright turned leader

_____ **4.** agreement to protect the atmosphere.

_____ **5.** ruled Britain through the 1980s

_____ **6.** Pope John Paul II's native land

_____ **7.** Solidarity leader

_____ **8.** in France led by François Mitterrand

_____ **9.** place from which Soviets, under Gorbachev's command, withdrew

_____ **10.** environmental conference in Rio de Janeiro, Brazil

**Column B**

**a.** Poland

**b.** Lech Walesa

**c.** Afghanistan

**d.** Conservatives

**e.** Earth Summit

**f.** Socialists

**g.** IRA

**h.** Commonwealth of Independent States

**i.** Montreal Protocol

**j.** Václav Havel

## Multiple Choice

*In the blank, write the letter of the choice that best completes the statement. (4 points each)*

_____ **11.** All of the following are provinces of the former Yugoslavia EXCEPT
    **a.** Serbia.
    **b.** Croatia.
    **c.** Latvia.
    **d.** Bosnia-Herzegovina.

_____ **12.** Mikhail Gorbachev called for the rebuilding of the Soviet economy, a policy called
    **a.** glasnost.
    **b.** collective security.
    **c.** perestroika.
    **d.** privatization.

_____ **13.** Both Turkey and Iraq have tried to combat
    **a.** uprisings by the Chechen people.
    **b.** outbreaks of anti-Buddhist violence.
    **c.** uprisings by the Kurdish people.
    **d.** the territorial expansionism of Saddam Hussein.

_____ **14.** In the late 1970s, dictatorial rule was replaced by democracy in
    **a.** France and Spain.
    **b.** Portugal and Spain.
    **c.** Latvia and Estonia.
    **d.** Latvia and Romania.

_____ **15.** The unity of Canada was threatened by the demands for independence of
    **a.** its French-speaking minority.
    **b.** its English-speaking minority.
    **c.** Brian Mulroney-led separatists.
    **d.** Pierre Trudeau-led separatists.

_____ **16.** Prime Minister Margaret Thatcher advocated all of the following EXCEPT
    **a.** dismantling social welfare programs.
    **b.** free-market economic policies.
    **c.** limiting the power of trade unions.
    **d.** the nationalization of private industry.

# Chapter 37 : Form
# Test : Ⓐ

_____ **17.** Many of the republics in the USSR resented the dominance of
    **a.** Russia.
    **b.** Germany.
    **c.** the United States.
    **d.** Lithuania.

_____ **18.** The condition in which the government spends more money than it earns in revenue is called
    **a.** a budget deficit.
    **b.** a trade deficit.
    **c.** a trade surplus.
    **d.** interdependency.

_____ **19.** Population is increasing most rapidly in
    **a.** the developed nations.
    **b.** the developing nations.
    **c.** the European Community.
    **d.** the CIS.

_____ **20.** The dictator Nicolae Ceauşescu was executed after a revolt toppled his government in
    **a.** Romania.
    **b.** Hungary.
    **c.** East Germany.
    **d.** Bulgaria.

_____ **21.** The island of Sri Lanka has been divided by conflict between the Sinhalese and
    **a.** Sunni Muslims.
    **b.** the Ossetians.
    **c.** the Tamils.
    **d.** the Serbs.

_____ **22.** The relationship between Greece and Turkey continues to be strained by
    **a.** the status of the island of Cyprus.
    **b.** Turkish support for Basque separatists.
    **c.** Turkey's desire to join NATO.
    **d.** Greece's desire to join NATO.

_____ **23.** Sending soldiers into Chechnya was ordered by
    **a.** Erich Honecker.
    **b.** Boris Yeltsin.
    **c.** Ronald Reagan.
    **d.** Brian Mulroney.

_____ **24.** The European Community expanded previous efforts toward integration of
    **a.** the International Monetary Fund.
    **b.** NATO.
    **c.** the Economic and Monetary Union.
    **d.** the Common Market.

_____ **25.** The fall of the Berlin Wall led rapidly to the reunification of
    **a.** Czechoslovakia.
    **b.** Yugoslavia.
    **c.** the USSR.
    **d.** Germany.

## Essay
_Answer one of the following questions on a separate sheet of paper. (10 points)_

**26a. Critical Thinking** Describe the changes that occurred in the relationship between the United States and the Soviet Union during the 1980s.

**26b. Critical Thinking** Provide two examples of the way the world's nations are becoming increasingly interdependent.

# Chapter 37 : *Form*
# Test : Ⓑ

**Score** _____

## Matching
*Match each item in Column A with an item in Column B by writing the correct letters in the blanks.*
*(3 points each)*

**Column A**

_____ **1.** held out for two years against reforms of 1989

_____ **2.** major factor in Yugoslavian breakup

_____ **3.** aimed at bringing peace to former Yugoslavia

_____ **4.** created "hole" in Iron Curtain by opening its borders

_____ **5.** guided Spain into democracy

_____ **6.** a result of global technology and trade

_____ **7.** policy of new openness in the USSR

_____ **8.** stateless Middle Eastern people

_____ **9.** Sri Lankan Buddhists

_____ **10.** East Germany's longtime leader

**Column B**

**a.** Sinhalese

**b.** glasnost

**c.** Erich Honecker

**d.** Juan Carlos I

**e.** interdependence

**f.** Albania

**g.** Kurds

**h.** Hungary

**i.** Dayton Treaty

**j.** nationalism

## Multiple Choice
*In the blank, write the letter of the choice that best completes the statement. (4 points each)*

_____ **11.** The Solidarity movement demanded better conditions for workers in
   **a.** Poland.
   **b.** Russia.
   **c.** Czechoslovakia.
   **d.** Hungary.

_____ **12.** In 1991 military leaders and secret police in the USSR attempted a coup against
   **a.** Boris Yeltsin.
   **b.** Lech Walesa.
   **c.** Mikhail Gorbachev.
   **d.** Alexander Kwasniewski.

_____ **13.** By the year 2050, at the present rate of growth, the world's population will reach
   **a.** 6 billion.
   **b.** 12 billion.
   **c.** 18 billion.
   **d.** 25 billion.

_____ **14.** In the 1980s, America's growing preference for fuel-efficient Japanese cars contributed to
   **a.** the budget deficit.
   **b.** the trade deficit.
   **c.** perestroika.
   **d.** privatization.

_____ **15.** Dispute over the ownership of Nagorno-Karabakh has created conflict between
   **a.** the United States and Canada.
   **b.** Spain and Portugal.
   **c.** Armenia and Azerbaijan.
   **d.** Greece and Turkey.

_____ **16.** As a consequence of reunification, Germany experienced
   **a.** a decrease in the level of unemployment.
   **b.** a decrease in the incidence of Neo-Nazi violence.
   **c.** a decrease in immigration from Eastern Europe.
   **d.** an increase in taxation to pay for economic restructuring.

# Chapter 37 : *Form*
# Test : Ⓑ

_____ **17.** In 1992 a meeting of European leaders in the Netherlands established
  **a.** the Commonwealth of Nations.
  **b.** the Commonwealth of Independent States.
  **c.** NATO.
  **d.** the European Union.

_____ **18.** The world's newly industrializing countries are referred to as
  **a.** interdependent nations.
  **b.** developing nations.
  **c.** Pacific Rim nations.
  **d.** nonnuclear nations.

_____ **19.** One important issue about which reformed Communists in Eastern Europe were concerned was
  **a.** more rapid privatization.
  **b.** budget deficit reduction.
  **c.** increased ethnic tension.
  **d.** social welfare program protection.

_____ **20.** In 1995 referendum voters in Quebec narrowly approved
  **a.** the province's independence.
  **b.** withdrawal from NATO.
  **c.** continued union with Canada.
  **d.** continued membership in the European Community.

_____ **21.** An international court issued charges of genocide against
  **a.** Bosnian Serb leaders.
  **b.** Russian leaders.
  **c.** Chechen leaders.
  **d.** Sri Lankan Tamil leaders.

_____ **22.** United States-Soviet Union tension began to diminish as President Reagan developed a working relationship with
  **a.** Boris Yeltsin.
  **b.** Mikhail Gorbachev.
  **c.** Lech Walesa.
  **d.** Helmut Kohl.

_____ **23.** Innovations as varied as industrial robots and computerized analyses of the weather have been made possible by the development of
  **a.** ultraviolet rays.
  **b.** genetic engineering.
  **c.** the modem.
  **d.** the microchip.

_____ **24.** Family and friends were reunited after the Brandenburg Gate was opened in
  **a.** Moscow.      **b.** Berlin.      **c.** Gdansk.      **d.** Sarajevo.

_____ **25.** Many of Northern Ireland's Protestant majority favor
  **a.** continued union with Great Britain.
  **b.** continued union with the Republic of Ireland.
  **c.** a merger with Great Britain.
  **d.** a merger with the Republic of Ireland.

## Essay

*Answer one of the following questions on a separate sheet of paper. (10 points)*

**26a. Critical Thinking** Compare and contrast the political leadership of England and France during the 1980s.

**26b. Critical Thinking** Discuss the relationship between the fall of communism and the creation of new independent states in Eastern Europe and central Asia.

# Unit 1 : Test

Score _____

## Matching

*Match each item in Column A with an item in Column B by writing the correct letters in the blanks.*
*(1 point each)*

**Column A**

_____ **1.** group of officials with civic responsibilities

_____ **2.** the scientific study of hominids

_____ **3.** seasonal wind

_____ **4.** their legal system emphasized payment over punishment

_____ **5.** one of the largest Neolithic villages

_____ **6.** Assyrian capital

_____ **7.** the Phoenician city-states formed one

_____ **8.** site of first government to rule all of Egypt

_____ **9.** a source of information about Fertile Crescent history

_____ **10.** made possible the translation of hieroglyphics

_____ **11.** includes the food, art, religion, language, and customs of a people

_____ **12.** developed a 22-character alphabet

_____ **13.** discovery site of early hominid bones

_____ **14.** one site of early urban civilization

_____ **15.** ruled by Hammurabi

_____ **16.** technique used to determine age of remains

_____ **17.** belief in one all-powerful god

_____ **18.** traditional tale of explanation

_____ **19.** Lebanon, Israel, Jordan

_____ **20.** period of great advancement in agricultural methods

**Column B**

**a.** anthropology

**b.** Aramis

**c.** Babylonian Empire

**d** the Bible

**e.** bureaucracy

**f.** Canaan

**g.** Çatal Hüyük

**h.** confederation

**i.** culture

**j.** Hittites

**k.** Indus Valley

**l.** Memphis

**m.** monotheism

**n.** monsoon

**o.** myth

**p.** Neolithic Revolution

**q.** Nineveh

**r.** Phoenicians

**s.** radiocarbon dating

**t.** Rosetta stone

## Multiple Choice

*In the blank, write the letter of the choice that best completes the statement. (2 points each)*

_____ **21.** The Babylonian calendar resolved the difference between solar and lunar years by

    **a.** adding an extra five-day week to certain months.

    **b.** adding an extra day to certain months.

    **c.** making solar months longer than lunar months.

    **d.** adding an extra month to certain years.

_____ **22.** The ability of people to settle in permanent communities was made possible by the development of

    **a.** agriculture.     **b.** metalwork.     **c.** stone tools.     **d.** stone huts.

# Unit 1

# Test

_____ **23.** All of the following social groups grew as a part of urban civilizations EXCEPT
    **a.** government officials.
    **b.** nomadic wanderers.
    **c.** artisans.
    **d.** merchants.

_____ **24.** From around 900 B.C. to 612 B.C., the most feared army in the Middle East was that of the
    **a.** Chaldeans.
    **b.** Israelites.
    **c.** Assyrians.
    **d.** Persians.

_____ **25.** The Sumerians wrote by
    **a.** scratching characters onto oracle bones.
    **b.** using papyrus scrolls as a paperlike medium.
    **c.** using vegetable-based inks.
    **d.** pressing sharpened reeds into wet clay tablets.

_____ **26.** A government that combines both political and religious leadership is called a
    **a.** monarchy.
    **b.** dynasty.
    **c.** bureaucracy.
    **d.** theocracy.

_____ **27.** The first prehuman hominids probably lived in
    **a.** North and South America.
    **b.** eastern and southern Africa.
    **c.** southeast Asia.
    **d.** the Bering Strait.

_____ **28.** Located between the Tigris and Euphrates, Mesopotamia's name means
    **a.** "land between the mountains."
    **b.** "land between the rivers."
    **c.** "land between the kingdoms."
    **d.** "land of two peoples."

_____ **29.** All of the following are people of the Fertile Crescent EXCEPT the
    **a.** Aramaeans.
    **b.** Phoenicians.
    **c.** Israelites.
    **d.** Harappans.

_____ **30.** Amenhotep broke with Egyptian religious tradition by advocating
    **a.** the elimination of the priestly class.
    **b.** the worship of a single deity, the sun-disk god.
    **c.** polytheism.
    **d.** the worship of many gods and goddesses.

_____ **31.** Long-distance hunting weapons such as the bow and arrow were used by
    **a.** the Cro-Magnons.
    **b.** the Neanderthals.
    **c.** *Homo habilis.*
    **d.** *Homo erectus.*

_____ **32.** According to the Bible, Moses led his people out of Egypt
    **a.** across the Gobi.
    **b.** to the Hanging Gardens of Babylon.
    **c.** to the top of Mount Tabor.
    **d.** across the Sinai Peninsula.

_____ **33.** The Chinese writing system was
    **a.** written horizontally from right to left.
    **b.** so complex that few ancient Chinese could read and write.
    **c.** the world's first written language.
    **d.** a major influence on the Harappan writing system.

_____ **34.** After the death of Solomon, the Israelites formed
    **a.** 12 tribes.
    **b.** a northern and southern kingdom.
    **c.** 6 coastal city-states.
    **d.** an alliance with the Philistines.

# Unit 1 : Test

_____ **35.** The ability of farmers to produce grain surpluses spurred the growth of
  **a.** large urban civilizations.       **c.** small nomadic bands.
  **b.** irrigation technology.           **d.** small agricultural villages.

_____ **36.** The Paleolithic period is also referred to as the
  **a.** Ice Age.       **b.** New Stone Age.       **c.** Old Stone Age.       **d.** Bronze Age.

_____ **37.** The Asian subcontinent is the site of present-day
  **a.** Egypt.                                  **c.** India, Pakistan, and Bangladesh.
  **b.** Israel, Jordan, Iraq, and Turkey.       **d.** China.

_____ **38.** Most historians regard Hammurabi's greatest accomplishment as
  **a.** the development of a written code of law.   **c.** the defeat of the Akkadian Empire.
  **b.** the reorganization of the Mesopotamian     **d.** the unification of the Sumerian
  tax system.                                           city-states.

_____ **39.** Like many other ancient cities, Anyang was
  **a.** built with a pyramid at its center.     **c.** laid out in a gridlike fashion.
  **b.** built with a palace and temple          **d.** inhabited mainly by artisans.
  at its center.

_____ **40.** The Egyptian writing system used picture symbols called
  **a.** _eddubas._       **b.** papyrus.       **c.** hieroglyphs.       **d.** cuneiform.

_____ **41.** The Lydian kingdom revolutionized trading by developing
  **a.** a character-based alphabet.     **c.** contracts and bills of sale.
  **b.** a network of Mediterranean      **d.** a money system.
  colonies.

_____ **42.** _Homo habilis_, the oldest hominids to manufacture tools, lived from about
  **a.** 50,000 to 10,000 years ago.     **c.** 1.6 million to 250,000 years ago.
  **b.** 100,000 to 10,000 years ago.    **d.** 2.5 million to 1.5 million years ago.

_____ **43.** Zoroaster preached that Ahura Mazda was
  **a.** the god leading the forces of evil.     **c.** an earth-mother goddess.
  **b.** the god leading the forces of good.     **d.** the all-powerful god of the sun.

_____ **44.** In early civilizations, city government officials were needed for all of the following reasons
  EXCEPT
  **a.** to supervise and protect trade.     **c.** to minimize the specialization of labor.
  **b.** to organize labor for large-scale   **d.** to distribute agricultural surpluses.
  construction.

_____ **45.** Technological and cultural change occurred with greatest frequency among
  **a.** _Homo habilis._   **b.** _Homo erectus._   **c.** _Homo sapiens._   **d.** _Australopithecus._

_____ **46.** Israelite resettlement of Canaan was hindered by all of the following EXCEPT
  **a.** their division into 12 tribes.        **c.** the resistance of the Philistines.
  **b.** the resistance of the Persians.       **d.** the resistance of the Canaanites.

# Unit 1

## Test

_____ **47.** King Nebuchadnezzar did all of the following EXCEPT
  **a.** build the Hanging Gardens in Babylon.   **c.** conquer Jerusalem.
  **b.** extend the Chaldean Empire as far west   **d.** conquer Greece.
  as Syria and Canaan.

_____ **48.** Myths about Yu the Great may be based on the attempts of ancient rulers to control the
  **a.** Huang He.   **b.** Ganges.   **c.** Nile.   **d.** Brahmaputra.

_____ **49.** The Israelites believed in a single all-powerful god called
  **a.** Ahriman.   **b.** Yahweh.   **c.** Ur.   **d.** Ahura Mazda.

_____ **50.** The city of Carthage was founded by
  **a.** Cyrus II.   **c.** King Solomon.
  **b.** the Hittites.   **d.** Phoenician colonists.

_____ **51.** The Nile River flows
  **a.** from the East African highlands through   **c.** from east to west through the Fertile
  Egypt to the Mediterranean.   Crescent.
  **b.** from north to south through the Fertile   **d.** through present-day Turkey to the
  Crescent.   Mediterranean.

_____ **52.** The Persians helped to facilitate increased trade by
  **a.** eliminating provincial tax collection.   **c.** expanding Phoenician sea routes.
  **b.** improving the Assyrian-built road   **d.** prohibiting the use of local languages
  network.   and dialects.

_____ **53.** The Cro-Magnons created all of the following EXCEPT
  **a.** long stone blockhouses.   **c.** cave paintings and sculpted artifacts.
  **b.** canoes capable of open-sea voyages.   **d.** metal plows.

_____ **54.** Upper-class citizens of ancient Egypt often lived in
  **a.** simple stone buildings along the   **c.** large estates with gardens, pools, and
  banks of the Nile.   orchards.
  **b.** clay buildings with wooden roofs.   **d.** small agricultural villages.

_____ **55.** The migration of people from one part of the world to another was
  **a.** greatly affected by changes in the earth's   **c.** made possible by the development
  climate.   of spoken language.
  **b.** brought to a halt during the Ice Ages.   **d.** an obstacle to technological
  development.

## Essay
_Answer one of the following questions on a separate sheet of paper. (10 points)_

**56a. Critical Thinking** Compare and contrast the ruling techniques and accomplishments of two
Fertile Crescent empires.

**56b. Critical Thinking** Describe the writing systems of the Egyptians, Chinese, and Phoenicians.
Which system was accessible to a greater percentage of the population?

# Unit 2
# Test

## Matching

*Match each item in Column A with an item in Column B by writing the correct letters in the blanks.*
*(1 point each)*

**Column A**

_____ **1.** capital of Malian Empire

_____ **2.** early Niger River valley civilization

_____ **3.** facilitated trade with China

_____ **4.** this collection escaped the Qin bonfires

_____ **5.** Athenian meeting for drink, dining, discussion

_____ **6.** displayer of great generosity during Makkah trip

_____ **7.** 400-year period of Chinese prosperity

_____ **8.** commanded troops and wrote the story of Oedipus

_____ **9.** early inhabitants of the Italian Peninsula

_____ **10.** Greek word meaning city-state

_____ **11.** to achieve freedom from rebirth

_____ **12.** "the father of history"

_____ **13.** home of the Greek gods

_____ **14.** home of the oracle

_____ **15.** language of the Aryans

_____ **16.** made it easier to move heavy objects

_____ **17.** government by a wealthy few

_____ **18.** located in Egypt, named after a Macedonian

_____ **19.** wrote verses based on Greek mythology

_____ **20.** Confucian principle advocating respect

**Column B**

**a.** Alexandria

**b.** Archimedes

**c.** Delphi

**d.** Etruscans

**e.** filial piety

**f.** Five Classics

**g.** Herodotus

**h.** Mansa Musa

**i.** Mount Olympus

**j.** nirvana

**k.** Nok

**l.** oligarchy

**m.** Ovid

**n.** *Pax Sinica*

**o.** polis

**p.** Sanskrit

**q.** Silk Road

**r.** Sophocles

**s.** symposium

**t.** Timbuktu

## Multiple Choice

*In the blank, write the letter of the choice that best completes the statement. (2 points each)*

_____ **21.** The Bantu kingdoms of Central and Southern Africa controlled the
    **a.** salt trade.
    **b.** copper and gold mines of the interior.
    **c.** pottery trade.
    **d.** Red Sea ports and associated trade routes.

_____ **22.** The first emperor of Rome to defend Christianity was
    **a.** Augustus.
    **b.** Augustine.
    **c.** Constantine.
    **d.** Theodosius.

# Unit 2
# Test

_____ **23.** A phalanx is a Greek military formation made up of
  **a.** rows of closely-arrayed foot soldiers.       **c.** archers on top of the Acropolis.
  **b.** warships escorting merchant vessels.          **d.** noblemen on horseback.

_____ **24.** The king who introduced Islamic culture to Mali was
  **a.** Mansa Musa.                                   **c.** Piankhi.
  **b.** Askia Muhammad.                               **d.** Sundiata Keita.

_____ **25.** The Hellenistic philosopher who advised people to ignore their emotions and accept difficult circumstances was named
  **a.** Zeno.            **b.** Diogenes.             **c.** Euclid.           **d.** Aristotle.

_____ **26.** The religion founded by Siddhartha Gautama is
  **a.** Buddhism.        **b.** Islam.                **c.** Stoicism.         **d.** Hinduism.

_____ **27.** The Chinese dynasty that ruled for more than 800 years was the
  **a.** Qin.             **b.** Shang.                **c.** Han.              **d.** Zhou.

_____ **28.** The Greek architectural ideal of the "golden mean" is best described as
  **a.** "nothing to excess."                          **c.** "achieving both extremes."
  **b.** "nothing but extremes."                       **d.** "complexity at any cost."

_____ **29.** According to Thucydides,
  **a.** only gods make history.                       **c.** only humans make history.
  **b.** only kings make history.                      **d.** history is the story of the Greeks.

_____ **30.** Spartan males began their military training at age
  **a.** 7.               **b.** 10.                   **c.** 15.               **d.** 18.

_____ **31.** The coastal city-states of East Africa developed a thriving trade
  **a.** with the farmers of the Sahel.                **c.** along the Niger River.
  **b.** through the Sahara.                           **d.** across the Indian Ocean.

_____ **32.** Court cases in democratic Athens were decided by
  **a.** a single judge.                               **c.** the unanimous vote of a 12-member jury.
  **b.** a panel of judges.                            **d.** the majority vote of a 201- to 1,001-member jury.

_____ **33.** The Chinese philosophy that emphasizes harmony between the individual and nature is
  **a.** Buddhism.        **b.** Confucianism.         **c.** Daoism.           **d.** Mandarinism.

_____ **34.** The author of _The Republic_ was
  **a.** Sophocles.       **b.** Socrates.             **c.** Herodotus.        **d.** Plato.

_____ **35.** The first Greek plays were written to
  **a.** stress human courage and compassion.          **c.** honor the founders of Athens.
  **b.** honor Dionysus, god of wine and fertility.    **d.** tell the story of the fall of Troy.

# Unit 2

# Test

_____ **36.** Major reforms of Athenian government between about 630 B.C. and 500 B.C. were enacted by a series of
   **a.** tyrants.
   **b.** draconians.
   **c.** democratic governments.
   **d.** oligarchies.

_____ **37.** Hippocrates is sometimes called
   **a.** "the father of Plato."
   **b.** "the father of history."
   **c.** "the father of the atom."
   **d.** "the father of medicine."

_____ **38.** The largest of the stone fortresses built by the Karanga people is
   **a.** the Great Zimbabwe.
   **b.** Zanzibar.
   **c.** Monomotapa.
   **d.** Timbuktu.

_____ **39.** In return for financing the Spartan navy, the Persians were to receive
   **a.** Athens.
   **b.** Ionia.
   **c.** Troy.
   **d.** Delos.

_____ **40.** The *Odyssey* tells the story of
   **a.** a war between the Mycenaeans and the Minoans.
   **b.** a war between the Mycenaeans and the Trojans.
   **c.** a war between the Athenians and the Spartans.
   **d.** the return of a Mycenaean king to his homeland.

_____ **41.** A belief in "relative truth" was characteristic of
   **a.** Socrates.
   **b.** Euripides.
   **c.** the Sophists.
   **d.** the Stoics.

_____ **42.** Roman writers produced all of the following EXCEPT
   **a.** the *Aeneid*.
   **b.** the *Book of Changes*.
   **c.** the *Metamorphoses*.
   **d.** *Meditations*.

_____ **43.** The economy of the early Aryans revolved around
   **a.** mining.
   **b.** cattle.
   **c.** agriculture.
   **d.** hunting.

_____ **44.** The western Roman Empire came to an end in the late
   **a.** A.D. 100s.
   **b.** A.D. 300s.
   **c.** A.D. 400s.
   **d.** A.D. 700s.

_____ **45.** The wealth of the Malian kingdom depended on
   **a.** possession of the Moroccan gold mines.
   **b.** the strength of its naval fleet.
   **c.** control of the trans-Saharan trade routes.
   **d.** control of the silk trade.

_____ **46.** Membership in the Athenian Council of 500 was determined by
   **a.** the ruling aristocracy.
   **b.** a yearly lottery.
   **c.** a voice vote of Assembly members.
   **d.** a written vote of all citizens.

_____ **47.** All of the following originated during India's Golden Age EXCEPT
   **a.** the concepts of infinity and zero.
   **b.** Arabic numerals.
   **c.** the *Panchatantra* tales.
   **d.** the *Rig-Veda*.

# Unit 2:
# Test

_____ **48.** The primary concern of Confucianism is

    **a.** the creation of social order based on ethical behavior.

    **b.** the harmonious relationship between humans and nature.

    **c.** the reconciliation of nature's opposing forces.

    **d.** escape from the cycle of rebirth.

_____ **49.** In 30 B.C., Octavian became Rome's undisputed leader only after the

    **a.** suicides of Antony and Cleopatra.

    **b.** defeat of Pompey's armies.

    **c.** assassination of Julius Caesar.

    **d.** death of Romulus and Remus.

_____ **50.** The principle that the accused should be considered innocent until proved guilty is a legacy of

    **a.** Athenian law.

    **b.** Confucian thought.

    **c.** early Christian teachings.

    **d.** Roman law.

_____ **51.** The Punic Wars were fought by

    **a.** Athens and Sparta.

    **b.** Rome and Greece.

    **c.** Rome and Carthage.

    **d.** Persia and Macedonia.

_____ **52.** After a series of migrations, the Bantu-speaking peoples became

    **a.** rulers of the kingdom of Axum.

    **b.** the majority of the population in North Africa.

    **c.** the majority in Kush.

    **d.** the dominant group in Africa south of the Sahara.

_____ **53.** The term *caste system* refers to the Indian social structure of

    **a.** *Brahma* and *ahimsa*.

    **b.** *varnas* and *jati*.

    **c.** *karma* and *dharma*.

    **d.** *Sudra* and *moksha*.

_____ **54.** The Mauryan ruler who conquered India and then renounced war was

    **a.** Chandragupta I.    **b.** Buddha.    **c.** Asoka.    **d.** Bimbisara.

_____ **55.** In 494 B.C., plebeian dissatisfaction with the patricians led them to

    **a.** overthrow the government of Romulus.

    **b.** refuse to serve in the Assembly of Centuries.

    **c.** destroy the Twelve Tables.

    **d.** refuse to serve in the Roman army.

## Essay
*Answer one of the following questions on a separate sheet of paper. (10 points)*

**56a. Critical Thinking** Describe the Chinese civil service system. Explain its origins, entrance requirements, and philosophical foundation.

**56b. Critical Thinking** Explain the role of trade and government in facilitating the spread of Islam in Africa.

# Unit 3 : Test

## Matching

*Match each item in Column A with an item in Column B by writing the correct letters in the blanks.*
*(1 point each)*

**Column A**

_____ **1.** in this period, Japan was obsessed with beauty

_____ **2.** members of the English middle class

_____ **3.** Native American capital in Andean highlands

_____ **4.** title meaning "great general"

_____ **5.** the Byzantine religion

_____ **6.** Vietnamese spirit house

_____ **7.** city that fell to Ottomans in A.D. 1453

_____ **8.** the great central Asian plain

_____ **9.** nobles who served higher-ranking lords

_____ **10.** controlled Jerusalem by Crusades' end

_____ **11.** imperial language of the Inca

_____ **12.** site of the House of Wisdom

_____ **13.** Frankish king crowned Roman emperor

_____ **14.** a Mesoamerican civilization

_____ **15.** Islamic places of worship

_____ **16.** salmon trap of the Northwest peoples

_____ **17.** settled by the Maya

_____ **18.** floating gardens of the Aztec

_____ **19.** the popes were in exile here

_____ **20.** "city of the prophet"

**Column B**

**a.** Avignon

**b.** Baghdad

**c.** burgesses

**d.** Charlemagne

**e.** *chinampas*

**f.** Constantinople

**g.** Cuzco

**h.** *dinh*

**i.** Eastern Orthodox

**j.** Heian

**k.** Madinah

**l.** mosques

**m.** Muslims

**n.** Olmec

**o.** Quechua

**p.** shogun

**q.** steppe

**r.** vassals

**s.** weir

**t.** Yucatán

## Multiple Choice

*In the blank, write the letter of the choice that best completes the statement. (2 points each)*

_____ **21.** Most medieval literature was written
   **a.** by monks.
   **b.** in the vernacular.
   **c.** in Latin.
   **d.** in Italian.

_____ **22.** The collapse of the Mayan civilization may have been caused by
   **a.** invasion by the Aztec.
   **b.** an agricultural breakdown caused by erosion and overfarming.
   **c.** the near-extinction of the bison.
   **d.** competition for land caused by Inca expansion.

_____ **23.** Elaborate, decorated books called illuminated manuscripts were first produced by
   **a.** Byzantine religious scholars.
   **b.** the Franciscans.
   **c.** Benedictine monks.
   **d.** the Ottoman Turks.

# Unit 3 :
# Test

_____ **24.** Beginning in the A.D. 800s, Carolingian lands were attacked by seafaring invaders called
  **a.** Magyars.
  **b.** Huns.
  **c.** Vikings.
  **d.** Slavs.

_____ **25.** The League of the Iroquois was formed by Native American groups from
  **a.** present-day California.
  **b.** present-day Guatemala.
  **c.** the Yucatán Peninsula.
  **d.** the northeastern part of the present-day United States.

_____ **26.** The Arabian Peninsula is located
  **a.** between the Black Sea and Constantinople.
  **b.** just north of the Black Sea.
  **c.** between the Red Sea and the Persian Gulf.
  **d.** just west of the Balkans.

_____ **27.** The conflict over Pope Gregory XI's successor became known as the
  **a.** Wars of the Roses.
  **b.** Babylonian Captivity.
  **c.** Exile.
  **d.** Great Schism.

_____ **28.** At its height, the Aztec Empire stretched from
  **a.** southern Alaska to northern California.
  **b.** the Yucatán Peninsula to Cuzco.
  **c.** Ecuador to northern Argentina.
  **d.** north-central Mexico to the border of Guatemala.

_____ **29.** The common law introduced by Henry II set up a system of
  **a.** chivalry.
  **b.** fiefs and manors.
  **c.** excommunication.
  **d.** equal justice.

_____ **30.** The largest land empire in history was ruled by the
  **a.** Vikings.
  **b.** Arabs.
  **c.** Mongols.
  **d.** Romans.

_____ **31.** By the A.D. 1300s, the Byzantine Empire consisted of
  **a.** the entire Balkan Peninsula.
  **b.** most of the Balkans, Italy, southern Spain, Syria, North Africa, and Asia Minor.
  **c.** Constantinople, Armenia, and Georgia.
  **d.** little more than Constantinople.

_____ **32.** The Third Crusade ended with the
  **a.** decisive victory of Richard I in Palestine.
  **b.** defeat of Seljuk Turks by French-led crusaders.
  **c.** defeat of the French at Agincourt.
  **d.** continued control of Jerusalem by Saladin.

_____ **33.** Ferdinand and Isabella did all of the following EXCEPT
  **a.** initiate the _Reconquista_.
  **b.** order the conversion of Jews and Muslims to Catholicism.
  **c.** set up the Spanish Inquisition.
  **d.** expel the Moors from Granada.

_____ **34.** The Mongol ruler accompanied by Marco Polo was
  **a.** Kublai Khan.　　**b.** Genghis Khan.　　**c.** Ogadai Khan.　　**d.** Helagu.

# Unit 3
# Test

_____ **35.** The Five Pillars of Islam are faith, prayer, almsgiving, fasting, and
    **a.** obedience for *shari'ah*.
    **b.** celebration of Ramadan.
    **c.** pilgrimage to Makkah.
    **d.** recitation of the Hadith.

_____ **36.** The Eastern Slavs became isolated from Europe during the period of
    **a.** Moscow's rule.
    **b.** Mongol rule.
    **c.** Byzantine rule.
    **d.** Yaroslav's rule.

_____ **37.** Many Japanese rituals and art forms are based on a form of Buddhism called
    **a.** Zen.
    **b.** Shinto.
    **c.** Genji.
    **d.** Shotoku.

_____ **38.** The system of economic ties that bound nobles and peasants is referred to as
    **a.** feudalism.
    **b.** chivalry.
    **c.** manorialism.
    **d.** the vassal system.

_____ **39.** While European monks were still copying texts by hand, Chinese monks had invented
    **a.** illuminated manuscripts.
    **b.** Cyrillic script.
    **c.** calligraphy.
    **d.** block printing.

_____ **40.** The capital of the Toltec Empire was
    **a.** Samarkand.
    **b.** Angkor Wat.
    **c.** Tenochtitlán.
    **d.** Tula.

_____ **41.** The legal heritage of Rome was preserved in the *Corpus of Civil Law*, compiled under order of
    **a.** Justinian.
    **b.** Charlemagne.
    **c.** Alfred the Great.
    **d.** Leo III.

_____ **42.** English control of French territory led to the
    **a.** *Reconquista*.
    **b.** Hundred Years' War.
    **c.** Wars of the Roses.
    **d.** Crusades.

_____ **43.** During the homage ceremony, a vassal pledged to
    **a.** lead a life of poverty and chastity.
    **b.** provide his lord with knights for battle.
    **c.** remain on the manor.
    **d.** obey the code of chivalry.

_____ **44.** Mosques feature a mihrab, or niche, indicating the
    **a.** place of the caliph.
    **b.** place of the Quran.
    **c.** direction to Makkah.
    **d.** direction to Baghdad.

_____ **45.** Spain first came under Islamic control during the rule of the
    **a.** Umayyads.
    **b.** Abbasids.
    **c.** Turks.
    **d.** Maimonides.

_____ **46.** Sanskrit and the religion of Hinduism were introduced into Southeast Asia by the
    **a.** Chinese.
    **b.** Indians.
    **c.** Koreans.
    **d.** Mongols.

# Unit 3 : Test

_____ **47.** With some exceptions, Europe between the A.D. 400s and 1100s is characterized by the absence of
  **a.** strong monarchs.
  **b.** stratified social hierarchies.
  **c.** powerful religious authorities.
  **d.** wars between rival feudal lords.

_____ **48.** The country that became known as the Hermit Kingdom because of its long isolation was
  **a.** Korea.
  **b.** Japan.
  **c.** Thailand.
  **d.** Indonesia.

_____ **49.** The primary function of merchant guilds was to
  **a.** encourage competition among journey-men.
  **b.** provide social benefits to artisans.
  **c.** establish standards for handcrafted goods.
  **d.** enforce price and trade restrictions.

_____ **50.** Bali became the only Indonesian island to maintain
  **a.** a Hindu religion and culture.
  **b.** a rice-based economy.
  **c.** trade with the Malay Peninsula.
  **d.** Islamic law.

_____ **51.** Shiites believe the Islamic leader
  **a.** must be a descendant of the Rightly Guided Caliphs.
  **b.** must be a descendant of Muhammad.
  **c.** can be any devout Muslim accepted by the people.
  **d.** should be decided by an election.

_____ **52.** Russian, Ukrainian, and Belarussian people descended from the
  **a.** Eastern Slavs.
  **b.** Ottoman Turks.
  **c.** Seljuk Turks.
  **d.** Slovenes.

_____ **53.** The economy of the early Arctic peoples of North America was based on
  **a.** maize farming.
  **b.** pottery trade.
  **c.** timber trade.
  **d.** hunting and fishing.

_____ **54.** The Dominicans and Franciscans were two groups of wandering preachers known as
  **a.** monks.
  **b.** friars.
  **c.** abbots.
  **d.** heretics.

_____ **55.** The Crusades contributed to the breakdown of feudalism because
  **a.** Muslims captured the property of feudal landholders.
  **b.** many peasants became noblemen.
  **c.** the authority of kings increased while many nobles were financially weakened.
  **d.** many peasants converted to Islam.

## Essay

_Answer one of the following questions on a separate sheet of paper. (10 points)_

**56a. Critical Thinking** Provide an overview of the spread of Christianity, Islam, Confucianism, Hinduism, or Buddhism during the period from A.D. 400 to A.D. 1500.

**56b. Critical Thinking** Identify several factors that contributed to the growth of cities in Europe during the Middle Ages.

# Unit 4 : Test

**Score** _____

## Matching

*Match each item in Column A with an item in Column B by writing the correct letters in the blanks.*
*(1 point each)*

**Column A**

_____ **1.** France's ruling dynasty from 1589

_____ **2.** attempted to retake Silesia

_____ **3.** bishops met here to redefine Catholic doctrine

_____ **4.** Renaissance cartographers owed much to him

_____ **5.** Muslim converts to Christianity

_____ **6.** Ottomans defeated here

_____ **7.** site of the Medicis' school for sculptors

_____ **8.** refused to admit children, bear arms, hold office

_____ **9.** Cortés was one

_____ **10.** the first to try and unite the warring daimyos

_____ **11.** Calvin set up theocracy here

_____ **12.** the head of the Ottoman bureaucracy

_____ **13.** most famous Christian humanist

_____ **14.** journey of enslaved Africans to the Americas

_____ **15.** home of Luther

_____ **16.** Persian capital under Shah Abbas

_____ **17.** Russian nobles in service to the czar

_____ **18.** English farmers and laborers

_____ **19.** master of 17-syllable poetry

_____ **20.** Africa's southern tip

**Column B**

**a.** Anabaptists

**b.** Bourbon

**c.** Cape of Good Hope

**d.** conquistador

**e.** *dvorianie*

**f.** Erasmus

**g.** Florence

**h.** Geneva

**i.** Germany

**j.** grand vizier

**k.** Isfahan

**l.** Lepanto

**m.** Maria Theresa

**n.** Matsuo Basho

**o.** Moriscos

**p.** Middle Passage

**q.** Oda Nobunaga

**r.** Ptolemy

**s.** Trent

**t.** yeomen

## Multiple Choice

*In the blank, write the letter of the choice that best completes the statement. (2 points each)*

_____ **21.** The Mogul Empire was eventually weakened by conflict between
   **a.** Muslim rulers and their Hindu subjects.
   **b.** Hideyoshi and the Christian missionaries.
   **c.** Shiite and Sunni Muslims.
   **d.** Sikh rulers and the Christian missionaries.

_____ **22.** All of the following were European writers of the Renaissance period EXCEPT
   **a.** Pierre Ronsard.
   **b.** François Rabelais.
   **c.** Christopher Marlowe.
   **d.** Hubert van Eyck.

# Unit 4 : Test

_____ **23.** Michelangelo did all of the following EXCEPT
   **a.** paint the ceiling of the Sistine Chapel.
   **b.** paint the *Last Supper*.
   **c.** study in Florence.
   **d.** design the dome of the new St. Peter's Basilica.

_____ **24.** In 1588 the Spanish Armada suffered a catastrophic defeat in the
   **a.** English Channel.
   **b.** Mediterranean.
   **c.** West Indies.
   **d.** Philippines.

_____ **25.** The Treaty of Tordesillas divided
   **a.** the unexplored world between Spain and Portugal.
   **b.** Mexico between Cortés and the Aztec.
   **c.** Dutch East India territory between England and the Netherlands.
   **d.** Hispaniola into two territories.

_____ **26.** The English theater flourished and Shakespeare came to prominence during the rule of
   **a.** Henry VII.
   **b.** Henry VIII.
   **c.** Edward VI.
   **d.** Elizabeth I.

_____ **27.** Peter the Great's rule was notable for his effort to
   **a.** isolate Russia from contact with Roman Catholic countries.
   **b.** achieve an alliance with Sweden and Poland.
   **c.** encourage the spread of western European learning and customs.
   **d.** increase the influence of the Orthodox Church leadership.

_____ **28.** The Taiping Rebellion lasted 14 years and weakened the
   **a.** Qing dynasty.
   **b.** Ming dynasty.
   **c.** Mogul Empire.
   **d.** Safavid Empire.

_____ **29.** All of the following regions remained predominantly Catholic during the Protestant Reformation EXCEPT
   **a.** southern Italy.
   **b.** Poland.
   **c.** Hungary.
   **d.** northern Germany.

_____ **30.** The Forbidden City is located in
   **a.** Agra.        **b.** Tokyo.        **c.** Beijing.        **d.** Kyoto.

_____ **31.** The Dutch colonial settlement on Manhattan Island was called
   **a.** New Amsterdam.
   **b.** Montreal.
   **c.** Jamestown.
   **d.** Nova Scotia.

_____ **32.** Frederick the Great rejected the pragmatic sanction by
   **a.** aligning Prussia with Spain.
   **b.** aligning Prussia with France.
   **c.** seizing Hapsburg territory.
   **d.** barring Protestant worship.

_____ **33.** Mercantilist theory in Europe held that a state's power could be measured by the
   **a.** strength of its army.
   **b.** size of its colonies.
   **c.** amount of bullion it possessed.
   **d.** amount of sugar, coffee, and spices it produced.

# Unit 4
# Test

_____ **34.** The blend of Protestant belief and Catholic practice that developed under Elizabeth I was called
  **a.** Calvinism.    **b.** Puritanism.    **c.** Anglicanism.    **d.** Anabaptism.

_____ **35.** A long-standing goal of Russian rulers was to
  **a.** halt the spread of Puritanism.    **c.** acquire greater access to the sea.
  **b.** improve the conditions of the serfs.    **d.** obtain control of the Spice Island trade.

_____ **36.** By the 1800s, most of the Philippine population had converted to
  **a.** Islam.    **b.** Buddhism.    **c.** Hinduism.    **d.** Catholicism.

_____ **37.** Labor-intensive farming refers to agriculture dependent on
  **a.** the labor of domesticated animals.    **c.** the labor of enslaved people.
  **b.** the use of terraces and paddle-wheel    **d.** human effort.
  pumps.

_____ **38.** The passage around South America's tip is called the
  **a.** Strait of Vespucci.    **c.** Strait of Good Hope.
  **b.** Strait of Magellan.    **d.** Middle Passage.

_____ **39.** Louis XIV became known as
  **a.** "the Lawgiver."    **b.** "the Sun King."    **c.** "Great Elector."    **d.** "the Terrible."

_____ **40.** The technique of painting in oils was developed by
  **a.** Flemish painters.    **c.** Japanese painters.
  **b.** Italian painters.    **d.** Byzantine painters.

_____ **41.** Investors shared the risks and profits of an overseas undertaking by forming
  **a.** government-chartered banks.    **c.** merchant guilds.
  **b.** banking families.    **d.** joint-stock companies.

_____ **42.** King James I's ascension to the English throne marked the end of
  **a.** the rule of Protestants in England.    **c.** Tudor rule.
  **b.** the rule of Catholics in England.    **d.** Hapsburg rule.

_____ **43.** Luther's most important principle stressed that salvation could be achieved by
  **a.** faith alone.    **c.** members of the church hierarchy only.
  **b.** the purchase of indulgences.    **d.** performing complex rituals.

_____ **44.** From the mid-1600s, the preferred language of European diplomacy and culture became
  **a.** English.    **b.** Spanish.    **c.** French.    **d.** Castilian.

_____ **45.** Japanese society during the Tokugawa period was marked by
  **a.** the elimination of mobility between    **c.** a weakening of the hierarchical class
  classes.    system.
  **b.** division into two classes, shogunate    **d.** the elimination of complex rituals and
  members and the rest of the population.    etiquette.

Name _____ Date _____ Class _____

# Unit 4 :
## Test

_____ **46.** By the 1600s, the primary economic unit in Europe was the
    **a.** city-state.    **b.** nation.    **c.** fief.    **d.** village.

_____ **47.** The missionaries of the order founded by Ignatius of Loyola in 1540 became known as the
    **a.** Loyalists.    **b.** Jesuits.    **c.** Benedictines.    **d.** Puritans.

_____ **48.** A Southeast Asian people who avoided colonization by the Europeans was the
    **a.** Thais.    **b.** Filipinos.    **c.** Indonesians.    **d.** Vietnamese.

_____ **49.** Many early Portuguese explorations of the Atlantic were sponsored by
    **a.** King Ferdinand.    **c.** John Cabot.
    **b.** Pedro Alvares Cabral.    **d.** Prince Henry.

_____ **50.** French involvement in the Thirty Years' War stemmed from the desire to
    **a.** support a fellow Roman Catholic monarch.    **c.** end England's possession of French territory.
    **b.** curb the power of the Austrian Hapsburgs.    **d.** slow the spread of Calvinism.

_____ **51.** The form of government based on the unlimited power of an individual or group is called
    **a.** feudalism.    **b.** absolutism.    **c.** mercantilism.    **d.** pragmatism

_____ **52.** After beginning the seclusion policy, Japanese rulers barred all Europeans EXCEPT the
    **a.** Spanish.    **b.** Portuguese.    **c.** Dutch.    **d.** Italians.

_____ **53.** The colonial economy in Brazil was based on
    **a.** its role as a center of spice and tea production.    **c.** cash crops such as sugarcane, tobacco, coffee, and cotton.
    **b.** silver and gold mining.    **d.** the export of enslaved labor.

_____ **54.** The spread of Renaissance ideals can best be described as
    **a.** spreading from Italy northward into Europe.    **c.** spreading from France southward into Italy.
    **b.** beginning in the Byzantine Empire and spreading east.    **d.** spreading from France westward into the rest of Europe.

_____ **55.** The first Protestant faith was founded by
    **a.** Erasmus.    **b.** Calvin.    **c.** Ignatius.    **d.** Luther.

## Essay
*Answer one of the following questions on a separate sheet of paper. (10 points)*

**56a. Critical Thinking** Describe Venice's rise to economic prominence. What factors contributed to its eventual decline?

**56b. Critical Thinking** Describe the origins of the Jesuits and their activity in one Asian country.

# Unit 5

# Test

**Score** _____

## Matching

*Match each item in Column A with an item in Column B by writing the correct letters in the blanks.*
*(1 point each)*

**Column A**

_____ **1.** site of Napoleon's final defeat

_____ **2.** gained independence despite Metternich's actions

_____ **3.** the French nobility

_____ **4.** founded by Quaker pacifist

_____ **5.** hoped to exclude James II from the throne

_____ **6.** led Reign of Terror

_____ **7.** German astronomer

_____ **8.** radical faction in the French National Convention

_____ **9.** prohibited imprisonment without just cause

_____ **10.** wrote *Common Sense*

_____ **11.** most prosperous segment of the Third Estate

_____ **12.** abolished serfdom in Austria

_____ **13.** Lord Protector of England

_____ **14.** Britain defeated the French navy here

_____ **15.** meeting of the European powers after Napoleon's defeat

_____ **16.** agreement that restored peace with the Catholic Church

_____ **17.** the return of the House of Stuart

_____ **18.** wave of violence inspired by the fall of the Bastille

_____ **19.** Newton studied here

_____ **20.** overthrew the Directory

**Column B**

**a.** the bourgeoisie

**b.** Cambridge

**c.** Congress of Vienna

**d.** Concordat of 1801

**e.** Oliver Cromwell

**f.** the Great Fear

**g.** the Greeks

**h.** habeas corpus

**i.** Joseph II

**j.** Kepler

**k.** the Mountain

**l.** Napoleon

**m.** Thomas Paine

**n.** Pennsylvania

**o.** the Restoration

**p.** Robespierre

**q.** Second Estate

**r.** Trafalgar

**s.** Waterloo

**t.** the Whigs

## Multiple Choice

*In the blank, write the letter of the choice that best completes the statement. (2 points each)*

_____ **21.** The editor of the *Encyclopédie* was
    **a.** Baron de Montesquieu.
    **b.** Denis Diderot.
    **c.** Sir Robert Walpole.
    **d.** Samuel Adams.

_____ **22.** William III gained the English throne in what came to be called the
    **a.** Restoration.
    **b.** English Civil War.
    **c.** Glorious Revolution.
    **d.** Cavalier Rebellion.

# Unit 5:
# Test

_____ **23.** Prerevolutionary French society was divided into three social groups called
    **a.** tithes.    **b.** estates.    **c.** *sans-culottes*.    **d.** directories.

_____ **24.** Cromwell's rule of England was marked by his imposition of
    **a.** Calvinist doctrine in the Church of England.
    **b.** Puritan rules of behavior.
    **c.** laws guaranteeing freedom of speech and religion.
    **d.** the National Covenant.

_____ **25.** Delegates to the French National Assembly who supported the king were known as
    **a.** radicals.    **b.** royalists.    **c.** moderates.    **d.** republicans.

_____ **26.** The Reign of Terror refers to the period in which
    **a.** the Girondists rooted out Jacobin supporters.
    **b.** King Louis XVI suppressed enemies of the monarchy.
    **c.** the Jacobins ruthlessly crushed their enemies.
    **d.** Napoleon's armies swept across Europe.

_____ **27.** In 1766, colonial protests forced the repeal of the
    **a.** Navigation Acts.    **b.** Act of Settlement.    **c.** Declaratory Act.    **d.** Stamp Act.

_____ **28.** The author of *Two Treatises of Government* was
    **a.** Voltaire.    **b.** William Penn.    **c.** John Locke.    **d.** Thomas Hobbes.

_____ **29.** The Puritans disapproved of
    **a.** symbols in the Catholic Church.
    **b.** English influence in the church.
    **c.** the simplification of church rituals.
    **d.** attempts to reform the Church of England.

_____ **30.** The scientist forced by the Catholic Church to recant his theories was
    **a.** Lavoisier.    **b.** Kepler.    **c.** Galileo.    **d.** Voltaire.

_____ **31.** British forces and American colonists fought as allies in the
    **a.** Glorious Revolution.
    **b.** French and Indian War.
    **c.** English Civil War.
    **d.** Seven Years' War.

_____ **32.** Jean-Jacques Rousseau advocated the
    **a.** beauties of nature and the pleasures of country life.
    **b.** value of personal religious experience.
    **c.** role of governmental institutions in preventing disorder.
    **d.** separation of government into independent branches.

_____ **33.** In the Act of Settlement, the English Parliament
    **a.** prohibited any Catholic from inheriting the English throne.
    **b.** guaranteed the right to a trial by jury.
    **c.** guaranteed the right of all Christians to worship freely.
    **d.** returned confiscated land to the Irish.

# Unit 5 : Test

_____ **34.** The Irish scientist Robert Boyle is regarded as responsible for
  **a.** discovering the cell.
  **b.** suggesting that mathematical formulas could describe the universe.
  **c.** inventing the microscope.
  **d.** establishing chemistry as a true science.

_____ **35.** Eighteenth-century Deist thought was often characterized by its denunciation of
  **a.** organized religion.
  **b.** Jacobin ideals.
  **c.** the concept of natural law.
  **d.** pacifism.

_____ **36.** The philosopher-mathematician who wrote _Discourse on Method_ was
  **a.** René Descartes.    **b.** Francis Bacon.    **c.** Hugo Grotius.    **d.** Thomas Hobbes.

_____ **37.** The Constitution of 1791 changed the structure of French government by
  **a.** abolishing the monarchy.
  **b.** increasing the power of the Catholic Church.
  **c.** suspending the unicameral legislature.
  **d.** limiting the powers of the king.

_____ **38.** The French joined the American side in the Revolutionary War after the defeat of the British at
  **a.** Yorktown.    **b.** Lexington.    **c.** Saratoga.    **d.** Concord.

_____ **39.** The Third Estate included all of the following groups EXCEPT
  **a.** artisans.    **b.** clergy.    **c.** peasants.    **d.** merchants.

_____ **40.** The Clarendon Code restored
  **a.** the House of Stuart to the throne.
  **b.** Anglicanism as England's state religion.
  **c.** absolute monarchy in Ireland.
  **d.** Calvinism in Scotland.

_____ **41.** The Prussian ruler known for his reforms and belief in Enlightenment ideas was
  **a.** Frederick II.    **b.** Charles II.    **c.** Joseph II.    **d.** Leopold II.

_____ **42.** Enlightenment-era intellectual gatherings were called
  **a.** commonwealths.
  **b.** philosophes.
  **c.** _sans-culottes_.
  **d.** salons.

_____ **43.** The Quebec Act closed Canadian territories to
  **a.** the English.
  **b.** the French.
  **c.** the American colonists.
  **d.** Native Americans.

_____ **44.** The theory that monarchs derive their power directly from God is
  **a.** deism.
  **b.** divine right.
  **c.** federalism.
  **d.** martial law.

_____ **45.** Antoine and Marie Lavoisier contributed greatly to the study of
  **a.** gravity.    **b.** oxygen.    **c.** anatomy.    **d.** the sun.

_____ **46.** The Methodist movement was led by
  **a.** John Wesley.
  **b.** Jean-Jacques Rousseau.
  **c.** Immanuel Kant.
  **d.** William Penn.

# Unit 5: Test

_____ **47.** The Estates-General was a rarely called meeting of
   **a.** European foreign ministers.
   **b.** the French, English, and Austrian monarchies.
   **c.** higher and lower clergy members.
   **d.** delegates from the three social classes of France.

_____ **48.** The _Declaration of the Rights of Man_ was influenced by all of the following EXCEPT
   **a.** the Carlsbad Decrees.
   **b.** The English Bill of Rights.
   **c.** Enlightenment philosophy.
   **d.** the Declaration of Independence.

_____ **49.** The United States Constitution split political authority among three branches, a division recommended by
   **a.** John Locke.
   **b.** Thomas Paine.
   **c.** Oliver Cromwell.
   **d.** Baron de Montesquieu.

_____ **50.** The Continental System prohibited European countries from
   **a.** lifting the Napoleonic Code.
   **b.** trading with the United States.
   **c.** trading with Russia.
   **d.** trading with England.

_____ **51.** The persecution of Puritans by Charles I and William Laud contributed to
   **a.** the Intolerable Acts.
   **b.** the Great Fear.
   **c.** the Great Migration.
   **d.** the Middle Passage.

_____ **52.** In _Leviathan_, Hobbes argues that
   **a.** people have the right to break their contract with government.
   **b.** violence and disorder are created by institutions.
   **c.** an assembly of nations is necessary to assure world peace.
   **d.** absolute monarchy is the best form of government.

_____ **53.** After the Reign of Terror, and before Napoleon's coup d'état, France was governed by
   **a.** the Jacobins.
   **b.** King Louis XVI.
   **c.** the Directory.
   **d.** the Second Estate.

_____ **54.** In a final attempt to avoid war, the Continental Congress proposed compromise in
   **a.** the Articles of Confederation.
   **b.** _Common Sense._
   **c.** the Olive Branch Petition.
   **d.** the Petition of Right.

_____ **55.** The Tennis Court Oath was a promise by Third Estate representatives
   **a.** not to disband until a constitution was written.
   **b.** to restore the French monarchy.
   **c.** to spread the ideas of liberalism across Europe.
   **d.** not to pay feudal dues.

## Essay

_Answer one of the following questions on a separate sheet of paper. (10 points)_

**56a. Critical Thinking** Identify two measures of the British government that angered American colonists. What was the response of the colonies to each?

**56b. Critical Thinking** Describe the extent of the Napoleonic Empire. How did Napoleon's rule contribute to the rise of nationalism in Europe?

# Unit 6 : Test

## Matching

*Match each item in Column A with an item in Column B by writing the correct letters in the blanks.*
*(1 point each)*

**Column A**

_____ **1.** Balzac, Dickens, Tolstoy

_____ **2.** the Dutch use of forced labor in Asia

_____ **3.** instigator of Panamanian split from Colombia

_____ **4.** invented by Eli Whitney

_____ **5.** theorized an "iron law of wages"

_____ **6.** someone who takes a risk by setting up a business

_____ **7.** self-governing territory

_____ **8.** governors who rule as royal representatives

_____ **9.** his first term became known as the Great Ministry

_____ **10.** Sardinian king who battled Austria

_____ **11.** rejecters of all tradition

_____ **12.** the devotion to the local interests of a region

_____ **13.** Adam Smith's study of economics

_____ **14.** proclaimed in 1870 by Catholic bishops

_____ **15.** made home-based weavers more productive

_____ **16.** Scottish-born African explorer

_____ **17.** de-emphasized reason

_____ **18.** gave all adult U.S. citizens the right to vote

_____ **19.** written by Charles Darwin

_____ **20.** aviation pioneers

**Column B**

**a.** Charles Albert

**b.** *The Wealth of Nations*

**c.** cotton gin

**d.** culture system

**e.** *The Descent of Man*

**f.** dominion

**g.** entrepreneur

**h.** flying shuttle

**i.** William Gladstone

**j.** David Livingstone

**k.** nihilists

**l.** Nineteenth Amendment

**m.** papal infallibility

**n.** realists

**o.** David Ricardo

**p.** romanticism

**q.** Theodore Roosevelt

**r.** sectionalism

**s.** viceroys

**t.** Wrights

## Multiple Choice

*In the blank, write the letter of the choice that best completes the statement. (2 points each)*

_____ **21.** Genetics, the science of heredity, was based on the work of
    **a.** Charles Darwin.
    **b.** Louis Pasteur.
    **c.** Gregor Mendel.
    **d.** Jean-Baptiste de Lamarck.

_____ **22.** The domestic system in Great Britain grew out of the demand for
    **a.** domestic servants.
    **b.** agricultural labor.
    **c.** glass products.
    **d.** woolens.

_____ **23.** All of the following eighteenth-century territorial names refer to regions in Africa EXCEPT
    **a.** the Orange Free State.
    **b.** Tripoli.
    **c.** Dahomey.
    **d.** Siam.

# Unit 6

## Test

_____ **24.** The reign of Napoleon III ended when he
    **a.** abdicated during the "Bloody Week."    **c.** lost the election of 1848.
    **b.** abdicated after _Les Trois Glorieuses._    **d.** was captured by the Prussians.

_____ **25.** José Martí died in battle while leading a
    **a.** Filipino revolt against American rule.    **c.** Mexican revolt against American rule.
    **b.** Panamanian revolt against Colombian rule.    **d.** Cuban revolt against Spanish rule.

_____ **26.** Impressionist painters sought to capture
    **a.** the greed of the growing middle class.    **c.** the impact a subject made on the senses.
    **b.** a realistic portrayal of life as it actually was.    **d.** the signs and symbols of industrialized society.

_____ **27.** The last great European power to achieve political unity was
    **a.** Great Britain.    **c.** France.
    **b.** Italy.    **d.** Germany.

_____ **28.** The daily life of most preindustrial rural villagers revolved around
    **a.** agriculture.    **c.** service to the king.
    **b.** small-craft production.    **d.** service to the clergy.

_____ **29.** The original inhabitants of New Zealand were the
    **a.** English.    **b.** Aborigines.    **c.** Maori.    **d.** Creoles.

_____ **30.** The creation of the dual monarchy in 1867 restored the independence of
    **a.** the Balkan states.    **c.** Bohemia.
    **b.** Hungary.    **d.** Romania.

_____ **31.** Irish leaders such as Charles Stewart Parnell fought for the implementation of
    **a.** the _Risorgimento._    **c.** the Corn Laws.
    **b.** home rule.    **d.** the May Laws.

_____ **32.** The first country to become industrialized was
    **a.** England.    **c.** Germany.
    **b.** France.    **d.** the United States.

_____ **33.** The highest level of colonial Latin America's social hierarchy was made up of
    **a.** _peninsulares._    **c.** mestizos.
    **b.** colonial-born white aristocrats.    **d.** Magyars.

_____ **34.** Belgium exercised particularly brutal and exploitative colonial rule in
    **a.** Ethiopia.    **c.** South Africa.
    **b.** the Congo.    **d.** the Gold Coast.

_____ **35.** The British Combination Acts of 1799 and 1800 banned the
    **a.** export of industrial technology.    **c.** emigration of skilled workers.
    **b.** formation of labor unions.    **d.** use of village land for farming or grazing.

# Unit 6

# Test

_____ **36.** Queensland, Victoria, and New South Wales were British colonies in
    **a.** Canada.
    **b.** New Zealand.
    **c.** India.
    **d.** Australia.

_____ **37.** All of the following were major contributors to the development of mass production EXCEPT
    **a.** Eli Whitney.
    **b.** Frederick Taylor.
    **c.** Henry Ford.
    **d.** Samuel Morse.

_____ **38.** By 1900 the majority of new immigrants to the United States came from
    **a.** northern Europe.
    **b.** southern and eastern Europe.
    **c.** Latin America.
    **d.** Australia, New Zealand, and Canada.

_____ **39.** British business leaders reacted positively to the ideas of
    **a.** Robert Owen.
    **b.** Francis Deak.
    **c.** Friedrich Engels.
    **d.** Adam Smith.

_____ **40.** After the events of 1848, Italian nationalists looked for leadership from
    **a.** Sardinia.
    **b.** Sicily.
    **c.** Venetia.
    **d.** the Papal States.

_____ **41.** Ivan Pavlov experimented with animals in order to
    **a.** understand evolutionary adaptation.
    **b.** examine the effect of stimuli on behavior.
    **c.** develop treatments for infectious disease.
    **d.** develop effective anesthetics for medical surgery.

_____ **42.** The Monroe Doctrine warned
    **a.** European powers not to interfere in the Western Hemisphere.
    **b.** European powers not to interfere with U.S. interests in the Philippines.
    **c.** the Japanese not to interfere with U.S. trade in Asia.
    **d.** the Japanese not to expand their colonial empire in Asia.

_____ **43.** According to Karl Marx, control of the means of production would eventually be seized by the
    **a.** bourgeoisie.
    **b.** proletariat.
    **c.** middle class.
    **d.** peasants.

_____ **44.** Vladimir Ilyich Ulyanov led the radical Russian
    **a.** Bolsheviks.
    **b.** Mensheviks.
    **c.** anarchists.
    **d.** nihilists.

_____ **45.** All of the following were British colonies EXCEPT
    **a.** Canada.
    **b.** Australia.
    **c.** Haiti.
    **d.** New Zealand.

_____ **46.** The French thinker Auguste Comte contributed to the development of
    **a.** quantum theory.
    **b.** atomic theory.
    **c.** the science of sociology.
    **d.** the science of heredity.

# Unit 6

## Test

_____ **47.** The worker-led Socialist government of Paris was called the
   **a.** Commune.
   **b.** Duma.
   **c.** Third Republic.
   **d.** National Assembly.

_____ **48.** From the beginning of the Industrial Revolution through 1850, the population of Europe
   **a.** declined from about 266 million to 140 million.
   **b.** increased from about 140 million to 266 million.
   **c.** remained roughly constant at about 140 million.
   **d.** remained roughly constant at about 266 million.

_____ **49.** The economic and political domination of one country by another is characteristic of
   **a.** nationalism.
   **b.** industrialism.
   **c.** imperialism.
   **d.** mercantilism.

_____ **50.** Some early factory owners used a "blacklist" to prevent the hiring of
   **a.** suspected union members.
   **b.** child labor.
   **c.** foreign workers.
   **d.** smallpox carriers.

_____ **51.** The founder of the Universal German Workingmen's Association was
   **a.** Karl Marx.
   **b.** Michael Bakunin.
   **c.** Camillo di Cavour.
   **d.** Ferdinand Lassalle.

_____ **52.** Money available to invest in labor, machinery, or raw materials is called
   **a.** income.
   **b.** natural resources.
   **c.** capital.
   **d.** profit.

_____ **53.** Victor Emmanuel II was able to gain control of the entire Italian Peninsula after
   **a.** Napoleon III withdrew French protection for the pope.
   **b.** the Austrians withdrew from Lombardy.
   **c.** Garibaldi surrendered his control of the south.
   **d.** the Sardinians defeated the papal army at Castelfidaro.

_____ **54.** Simón Bolívar liberated all of the following present-day countries from Spain EXCEPT
   **a.** Colombia.
   **b.** Panama.
   **c.** Brazil.
   **d.** Ecuador.

_____ **55.** The artists Paul Cézanne and Georges Seurat are associated with
   **a.** romanticism.
   **b.** realism.
   **c.** symbolism.
   **d.** Postimpressionism.

## Essay

_Answer one of the following questions on a separate sheet of paper. (10 points)_

**56a. Critical Thinking** Describe the role played by Otto von Bismarck in the unification of Germany.

**56b. Critical Thinking** Identify one supporter and one critic of laissez-faire economics. Contrast their beliefs.

# Unit 7 Test

Score _____

## Matching

*Match each item in Column A with an item in Column B by writing the correct letters in the blanks.*
*(1 point each)*

**Column A**

_____ **1.** loser in struggle to succeed Lenin

_____ **2.** British pledge of support for Jewish homeland

_____ **3.** term describing Gandhi's nonviolent protests

_____ **4.** Germany's "lightning war" strategy

_____ **5.** the murder of European Jews, among others, by the Germans

_____ **6.** included Russia, France, Great Britain

_____ **7.** site of massive Allied evacuation

_____ **8.** the "Desert Fox"

_____ **9.** place where Allies met to discuss Italian campaign

_____ **10.** led by Mao Zedong

_____ **11.** political philosophy of the Bolsheviks

_____ **12.** proposed by Woodrow Wilson

_____ **13.** leader whose early plea to unite against Hitler was ignored

_____ **14.** invaded by Japan

_____ **15.** compulsory military service by civilians

_____ **16.** Labour party leader and British prime minister

_____ **17.** site of a disastrous Russian defeat in World War I

_____ **18.** went to London to press cause of independence

_____ **19.** American literary movement

_____ **20.** early twentieth-century abstract art form

**Column B**

**a.** Balfour Declaration

**b.** blitzkrieg

**c.** Casablanca

**d.** communism

**e.** conscription

**f.** cubism

**g.** Dunkirk

**h.** Harlem Renaissance

**i.** Holocaust

**j.** Jomo Kenyatta

**k.** League of Nations

**l.** Long March

**m.** Ramsay MacDonald

**n.** Manchuria

**o.** Erwin Rommel

**p.** satyagraha

**q.** Joseph Stalin

**r.** Tannenberg

**s.** Triple Entente

**t.** Leon Trotsky

## Multiple Choice

*In the blank, write the letter of the choice that best completes the statement. (2 points each)*

_____ **21.** The kulaks suffered greatly because of
    **a.** the Nuremberg Laws.
    **b.** Stalin's collectivization program.
    **c.** the repressive policies of Mussolini.
    **d.** Great Depression-era unemployment.

_____ **22.** The boycott was developed into an effective method of protesting British rule by
    **a.** Mohammed Ali Jinnah.
    **b.** Mohandas K. Gandhi.
    **c.** Mao Zedong.
    **d.** Lázaro Cárdenas.

# Unit 7 :
# Test

_____ **23.** The plan for an attack on Pearl Harbor was developed by
    **a.** Winston Churchill.             **c.** Erwin Rommel.
    **b.** Isoroku Yamamoto.          **d.** Dwight D. Eisenhower.

_____ **24.** Archduke Francis Ferdinand was assassinated by
    **a.** Russian Socialists.            **c.** Italian Fascists.
    **b.** Serbian nationalists.         **d.** German Communists.

_____ **25.** Many historians see the major turning point in World War II as the
    **a.** Battle of the Bulge.            **c.** British victory at Singapore.
    **b.** American victory in the Philippines.     **d.** Soviet victory at Stalingrad.

_____ **26.** Roosevelt, Churchill, and Stalin met to discuss the coming postwar era at
    **a.** Nuremberg.      **b.** Warsaw.      **c.** Yalta.      **d.** Berlin.

_____ **27.** Japan's invasion of Manchuria demonstrated the growing political power of
    **a.** the Communists.           **c.** the emperor.
    **b.** Prime Minister Osachi Hamaguchi.     **d.** the military.

_____ **28.** In the 1920s, resistance to the American invasion of Nicaragua was led by
    **a.** Getúlio Vargas.           **c.** Augusto César Sandino.
    **b.** Joshua Reuben Clark.       **d.** Anastasio Somoza.

_____ **29.** Chiang Kai-shek and Mao Zedong suspended their conflict and joined forces against the
    **a.** Communist party.   **b.** Guomindang.     **c.** Japanese.     **d.** British.

_____ **30.** The use of poison gas was introduced into World War I by the
    **a.** French.      **b.** Russians.      **c.** English.      **d.** Germans.

_____ **31.** By abandoning the Twenty-One Demands, Japan
    **a.** ended its boycott on American goods.     **c.** recognized Western interests in China.
    **b.** relinquished its support for an Open      **d.** recognized Chinese control of
        Door trade policy.                       Manchuria.

_____ **32.** _Kristallnacht_ is the name given to
    **a.** an attack by Nazis on Jewish homes and     **c.** the burning of the German legislative
        businesses.                          building.
    **b.** Hitler's purge of his radical supporters.     **d.** Hitler's law that suppressed freedom of
                                            speech and religion.

_____ **33.** The Allied campaign in the Pacific called for
    **a.** a direct assault on Japan from the south     **c.** sporadic attacks using the convoy
        and east.                           system.
    **b.** a direct assault on Japan by the Russians.     **d.** an island-by-island leapfrog approach.

_____ **34.** The country that produced a major share of the world's manufactured goods by the 1920s
    was
    **a.** England.      **b.** the United States.   **c.** Japan.      **d.** Germany.

# Unit 7

# Test

_____ **35.** The three-point program of the Russian soviets called for all of the following EXCEPT
    **a.** the transfer of land to the peasantry.
    **b.** an immediate peace and end to the war effort.
    **c.** the immediate abdication of the czar.
    **d.** the control of factories by the workers.

_____ **36.** In 1914 Russia sided with Serbia after receiving diplomatic assurances of
    **a.** French support.
    **b.** French neutrality.
    **c.** Belgian neutrality.
    **d.** British neutrality.

_____ **37.** All of the following were American World War II military leaders EXCEPT
    **a.** George Patton.
    **b.** Clement Attlee.
    **c.** Douglas MacArthur.
    **d.** Chester W. Nimitz.

_____ **38.** The government of the newly formed USSR was controlled primarily by
    **a.** Communist party leaders.
    **b.** Red Army generals.
    **c.** peasant committees.
    **d.** proletariat committees.

_____ **39.** Through 1940 America maintained its neutrality while supplying Britain via its
    **a.** collective security policy.
    **b.** scorched-earth policy.
    **c.** appeasement policy.
    **d.** cash-and-carry policy.

_____ **40.** The Commonwealth of Nations was a voluntary association that linked
    **a.** the United States and Latin American countries.
    **b.** countries with democratic governments.
    **c.** countries that had renounced war as a means of settling disputes.
    **d.** Great Britain and its former colonies.

_____ **41.** During the dictatorship of Juan Vicente Gómez, the Venezuelan oil industry was
    **a.** controlled by American and European companies.
    **b.** controlled by Mexican companies.
    **c.** nationalized by the Venezuelan government.
    **d.** controlled by Venezuelan companies.

_____ **42.** A long-standing dispute between France and Germany concerned the territory of
    **a.** Alsace-Lorraine.
    **b.** Bosnia-Herzegovina.
    **c.** Austria-Hungary.
    **d.** Schleswig and Holstein.

_____ **43.** In 1923 the French tried to ensure that Germany paid its war debts by sending troops into
    **a.** the Ruhr Valley.   **b.** the Reichstag.   **c.** Berlin.   **d.** Nuremberg.

_____ **44.** In 1933 the Manchurian incident revealed the weakness of
    **a.** the Japanese military.
    **b.** the Russian military.
    **c.** the League of Nations.
    **d.** Mussolini.

_____ **45.** The Treaty of Brest-Litovsk
    **a.** created a separate peace between Russia and Germany.
    **b.** created a truce between the Whites and the Reds.
    **c.** divided the Ottoman Empire among Russia, France, and England.
    **d.** ended all hostilities in World War I.

# Unit 7
# Test

_____ **46.** Hitler's territorial expansion did not stir Western military action until his invasion of
    **a.** Czechoslovakia.   **b.** Poland.     **c.** Austria.     **d.** the Rhine Valley.

_____ **47.** The countries that were allied with Austria-Hungary in World War I became known as the
    **a.** Allied Powers.   **b.** Central Powers.   **c.** Axis.     **d.** Whites.

_____ **48.** The former socialist who became fascist leader of the Blackshirts was
    **a.** Benito Mussolini.       **c.** Joseph Stalin
    **b.** Victor Emmanuel III.     **d.** Adolf Hitler.

_____ **49.** Italy and Germany declared war on the United States, honoring the terms of the
    **a.** Munich Pact.         **c.** Tripartite Pact.
    **b.** Atlantic Charter.       **d.** Treaty of Versailles.

_____ **50.** In 1929 Nigerian women protesting British tax policies
    **a.** succeeded in getting unfair taxes     **c.** forced the British to grant Nigeria
       repealed.               independence.
    **b.** were massacred by British troops.   **d.** were sent into exile in Kenya.

_____ **51.** The Fourteen Points plan of Woodrow Wilson endorsed all of the following EXCEPT
    **a.** the establishment of an assembly of   **c.** the payment of reparations for damage
       nations.               caused by the war.
    **b.** the right to self-rule by all nations.   **d.** an end to secret alliances.

_____ **52.** In the 1920s, Latin American countries were heavily dependent on global demand for their
    **a.** raw materials.         **c.** industrial machinery.
    **b.** manufactured goods.      **d.** investment capital.

_____ **53.** The developer of the theory of relativity was
    **a.** Sigmund Freud.        **c.** Albert Einstein.
    **b.** Arnold Schoenberg.      **d.** Walter Gropius.

_____ **54.** The aim of a united independent India was opposed by
    **a.** Jawaharlal Nehru.       **c.** the Muslim League.
    **b.** the Indian National Congress.   **d.** Mahatma Gandhi.

_____ **55.** All of the following military developments contributed to the defeat of the German alliance
    during World War I EXCEPT the
    **a.** arrival of American troops in France.   **c.** surrender of the Turks.
    **b.** defeat of the Austro-Hungarians by Italy.   **d.** defeat of the Red Army in Russia.

## Essay
*Answer one of the following questions on a separate sheet of paper. (10 points)*

**56a. Critical Thinking** Provide a summary of the Spanish Civil War. Discuss the role of foreign forces in the conflict.

**56b. Critical Thinking** Among the nations that formed the Axis alliance, what dissatisfactions resulted from the peace settlements and institutions that arose out of World War I?

# Unit 8 : Test

Score _____

## Matching

*Match each item in Column A with an item in Column B by writing the correct letters in the blanks.*
*(1 point each)*

**Column A**

_____ **1.** 1945 document drafted in San Francisco

_____ **2.** CIA-backed attempt to topple Castro

_____ **3.** small republic off tip of Malay Peninsula

_____ **4.** Indochinese Communists

_____ **5.** agreement setting up a united Europe

_____ **6.** organization that makes loans to developing nations

_____ **7.** treaty linking United States, Australia, New Zealand

_____ **8.** capital of South Korea

_____ **9.** Soviet-East European military agreement

_____ **10.** founded by 32 African nations in 1963

_____ **11.** site of massive Egyptian dam

_____ **12.** one signer of SALT Treaty

_____ **13.** told of Soviet prison camps in *The Gulag Archipelago*

_____ **14.** a threat to the peoples of the Sahel

_____ **15.** anti-Somoza alliance took his name

_____ **16.** Mao's ambitious but disastrous economic program

_____ **17.** could ease water shortage in Middle East

_____ **18.** contributed to high inflation in 1970s

_____ **19.** Zaire's long-ruling dictator

_____ **20.** present-day Sri Lanka

**Column B**

**a.** ANZUS

**b.** Aswan

**c.** Bay of Pigs

**d.** Leonid Brezhnev

**e.** Ceylon

**f.** desalination

**g.** desertification

**h.** Great Leap Forward

**i.** IMF

**j.** OAU

**k.** oil embargo

**l.** Augusto Sandino

**m.** Seoul

**n.** Mobutu Sese Seko

**o.** Singapore

**p.** Alexander Solzhenitsyn

**q.** Treaty of Maastricht

**r.** UN Charter

**s.** Vietminh

**t.** Warsaw Pact

## Multiple Choice

*In the blank, write the letter of the choice that best completes the statement. (2 points each)*

_____ **21.** All of the following Asian nations were ruled by Communist governments during the 1970s EXCEPT

    **a.** Laos.    **b.** Vietnam.    **c.** Cambodia.    **d.** Thailand.

_____ **22.** During the 1980s, the United States was involved in military encounters with

    **a.** Libya.    **b.** Algeria.    **c.** South Africa.    **d.** Nigeria.

_____ **23.** In 1999 the United States will surrender its control of

    **a.** Hong Kong.              **c.** the Panama Canal.

    **b.** OPEC.                  **d.** the Falkland Islands.

# Unit 8

## Test

_____ **24.** Alarm over Dubček's 1968 reforms caused the Soviets to send troops into
    **a.** Hungary.     **b.** Yugoslavia.     **c.** Poland.     **d.** Czechoslovakia.

_____ **25.** The UN Security Council couldn't settle U.S.-USSR disputes because
    **a.** China usually sided with the U.S.
    **b.** both the U.S. and the USSR possessed the veto power in the council.
    **c.** France usually sided with the USSR.
    **d.** the General Assembly had responsibility for political and military disputes.

_____ **26.** After the withdrawal of coalition troops from Iraq, Saddam Hussein
    **a.** invaded Kuwait.
    **b.** suppressed rebellions by the Kurds and the Shiite.
    **c.** invaded Turkey.
    **d.** immediately complied with all terms of the cease-fire agreement.

_____ **27.** During the period of Carlos Menem's leadership, Argentina
    **a.** was terrorized by roaming death squads.
    **b.** became one of the world's wealthiest nations.
    **c.** lost a military conflict to Great Britain.
    **d.** brought hyperinflation under control.

_____ **28.** General Douglas MacArthur headed the occupation government of
    **a.** West Germany.     **b.** East Germany.     **c.** Japan.     **d.** North Korea.

_____ **29.** In post-Communist Yugoslavia, rising nationalism led to
    **a.** demands for reunification.
    **b.** the breakup of the state into smaller republics.
    **c.** diminished ethnic conflict.
    **d.** the consolidation of the state into one large republic.

_____ **30.** Cuba's economy in the 1990s was devastated by
    **a.** shrinking Soviet support since the fall of communism.
    **b.** low world market prices for oil.
    **c.** the lifting of the American embargo on trade.
    **d.** high world market prices for sugar.

_____ **31.** The war in Algeria helped bring about the collapse of
    **a.** France's Fourth Republic.
    **b.** Nkrumah's Socialist government.
    **c.** the Afrikaner government.
    **d.** Haile Selassie's rule.

_____ **32.** Support for the U.S. effort in Vietnam decreased after
    **a.** bitter fighting during the Tet Offensive.
    **b.** the decisive loss at Dien Bien Phu.
    **c.** the surprise invasion at Inchon.
    **d.** the Soviet Union occupied the northern half of the country.

_____ **33.** The civil war in Lebanon stemmed from conflict between
    **a.** Jews and Arabs.
    **b.** Jews and Muslims.
    **c.** Christians and Muslims.
    **d.** Christians and Jews.

_____ **34.** During the rule of Jawaharlal Nehru, India tried to maintain a
    **a.** firm alliance with the Soviet Union.
    **b.** firm alliance with China.
    **c.** firm alliance with the United States.
    **d.** policy of nonalignment.

# Unit 8:
## Test

_____ **35.** African countries with one-product economies are constantly at the mercy of
   **a.** colonial governments.
   **c.** changing world market prices.
   **b.** unstable coalition governments.
   **d.** the threat of ethnic conflict.

_____ **36.** The German leader whose _Ostpolitik_ policies aimed to reduce tension with the Soviet Bloc was
   **a.** Georges Pompidou.
   **c.** Konrad Adenauer.
   **b.** Willie Brandt.
   **d.** Clement Attlee.

_____ **37.** Under Presidents Reagan and Bush, increased military spending was a factor in the growth of America's
   **a.** budget deficit.
   **c.** balanced budget.
   **b.** trade surplus.
   **d.** population.

_____ **38.** The policy of containment adopted by Truman in 1947 was designed to
   **a.** stimulate economic prosperity in Western Europe.
   **c.** discourage the resurgence of German expansionism.
   **b.** keep communism within its existing borders.
   **d.** prevent emigration from Eastern Europe.

_____ **39.** Burundi and Rwanda were torn by ethnic conflict between the Hutu and the
   **a.** Afrikaners.　　**b.** Tutsi.　　**c.** Kikuyu.　　**d.** Somalis.

_____ **40.** Opposition mounted to France's policy of conducting nuclear tests in
   **a.** France.　　**b.** Algeria.　　**c.** Indochina.　　**d.** the South Pacific.

_____ **41.** Gamal Abdel Nasser negotiated the British withdrawal from
   **a.** Palestine.　　**b.** the Suez Canal.　　**c.** East Jerusalem.　　**d.** Transjordan.

_____ **42.** Zapatista rebels opposed NAFTA, claiming that it would result in
   **a.** the handover of Mexican land to large corporations.
   **c.** high tariffs on Mexican exports to the United States.
   **b.** the handover of Cuban land to large corporations.
   **d.** high tariffs on Cuban exports to the United States.

_____ **43.** Supporters of China's Cultural Revolution called for
   **a.** an end to book burning and censorship.
   **c.** a return to pre-Communist traditions.
   **b.** an end to the influence of the pragmatists.
   **d.** the breaking of all ties with the Soviet Union.

_____ **44.** A French Canadian himself, Jean Chretien opposed
   **a.** Quebec separatism.
   **c.** the building of the St. Lawrence Seaway.
   **b.** passage of the Official Languages Act.
   **d.** the English separatism of the Parti Quebecois.

_____ **45.** Opposition to Western influence has led to a rise in Middle Eastern
   **a.** communism.　　**b.** materialism.　　**c.** fundamentalism.　　**d.** Zionism.

# Unit 8

# Test

_____ **46.** In 1947 British India was divided into two nations—India and
- **a.** Sri Lanka.
- **b.** Pakistan.
- **c.** Bangladesh.
- **d.** Vietnam.

_____ **47.** During the 1950s, Turkey became a member of
- **a.** NATO.
- **b.** the Organization of African Unity.
- **c.** the Arab League.
- **d.** the UAR.

_____ **48.** The Dalai Lama has led a worldwide campaign against Communist Chinese rule of
- **a.** Laos.
- **b.** Korea.
- **c.** Taiwan.
- **d.** Tibet.

_____ **49.** Peru's Shining Path rebel movement was defeated by the government of
- **a.** Salvador Allende.
- **b.** Alberto Fujimori.
- **c.** Isabel Perón.
- **d.** Margaret Thatcher.

_____ **50.** High interest rates and a global recession in the 1980s weakened the
- **a.** ability of Latin American countries to repay foreign debts.
- **b.** desire of Eastern Europeans to escape Soviet dominance.
- **c.** ability of West European countries to join the Common Market.
- **d.** desire of Western Europeans to create a common currency.

_____ **51.** Sri Lankan rebels are fighting to win self-rule for the
- **a.** Kurdish minority.
- **b.** Sinhalese minority.
- **c.** Chechen minority.
- **d.** Tamil minority.

_____ **52.** The 38th parallel became an important dividing line between
- **a.** East and West Germany.
- **b.** North and South Korea.
- **c.** China and Taiwan.
- **d.** North and South Vietnam.

_____ **53.** A growing field of science is genetic engineering, which involves the
- **a.** distribution of water supplies to arid areas.
- **b.** alteration of cells to produce new life-forms.
- **c.** creation of an infrastructure for global communication.
- **d.** creation of chemicals that protect the ozone layer.

_____ **54.** A major obstacle to an Israeli-Syrian peace agreement is control of
- **a.** Jordan.
- **b.** the Gaza Strip.
- **c.** the Golan Heights.
- **d.** the Sinai Peninsula.

_____ **55.** Under apartheid, black South Africans were often forced to live in segregated townships such as
- **a.** Addis Ababa.
- **b.** Eritrea.
- **c.** Biafra.
- **d.** Soweto.

## Essay
*Answer one of the following questions on a separate sheet of paper. (10 points)*

**56a.** **Critical Thinking** Describe the steps taken by Europe toward increased regional unity and economic integration in the period following World War II.

**56b.** **Critical Thinking** Discuss how social inequality and the cold war contributed to civil conflicts in Latin America.

ANSWERS

Chapter 1 Test Form A, pp. 1–2

| | | | | |
|---|---|---|---|---|
| **1.** g | **6.** i | **11.** b | **16.** c | **21.** a |
| **2.** h | **7.** e | **12.** d | **17.** d | **22.** a |
| **3.** b | **8.** j | **13.** a | **18.** b | **23.** d |
| **4.** d | **9.** f | **14.** d | **19.** a | **24.** d |
| **5.** c | **10.** a | **15.** b | **20.** b | **25.** b |

**26a.** *Student essays will vary. Here is a sample:*
The primary reason for the formation of governing bodies was the need of city inhabitants to organize agriculture and trade. The production of surplus food on which city residents were dependent demanded the creation of such structures as canals, dams, reservoirs, and grain storage facilities. These structures could be built only by an organized labor force. Officials were needed to organize and direct this labor force. In addition, the trade routes on which city economies depended were vulnerable to attack by nomadic groups. Cities required governing bodies to hire or maintain armed forces to protect their territory and trade.

**26b.** *Student essays will vary. Here is a sample:*
Two methods scientists use to learn about early hominids are radiocarbon dating and the comparison of their bones. Scientists use radiocarbon dating to determine the age of organic remains. By measuring the amount of radioactive carbon left in the remains of an early hominid, scientists can figure out when that creature lived and died. Scientists also examine the size and shape of early hominid bones. Bone structure can indicate various things such as weight, height, and the ability to walk upright or climb.

Chapter 1 Test Form B, pp. 3–4

| | | | | |
|---|---|---|---|---|
| **1.** f | **6.** g | **11.** a | **16.** b | **21.** b |
| **2.** a | **7.** d | **12.** a | **17.** c | **22.** a |
| **3.** e | **8.** i | **13.** c | **18.** a | **23.** b |
| **4.** j | **9.** c | **14.** b | **19.** d | **24.** d |
| **5.** h | **10.** b | **15.** a | **20.** c | **25.** c |

**26a.** *Student essays will vary. Here is a sample:*
Prior to the development of agriculture, people couldn't count on a regular food supply and had to concentrate on obtaining food. With the agricultural advances of the Neolithic Revolution came a regular food supply and agricultural surplus that allowed some people to earn a living in occupations besides food production.

**26b.** *Student essays will vary. Here is a sample:*
Although both were hunter-gatherers, the Cro-Magnons far surpassed the Neanderthals in technological ability. Neanderthals had the ability to use fire and to create stone and bone tools, knives, and hunting weapons. They learned to take shelter in caves and cliffs and to make primitive clothing from animal skins. The Cro-Magnons achieved a much greater level of technological sophistication. They created needles and sewed fitted clothing. They improved on the hunting technology of the Neanderthals by inventing long-distance hunting weapons such as the bow and arrow. They also made canoes, using stone axes to chop down trees, and eventually developed permanent homes rather than sheltering only in caves and under cliffs.

Chapter 2 Test Form A, pp. 5–6

| | | | | |
|---|---|---|---|---|
| **1.** j | **6.** i | **11.** b | **16.** a | **21.** d |
| **2.** a | **7.** d | **12.** a | **17.** d | **22.** c |
| **3.** h | **8.** b | **13.** c | **18.** b | **23.** b |
| **4.** g | **9.** e | **14.** d | **19.** a | **24.** a |
| **5.** f | **10.** c | **15.** c | **20.** d | **25.** a |

**26a.** *Student essays will vary. Here is a sample:*
The seasonal flooding of the rivers of the Indus-Ganges plain was caused by the rains of the southwest monsoon. This flooding helped to enrich the soil and provide fertile agricultural areas for Indus Valley inhabitants; without it, they couldn't grow crops. Sometimes, however, this flooding was too great, destroying villages and drowning animals.

Silt deposits brought by the flooding of the Huang He also provided fertile agricultural areas to its nearby inhabitants. Yet when this flooding, caused by melting snow and monsoon rains, was too great, it brought such destruction that the river became known as "the Great Sorrow."

**26b.** *Student essays will vary. Here is a sample:*
   Historians have divided the Egyptian dynasties into three periods, the Old Kingdom, the Middle Kingdom, and the New Kingdom. The Old Kingdom began with Narmer's unification of the entire country and the building of a capital in Memphis. A national government was established with a large bureaucracy. Labor was mobilized to build a network of dams, irrigation canals, and the pyramids.
   During the Middle Kingdom, the kings of Memphis lost their power, and a new capital, Thebes, was constructed in Upper Egypt. Egyptian territory expanded to include Nubia, but eventually Egypt was invaded and defeated by the Hyksos.
   The New Kingdom was established with the overthrow of the Hyksos by the Egyptian prince Ahmose, the first Egyptian ruler to assume the title "pharaoh." During this period, Egyptian rulers built the tombs and temples of the Valley of the Kings. Eventually the kingdom split in two, and a weakened Egypt again came under the control of foreign invaders.

## Chapter 2 Test Form B, pp. 7–8

| | | | | |
|---|---|---|---|---|
| **1.** d | **6.** b | **11.** d | **16.** a | **21.** a |
| **2.** j | **7.** g | **12.** d | **17.** b | **22.** a |
| **3.** i | **8.** c | **13.** c | **18.** b | **23.** b |
| **4.** h | **9.** a | **14.** c | **19.** d | **24.** a |
| **5.** f | **10.** e | **15.** c | **20.** a | **25.** a |

**26a.** *Student essays will vary. Here is a sample:*
   Egyptian society was marked by great social stratification. At the very top of Egyptian society were the kings, who served as both religious and political rulers. They were joined in the upper level by other royalty, nobles, and priests. This class controlled political and religious affairs.
   The middle class carried out commercial activity and included artisans, merchants, and scribes. The vast majority of Egyptians formed the lower class. This included farmers, laborers, and the servants of the priests and nobles.

**26b.** *Student essays will vary. Here is a sample:*
   The Sumerians were the probable architects of several important firsts. Their city-states such as Ur and Uruk were probably the world's first cities. They also developed cuneiform, a pictographic writing system that may be the world's oldest written language. The early *Gilgamesh* epic was written in cuneiform.
   The Sumerians were responsible for many technological innovations such as the wagon wheel, the arch, the potter's wheel, and the sundial. They also ushered in the Bronze Age by learning to create this metal alloy out of copper and tin.

## Chapter 3 Test Form A, pp. 9–10

| | | | | |
|---|---|---|---|---|
| **1.** g | **6.** i | **11.** b | **16.** a | **21.** d |
| **2.** j | **7.** c | **12.** d | **17.** d | **22.** c |
| **3.** d | **8.** e | **13.** c | **18.** c | **23.** c |
| **4.** h | **9.** f | **14.** a | **19.** b | **24.** a |
| **5.** b | **10.** a | **15.** b | **20.** b | **25.** d |

**26a.** *Student essays will vary. Here is a sample:*
   Zoroaster preached of the existence of two gods locked in a ongoing struggle—Ahura Mazda, leader of the forces of good, and Ahriman, leader of the forces of evil. According to his teachings, humans had to make a choice about which god to fight for. Those who fought for good would be rewarded with eternal life. Those who fought for evil would suffer in a hell-like afterlife.
   These teachings differed markedly from common polytheistic beliefs of the day. Many early peoples worshiped a multitude of gods who represented elements or natural forces such as sun or fire. These gods were often capricious, and humans were seen as having little control over their own fate. In contrast, Ahura Mazda and Ahriman represented opposing moral forces. Humans could decide their eternal destiny by choosing between the two.

**26b.** *Student essays will vary. Here is a sample:*
   The first Israelites settled in Canaan around 1900 B.C. They remained there until forced by drought and famine to migrate to Egypt. To escape enslavement by the pharaohs, the Israelites departed Egypt in the 1200s B.C. to return to Canaan.

Internal divisions made the Israelites susceptible to a series of invasions that began in the 700s B.C. The invasion of the Assyrians scattered the people of the northern tribes throughout Mesopotamia. Many residents of Jerusalem were carried off to Babylon and enslaved by the Chaldeans in 586 B.C. During the period of the Persian Empire, some of the dispersed Israelites returned to Jerusalem.

## Chapter 3 Test Form B, pp. 11–12

| | | | | |
|---|---|---|---|---|
| **1.** i | **6.** j | **11.** a | **16.** a | **21.** d |
| **2.** c | **7.** d | **12.** c | **17.** b | **22.** d |
| **3.** g | **8.** f | **13.** a | **18.** a | **23.** d |
| **4.** b | **9.** e | **14.** c | **19.** b | **24.** a |
| **5.** a | **10.** h | **15.** d | **20.** c | **25.** b |

**26a.** *Student essays will vary. Here is a sample:*
Abraham and Moses were both important Israelite leaders. Abraham was the first leader of the Israelites. A trader and herder, he migrated in 1900 B.C. from the city of Ur to the land of Canaan. According to the Bible, he made a covenant with God, who promised a great nation to Abraham's descendants if they remained faithful to God.

Around 1200 B.C. Moses directed the Israelites' escape from Egypt after a period of enslavement. As he led them across the Sinai Desert back toward Canaan, he renewed the covenant made by Abraham, receiving and accepting the Ten Commandments.

**26b.** *Student essays will vary. Here is a sample:*
The Phoenicians are an example of a people whose development was greatly influenced by geographic and environmental factors. Because the land they inhabited was not suitable for agriculture, the Phoenician economy developed instead around seafaring, and they built their towns and cities on the Mediterranean coast. Their ability to become sailors and sea traders was aided by the natural abundance of cedar forests that provided not only wood for shipbuilding but also cedar logs, a valuable trading commodity. The Phoenicians used their geography and environment to take control of shipping and trade and set up a network of colonies and trading posts around the Mediterranean.

## Chapter 4 Test Form A, pp. 13–14

| | | | | |
|---|---|---|---|---|
| **1.** h | **6.** b | **11.** b | **16.** d | **21.** b |
| **2.** j | **7.** i | **12.** d | **17.** a | **22.** b |
| **3.** d | **8.** c | **13.** a | **18.** d | **23.** d |
| **4.** g | **9.** f | **14.** c | **19.** c | **24.** c |
| **5.** e | **10.** a | **15.** b | **20.** b | **25.** d |

**26a.** *Answers will vary. Here is a sample:*
The Peloponnesian War was fought between Sparta and its allied city-states and Athens and its allied city-states. The Spartan-led side was also backed by Persia.

One major factor in the war was the Persian desire for greater influence in the Aegean and its desire to regain Ionia, a city-state it had lost during the Persian Wars. In exchange for its return, Persia agreed to support and finance the Spartan side.

Another factor was increasing resentment of Athens's growing power and affluence by the other Greek city-states. Sparta and other city-states that had cooperated with Athens during the Persian Wars now began to see Athens rather than Persia as their chief threat.

**26b.** *Answers will vary. Here is a sample:*
The Spartan educational system was characterized by its emphasis on military and physical training. The aim was to prepare men to become soldiers. Training was compulsory and began at age seven. Boys were taken away from home and trained in reading, writing, and fighting. Their athletic training program produced great athletes, and women as well as men were trained in athletics.

Athenian education was also compulsory, for male children only, but the aim was to create citizens rather than soldiers. Like their Spartan counterparts, boys began school at age seven, but they were educated by tutors or in private schools, not in barracks. The range of subjects taught was much greater, including public speaking, math, and art. Athletics was part of the curriculum, but it was not emphasized to the same degree as in Sparta.

# Chapter 4 Test Form B, pp. 15–16

| | | | | |
|---|---|---|---|---|
| **1.** b | **6.** g | **11.** d | **16.** b | **21.** d |
| **2.** f | **7.** c | **12.** c | **17.** a | **22.** a |
| **3.** h | **8.** a | **13.** a | **18.** b | **23.** b |
| **4.** i | **9.** j | **14.** c | **19.** c | **24.** c |
| **5.** d | **10.** e | **15.** a | **20.** d | **25.** d |

**26a.** *Answers will vary. Here is a sample:*

The Peloponnesian War was an economic, social, and political disaster for the Greek city-states. Agriculture was damaged, as fields and orchards had been destroyed. Unemployment was widespread. Greeks—first the Spartans and then the Thebans—lost faith in their political systems, as the rulers of the city-states proved cruel or incompetent. Finally, the city-states never regained the cooperation that allowed them to withstand invasion during the Persian Wars. Weakened by infighting, they were unable to resist when the Macedonians invaded.

**26b.** *Answers will vary. Here is a sample:*

The Greeks were a polytheistic people who worshiped a great number of gods and goddesses. Each Greek community chose one of these gods as its special protector. In general, these deities were believed to have human forms and qualities—they married, fought, and played tricks on each other—but they also were believed to possess superhuman powers.

The most important gods lived on a Greek mountain called Mount Olympus. Zeus was the chief god, ruler of the sky and the weather. He was worshiped equally by all Greek communities. Dionysus was the god of wine and fertility. The first plays were outdoor performances held in his honor.

# Chapter 5 Test Form A, pp. 17–18

| | | | | |
|---|---|---|---|---|
| **1.** h | **6.** c | **11.** d | **16.** d | **21.** c |
| **2.** j | **7.** d | **12.** c | **17.** b | **22.** b |
| **3.** f | **8.** e | **13.** c | **18.** a | **23.** d |
| **4.** i | **9.** a | **14.** b | **19.** b | **24.** a |
| **5.** b | **10.** g | **15.** d | **20.** d | **25.** b |

**26a.** *Student essays will vary. Here is a sample:*

Two major playwrights of ancient Greece were the tragedians Sophocles and Aeschylus. Of the many plays Aeschylus wrote during the 400s B.C., only a few have survived. One of these is a trilogy called the *Oresteia*. Known for its use of language, the *Oresteia* described the murder of King Agamemnon by his wife and the consequences of one generation's actions on the next. Like other Greek tragedies, the plays of Aeschylus depicted characters struggling against fate.

Sophocles had served in the Athenian army and witnessed the suffering that occurred during war. His plays stressed suffering as an unavoidable part of life. His character King Oedipus, for example, kills his father and marries his mother, then blinds himself in despair.

**26b.** *Student essays will vary. Here is a sample:*

The first two noted Greek historians were Herodotus and Thucydides. Herodotus, who chose the Persian Wars as his subject matter, is considered to have created the discipline of history by attempting to separate fact from legend. To record the history of the Persian Wars, he traveled to the sites where the wars took place, conducted interviews, and checked the reliability of his sources. In addition to political and military history, he documented the religion, customs, and notable people of the places he visited.

Thucydides chose the Peloponnesian War as his subject matter. Like Herodotus, he visited many of the places about which he wrote. He was, however, a more rigorous and accurate historian than Herodotus, examining documents, accepting only eyewitness accounts, and rejecting supernatural explanations for events.

# Chapter 5 Test Form B, pp. 19–20

| | | | | |
|---|---|---|---|---|
| **1.** j | **6.** g | **11.** c | **16.** d | **21.** a |
| **2.** f | **7.** e | **12.** b | **17.** a | **22.** b |
| **3.** h | **8.** d | **13.** c | **18.** d | **23.** d |
| **4.** a | **9.** c | **14.** a | **19.** c | **24.** a |
| **5.** b | **10.** i | **15.** d | **20.** c | **25.** a |

**26a.** *Student essays will vary. Here is a sample:*

The development of a Hellenistic culture out of a combination of Greek and Middle Eastern cultures was largely the legacy of Alexander the Great. The creation of a large empire by Alexander that encompassed both the Greek city-states and the Middle East created an opportunity for cultural diffusion between the two regions. Alexander encouraged this diffusion by actively promoting the meeting of "East and West," promoting intermarriage of Greeks and Persians, setting up his capital in Babylon, and adopting Persian customs while facilitating the spread of the Greek language. Economic links such as intercity trade, the free migration of labor, and the use of a common currency also promoted the growth of a common culture that continued to flourish after Alexander's death.

**26b.** *Student essays will vary. Here is a sample:*
The political philosophies of Plato and Aristotle were vastly different. Plato's political philosophy advocated limiting individual freedom and was based on a distrust of both the individual and the lower classes. In his view, only the most intelligent were capable of ruling. Only a government run by philosopher-kings could rule properly and prevent social disorder.

Aristotle, in contrast, approved of many different types of government. In fact, he thought the best form of government balanced monarchy, aristocracy, and democracy, in one system. The optimal ruling class was not an elite upper class but the middle class.

## Chapter 6 Test Form A, pp. 21–22

| | | | | |
|---|---|---|---|---|
| 1. e | 6. h | 11. c | 16. b | 21. a |
| 2. i | 7. j | 12. c | 17. d | 22. b |
| 3. b | 8. a | 13. c | 18. c | 23. a |
| 4. c | 9. g | 14. b | 19. a | 24. d |
| 5. f | 10. d | 15. b | 20. a | 25. c |

**26a.** *Student essays will vary. Here is a sample:*
Although the Italian peninsula has miles of Mediterranean coastline, the Italian coast tends to be rocky or marshy. Italy has few natural harbors, and this may have discouraged its development as a seafaring region. In addition, Italy had an abundance of fertile soil enriched by the mountain streams of the Alps. This probably reduced the need to travel great distances for trade.

**26b.** *Student essays will vary. Here is a sample:*
All three Punic Wars occurred between the Romans and the Carthaginians. The First Punic War began over Sicily and the channel that separated it from Italy. Carthage had initial naval superiority, but Rome built more ships and developed tactics that eventually forced

Carthage to give in. Carthage gave up control of Sicily and paid Rome an indemnity for damages.

The Second Punic War began when a Carthaginian general named Hannibal seized a Roman city in Spain and then attacked the empire on Italian territory, crossing over the Alps. The Romans withstood Hannibal in Italy and then attacked Carthage itself. Again, Carthage gave up control of territory and paid an indemnity.

In the third war, Rome destroyed Carthage completely to gain control of the western Mediterranean.

## Chapter 6 Test Form B, pp. 23–24

| | | | | |
|---|---|---|---|---|
| 1. c | 6. a | 11. b | 16. a | 21. d |
| 2. j | 7. h | 12. a | 17. d | 22. d |
| 3. f | 8. i | 13. c | 18. d | 23. b |
| 4. e | 9. g | 14. c | 19. b | 24. c |
| 5. b | 10. d | 15. a | 20. a | 25. c |

**26a.** *Student essays will vary. Here is a sample:*
The decline of the Roman Empire was caused by a combination of economic, political, and external factors. Economic problems were many. Some were caused by political instability while others added to this instability. For example, the large empire couldn't afford the cost of maintaining the large army necessary to protect itself. In addition, treasury money was wasted by the lavish spending of emperors. To pay soldiers, rulers raised taxes. These increased taxes led to more political unrest and food shortages as farmers abandoned their land.

External factors included the increasing pressure of Germanic tribes entering and attacking the empire. Attacks by the Germans were followed by attacks by the Huns from central Asia. The devastation they caused allowed the Germans to take over Rome completely after the Huns finally retreated.

**26b.** *Student essays will vary. Here is a sample:*
During the Republic, Roman government had two branches, executive and legislative. The executive branch was headed by officials known as consuls who were elected for one-year terms. The legislative branch initially consisted of two bodies, the Assembly of Centuries and the Senate. Although the Assembly of Centuries elected the executive-branch officials, the Senate

was the more powerful lawmaking body. These institutions chiefly served the interests of the patrician class, and only members of that class could serve in public office.

Over time these legislative bodies were joined by the Assembly of Tribunes, which represented the plebeian class and gained the right to make laws in 287 B.C.

## Chapter 7 Test Form A, pp. 25–26

| | | | | |
|---|---|---|---|---|
| **1.** c | **6.** h | **11.** a | **16.** b | **21.** d |
| **2.** i | **7.** f | **12.** b | **17.** a | **22.** c |
| **3.** a | **8.** b | **13.** a | **18.** d | **23.** d |
| **4.** j | **9.** d | **14.** c | **19.** d | **24.** b |
| **5.** g | **10.** e | **15.** c | **20.** c | **25.** b |

**26a.** *Student essays will vary. Here is a sample:*
Trade played an important role in shaping the culture of East African city-states. Trade brought merchants from Persia and the Arabian Peninsula to the East African coast along with their religion, culture, and languages. The culture of the city-states thus reflected a mixture of Islamic and Bantu influences. Many of the people of these cities adopted Islam, wrote in an alphabet derived from Arabic, and spoke Swahili, a Bantu language that contained many Arabic and Persian words.

**26b.** *Student essays will vary. Here is a sample:*
Timbuktu is located in West Africa on the southern edge of the Sahara and was the capital of the kingdom of Mali during the reign of Mansa Musa. Under Musa it became a center of Islamic art and learning and the site of his palace. The city thrived during the era of salt and gold caravans but was captured by the Berbers after Musa's death. It came under Songhai control during the reign of Sunni Ali.

## Chapter 7 Test Form B, pp. 27–28

| | | | | |
|---|---|---|---|---|
| **1.** c | **6.** f | **11.** c | **16.** a | **21.** d |
| **2.** g | **7.** b | **12.** d | **17.** c | **22.** d |
| **3.** h | **8.** d | **13.** b | **18.** a | **23.** c |
| **4.** i | **9.** j | **14.** a | **19.** d | **24.** d |
| **5.** a | **10.** e | **15.** b | **20.** b | **25.** b |

**26a.** *Student essays will vary. Here is a sample:*
The trans-Saharan caravan trade involved the transportation and exchange of goods between cities in North Africa and West Africa. Traders from Islamic cities in North Africa sent cloth, metal products, and other goods from Morocco and Spain south to such West African kingdoms such as Ghana, Mali, and that of the Songhai. In return, gold and produce from Ghana and other sub-Saharan regions were sent north. Control of the trade routes brought prosperity to the empires of the region, and cultural contact brought by trade helped spread Islam to West Africa.

**26b.** *Student essays will vary. Here is a sample:*
Except for a thin fertile strip near the Mediterranean coast, North Africa is dominated by the Sahara, a sand-and-rock-filled region spanning the continent from west to east. South of the Sahara is sub-Saharan Africa. This area begins with a high plateau called the Sahel. The Sahel is mainly made up of grassland called savannas. To the east are several high mountains and the Great Rift Valley, which continues south to South Africa. In the west, below the Sahel, is an equatorial rain forest, followed by another area of desert, and finally the fertile highlands of South Africa.

## Chapter 8 Test Form A, pp. 29–30

| | | | | |
|---|---|---|---|---|
| **1.** i | **6.** a | **11.** c | **16.** d | **21.** d |
| **2.** f | **7.** d | **12.** b | **17.** c | **22.** a |
| **3.** h | **8.** j | **13.** b | **18.** c | **23.** c |
| **4.** b | **9.** c | **14.** a | **19.** b | **24.** b |
| **5.** g | **10.** e | **15.** a | **20.** a | **25.** a |

**26a.** *Student essays will vary. Here is a sample:*
Two major principles of the Hindu religion are dharma and karma. Obedience to the principle of dharma involves following one's duty. The duties of an individual might vary according to age, sex, social standing, or occupation. But regardless of the exact nature of a person's obligations, they have to be followed even if it means hardship or personal cost.

Karma is the principle behind the cycle of rebirth. According to Hinduism, a person's soul is reincarnated after death; it passes into another form for the next life. The concept of karma means that the form taken in this next life is determined by how a person lived in his or her previous existence. Those who have lived properly will pass into a higher form.

**26b.** *Student essays will vary. Here is a sample:*
   Cattle provided the basis of the Aryan economy. The Aryans were originally a nomadic-herding people who depended on cattle for food and trade. Wealth was measured by the size of one's herd, and cattle raids were common between tribes. Even after the Aryans began farming in the Indus Valley, cattle remained so important that to maintain the herds the eating of meat was prohibited.

## Chapter 8 Test Form B, pp. 31–32

| | | | | |
|---|---|---|---|---|
| **1.** i | **6.** a | **11.** b | **16.** d | **21.** b |
| **2.** g | **7.** f | **12.** d | **17.** b | **22.** c |
| **3.** e | **8.** h | **13.** a | **18.** a | **23.** c |
| **4.** d | **9.** c | **14.** c | **19.** d | **24.** a |
| **5.** j | **10.** b | **15.** a | **20.** b | **25.** c |

**26a.** *Student essays will vary. Here is a sample:*
   Two of the great texts of the ancient Indian civilization are the *Mahabharata* and the *Upanishads.* The *Mahabharata* is a 100,000-verse epic poem that tells the story of a power struggle between two families. The product of several authors, it contains many discussions of philosophy and religion, including the section called the *Bhagavad Gita.*
   The *Upanishads* are a collection of writings by various religious thinkers of the period between 800 B.C. and 400 B.C. It is one of the important books of Hindu thought, and its study was encouraged by the Gupta rulers.

**26b.** *Student essays will vary. Here is a sample:*
   The caste system in India around 500 B.C. consisted of four major social classes: warriors, priests, common people, and servants. In addition, there was a fifth group of people of such low status they were outside the caste system altogether. Each of the classes, or *varnas*, had its own occupations and duties.
   Two major changes occurred in this system after it was brought to India by the Aryans. The first was the occupation of the highest place in the social hierarchy by the priestly class, who replaced the warrior class in that position. The

second change was the division of each *varna* into subgroups called *jati*. Each subgroup had the same occupation and customs and occupied a specific place within the *varna* itself.

## Chapter 9 Test Form A, pp. 33–34

| | | | | |
|---|---|---|---|---|
| **1.** g | **6.** e | **11.** c | **16.** a | **21.** a |
| **2.** b | **7.** i | **12.** b | **17.** c | **22.** d |
| **3.** j | **8.** d | **13.** a | **18.** d | **23.** d |
| **4.** a | **9.** h | **14.** a | **19.** a | **24.** b |
| **5.** f | **10.** c | **15.** b | **20.** c | **25.** d |

**26a.** *Student essays will vary. Here is a sample:*
   Both Daoism and Confucianism focus on the way people should live, but they differ greatly in their emphasis and principles. The primary concern of Confucian thought is the prevention of civil disorder. Confucius emphasized the importance of accepting one's role within the structures of the family and society. He stressed the need to conduct relationships in a respectful manner. In contrast, Daoism does not demand that humans live in a given social structure. Instead, Daoist teaching emphasizes the renunciation of ambition and the importance of living in harmony with nature.
   Both philosophies had great impact. Confucianism provided the basis for Han government and influenced Chinese society for more than 2,000 years. Daoism's emphasis on harmony with nature had a particular influence on the arts.

**26b.** *Student essays will vary. Here is a sample:*
   Han-era social structure was divided into three main classes. At the top of Chinese society were the landowners. This class was predominantly wealthy, although over time individual fortunes diminished as property was divided by inheritance.
   At the middle level were the peasants, who made up some 90 percent of the population. Living in rural villages, the peasantry faced a difficult existence, having to pay rent to the landowners, contribute taxes and labor to the government, and face the threats of famine and flood.
   The merchant class included shopkeepers, traders, and bankers. This class, while often wealthy, was held in contempt by Chinese society as Confucian teaching denigrated the pursuit of profit.

## Chapter 9 Test Form B, pp. 35–36

| | | | | |
|---|---|---|---|---|
| **1.** d | **6.** j | **11.** d | **16.** d | **21.** a |
| **2.** b | **7.** i | **12.** a | **17.** c | **22.** c |
| **3.** g | **8.** f | **13.** d | **18.** d | **23.** b |
| **4.** e | **9.** a | **14.** b | **19.** b | **24.** c |
| **5.** h | **10.** c | **15.** b | **20.** c | **25.** d |

**26a.** *Student essays will vary. Here is a sample:*

Three groups that might have been unhappy with the rule of Qin Shihuangdi include the local lords, the peasant class, and the scholars. The local lords saw their power sharply curtailed by Qin Shihuangdi. His policy of dividing China into military districts prevented them from challenging the central government. They were further weakened by land taxes and confiscation. The peasantry were the victims of Qin's large-scale building programs that required huge amounts of forced labor—300,000 men for the Great Wall alone. The scholars would have been unhappy with the imposition of book burnings and censorship. Hundreds who disagreed with Qin's order not to discuss the past were put to death.

**26b.** *Student essays will vary. Here is a sample:*

The overland trade routes that stretched from China to the Mediterranean became known as the Silk Road. This network of trails led from China's Pacific coast across western China and continued through the deserts and mountains of central Asia. Expanded during the Han dynasty, the network provided a means for traders to exchange Chinese commodities—the most important being silk—for products from the Middle East and Europe.

## Chapter 10 Test Form A, pp. 37–38

| | | | | |
|---|---|---|---|---|
| **1.** f | **6.** i | **11.** c | **16.** b | **21.** a |
| **2.** d | **7.** e | **12.** a | **17.** c | **22.** c |
| **3.** a | **8.** h | **13.** c | **18.** a | **23.** d |
| **4.** j | **9.** c | **14.** b | **19.** b | **24.** b |
| **5.** b | **10.** g | **15.** a | **20.** d | **25.** d |

**26a.** *Student essays will vary. Here is a sample:*

After the fall of Rome, classical knowledge was preserved by Byzantine determination to record the culture and scholarship of the ancient Greeks and Romans. Under Justinian, a commission of scholars preserved Rome's legal heritage by compiling the old laws of Rome into a collection of books. This later became the basis for the legal systems of much of Europe. Other scholars copied and preserved the literary, philosophical, and scientific works of Greece and Rome, as well as Christian theological texts. The government encouraged this scholarship by emphasizing education and setting up schools such as the University of Constantinople.

**26b.** *Student essays will vary. Here is a sample:*

Two factors that contributed to the fall of the Byzantine Empire were the schism between the churches and attacks of invading armies. The Byzantine Empire came under continual attack by invaders including Germanic tribes, Persians, and Arabs. These attacks gradually decreased Byzantine territory. The schism, or separation of the Eastern and Western Churches, also weakened the empire greatly. Not only did it make the Byzantines more susceptible to Turkish invasion, but forces under control of the Western Church began to pressure Constantinople from the West.

## Chapter 10 Test Form B, pp. 39–40

| | | | | |
|---|---|---|---|---|
| **1.** h | **6.** d | **11.** c | **16.** a | **21.** a |
| **2.** f | **7.** j | **12.** a | **17.** d | **22.** d |
| **3.** e | **8.** a | **13.** b | **18.** c | **23.** d |
| **4.** b | **9.** g | **14.** b | **19.** d | **24.** b |
| **5.** i | **10.** c | **15.** c | **20.** b | **25.** c |

**26a.** *Student essays will vary. Here is a sample:*

The Eastern Slavs owed much of their culture and religious heritage to the Byzantines. Eastern Slavic culture was shaped by the Eastern Orthodox religion, so much so that Moscow became the center of the religion after Constantinople's fall. Cyrillic, the Slavic alphabet, was developed by a Byzantine missionary. This allowed the translation of the Bible into Slavic languages and helped to spread Byzantine religion and culture to Slavic peoples. The art and architecture of Moscow were also greatly influenced by the Byzantines.

**26b.** *Student essays will vary. Here is a sample:*

The Eastern and Western Churches disagreed over numerous issues beginning in the A.D. 300s. One major issue was leadership. The Western Church claimed that the pope was

**188**     Chapter and Unit Tests                                   *World History*

supreme leader over both churches, but the Eastern Church would not accept a subordinate role for its patriarchs. Another source of conflict was the involvement of the Western Church in the Byzantine clergy's dispute about icons. The Western and Eastern Churches also disputed the control of new churches in the Balkan Peninsula. Eventually, these conflicts led to a schism, or complete separation of the two churches, in A.D. 1054.

## Chapter 11 Test Form A, pp. 41–42

| | | | | |
|---|---|---|---|---|
| **1.** d | **6.** a | **11.** b | **16.** c | **21.** d |
| **2.** j | **7.** c | **12.** b | **17.** b | **22.** a |
| **3.** f | **8.** b | **13.** a | **18.** b | **23.** b |
| **4.** i | **9.** e | **14.** c | **19.** d | **24.** c |
| **5.** g | **10.** h | **15.** d | **20.** a | **25.** c |

**26a.** *Student essays will vary. Here is a sample:*

The role of women in early Islamic society was largely defined by their relationship to men. Women were expected to carry out their defined roles as wives, mothers, or daughters. Women expected to be treated well by their husbands and were granted specific rights. They had the right to inherit and control property and to keep that property even in the cases of divorce or remarriage.

In general, the women had more rights and protections than they did in pre-Islamic society. For example, while the common practice of polygamy was allowed to continue under Islam, men were limited to four wives whom they had to treat equally. In addition, the tribal practice of killing unwanted female children was forbidden.

**26b.** *Student essays will vary. Here is a sample:*

Islamic scholars made breakthroughs in medicine and mathematics during the Abbasid Empire. In mathematics, Arab scholars made great advances in geometry and invented algebraic equations. They also adopted the numerical symbols and the zero concept of the Gupta mathematicians, and used them to develop the place-value system.

Two Islamic scholars who contributed to the field of medicine were al-Razi and Ibn Sina. Al-Razi wrote a medical encyclopedia that described the origins of and differences among diseases. Ibn Sina wrote the *Canon of Medicine*, an encyclopedia of the accumulated medical knowledge of the time. The book offered advice for the treatment of many diseases.

## Chapter 11 Test Form B, pp. 43–44

| | | | | |
|---|---|---|---|---|
| **1.** f | **6.** h | **11.** c | **16.** c | **21.** b |
| **2.** i | **7.** e | **12.** a | **17.** a | **22.** d |
| **3.** a | **8.** g | **13.** a | **18.** a | **23.** c |
| **4.** c | **9.** b | **14.** b | **19.** b | **24.** b |
| **5.** j | **10.** d | **15.** d | **20.** d | **25.** c |

**26a.** *Student essays will vary. Here is a sample:*

The city of Makkah is central both to Islamic history and to the practice of its adherents. Makkah is the birthplace of Muhammad, founder and prophet of Islam. It is the city where Muhammad first shared the revelations he received from Gabriel and to which he returned after the migration to Madinah. The spiritual home of Islam, Makkah is the location of the Kaaba, the religion's most sacred place of worship.

The city is important to the practice of Islam today. A pilgrimage there is mandatory for every able-bodied Muslim at least once during his or her lifetime.

**26b.** *Student essays will vary. Here is a sample:*

The name "Rightly Guided Caliphs" refers to the first four Muslim leaders to succeed Muhammad after his death. The first Caliph was Muhammad's friend and father-in-law Abu Bakr, the fourth caliph his son-in-law Ali. They are respected for following the example of Muhammad and exercising good leadership. During the reigns of these four leaders, Islam spread beyond the Arabian Peninsula, and Arab armies conquered much of the area held by the Byzantines and Persians. The election of Ali, the last of these caliphs, caused a split among Muslims and caused the division of believers into the Shiite and the Sunni.

## Chapter 12 Test Form A, pp. 45–46

| | | | | |
|---|---|---|---|---|
| **1.** h | **6.** j | **11.** b | **16.** d | **21.** a |
| **2.** e | **7.** i | **12.** c | **17.** b | **22.** b |
| **3.** d | **8.** f | **13.** b | **18.** b | **23.** c |
| **4.** c | **9.** g | **14.** a | **19.** a | **24.** d |
| **5.** a | **10.** b | **15.** d | **20.** d | **25.** a |

**26a.** *Student essays will vary. Here is a sample:*

The Carolingian dynasty was named after the Frankish king Charlemagne, whose name in Latin is Carolus Magnus. Under Charlemagne's rule, Carolingian territory expanded and became known as the Frankish Empire. He was crowned Roman emperor by the pope, and his kingdom encompassed much of western Europe.

The collapse of the empire was caused by internal feuding and outside invasion. After Charlemagne's death, the empire passed to his son, who was not able to maintain control. Carolingian lands were split in three by Charlemagne's grandsons, and their weakened kingdoms became subject to attacks by three sets of invaders, the Muslims, the Slavs, and the Vikings.

**26b.** *Student essays will vary. Here is a sample:*

During the feudal era, local lords gained many of the traditional powers of kings and government. These included the power to mint coins, dispense justice, and, most important, raise armies. They received grants of land from the king and wielded near-total authority within these holdings.

The major advantage to European monarchs of the feudal system was making the lords bear the economic cost of raising an army—buying horses and military equipment for soldiers. In return for the land and authority over it, lords had to swear loyalty to the king and periodically provide him with well-equipped knights for the royal army.

## Chapter 12 Test Form B, pp. 47–48

| | | | | |
|---|---|---|---|---|
| **1.** d | **6.** b | **11.** b | **16.** b | **21.** d |
| **2.** i | **7.** e | **12.** c | **17.** c | **22.** c |
| **3.** a | **8.** c | **13.** b | **18.** d | **23.** b |
| **4.** f | **9.** h | **14.** b | **19.** c | **24.** c |
| **5.** j | **10.** g | **15.** d | **20.** a | **25.** a |

**26a.** *Student essays will vary. Here is a sample:*

Viking military technology and the lack of strong central authorities combined to make Europe vulnerable to Viking attacks. The Vikings traveled from their native Scandinavia in long ships that could navigate both the Atlantic Ocean and European rivers. Light and fast, these boats enabled the Vikings to arrive and retreat quickly, bypassing European defenses.

In addition, internal divisions among European rulers after the death of Charlemagne made it difficult for them to resist the Vikings. The already weak authority of the rulers became weaker under successive attacks, and their holdings became even more vulnerable to invaders.

**26b.** *Student essays will vary. Here is a sample:*

The monks of the Middle Ages lived in monasteries under the leadership of an abbot. They made vows of poverty and chastity, and tended to live simple, self-sufficient lives. At the monasteries, monks often provided educational and medical services for nearby communities and were leaders in the call for religious reform.

Friars also lived a simple existence without possessions. Unlike the monks who lived apart from the community, friars wandered from place to place preaching Christianity. They lived by monastic rules among the villagers to whom they preached, and they depended on the charity of the community to survive.

## Chapter 13 Test Form A, pp. 49–50

| | | | | |
|---|---|---|---|---|
| **1.** c | **6.** e | **11.** c | **16.** b | **21.** d |
| **2.** d | **7.** b | **12.** a | **17.** d | **22.** d |
| **3.** g | **8.** i | **13.** d | **18.** b | **23.** a |
| **4.** j | **9.** h | **14.** d | **19.** a | **24.** c |
| **5.** a | **10.** f | **15.** b | **20.** c | **25.** a |

**26a.** *Student essays will vary. Here is a sample essay:*

The Crusades brought lasting economic, technological, and cultural benefits to Europe. Increased trade resulting from European contact with the Mediterranean world brought a great variety of goods from the Middle East and China. Markets were also created for European textiles, and economic prosperity came to trading cities such as Genoa and Flanders.

The arrival of classic texts preserved by Byzantine and Muslim scholars helped to renew European intellectual life. Literature and the arts flourished as a result of this contact.

The level of technology increased as well, as Europeans learned about the weaponry, map-making, and shipbuilding and navigation techniques of the Muslim world.

**26b.** *Student essays will vary. Here is a sample:*

The Hundred Years' War demonstrated the obsolescence of both feudal weaponry and military organization. The use, begun by the English, of innovative distance weapons such as the Welsh longbow, cannons, and other firearms made foot soldiers more valuable in war than mounted knights. Feudal weaponry such as swords and crossbows were meant for close combat and were useless at a distance.

Military units made up of feudal knights became inferior to large armies made up of hired soldiers. Maintaining and supplying these armies was beyond the capability of feudal lords, so the responsibility for raising armies reverted to the monarchies.

## Chapter 13 Test Form B, pp. 51–52

| | | | | |
|---|---|---|---|---|
| **1.** e | **6.** b | **11.** a | **16.** c | **21.** d |
| **2.** d | **7.** i | **12.** c | **17.** d | **22.** d |
| **3.** a | **8.** j | **13.** a | **18.** c | **23.** c |
| **4.** f | **9.** c | **14.** d | **19.** b | **24.** a |
| **5.** h | **10.** g | **15.** b | **20.** a | **25.** c |

**26a.** *Student essays will vary. Here is a sample:*

Both merchant and craft guilds were business associations that originated in Europe during the A.D. 1100s. Merchant guilds were composed of local traders. They joined together to maintain price levels and discourage competition by restricting the ability of foreigners to trade in their areas. Craft guilds were made up of artisans such as carpenters and seamstresses. These guilds established rules about prices, wages, and work practices. In addition, craft guilds established quality standards for the goods their members manufactured. Both merchant and craft guilds provided a variety of social, religious, and economic services for their members.

**26b.** *Student essays will vary. Here is a sample:*

Vernacular is the language of everyday speech native to a particular region. For example, the vernacular of England is English; of France, French. The use of vernacular language in literature and religious texts had two major effects. Literature in vernacular language was accessible to far more people than it would have been in Latin, the language previously used for scholarly and religious writing. In addition, the translation of religious texts into vernacular

languages such as English and Czech allowed people to read them for themselves. They no longer had to depend on the interpretation of religious ideas from clergy members. The use of the vernacular also helped to strengthen the national identities of the people in Europe's separate kingdoms.

## Chapter 14 Test Form A, pp. 53–54

| | | | | |
|---|---|---|---|---|
| **1.** g | **6.** e | **11.** a | **16.** b | **21.** a |
| **2.** d | **7.** f | **12.** b | **17.** d | **22.** c |
| **3.** a | **8.** h | **13.** d | **18.** c | **23.** c |
| **4.** j | **9.** b | **14.** a | **19.** d | **24.** d |
| **5.** i | **10.** c | **15.** c | **20.** b | **25.** d |

**26a.** *Student essays will vary. Here is a sample:*

The Japanese samurai adopted the form of Buddhism brought to Japan by the scholar Eisai. This form, called Zen Buddhism, emphasized the need for the individual to live in harmony with nature. Practitioners of Zen believed that harmony could be achieved through meditation and bodily discipline rather than the study of religious texts. Zen practice of ritual and meditation was beneficial to samurai warriors because it helped them to act instinctively without distraction. Military skills such as archery could be improved through the concentration Zen practice afforded.

**26b.** *Student essays will vary. Here is a sample:*

Both the Vietnamese and Korean cultures were heavily influenced by the Chinese. Vietnam was dominated by the Chinese for more than 1,000 years beginning around 200 B.C. The Vietnamese adopted writing based on Chinese characters and adopted aspects of Chinese belief systems and government, including a civil service based on Confucian principles.

The Koreans were ruled by Han Chinese for a period beginning around 100 B.C. In that time and the period after the Koreans regained control, Korea borrowed greatly from the Chinese, adopting Chinese arts and sciences, and elements of Confucian and Buddhist thought. Chinese influence again grew strong during the Yi dynasty at the end of the A.D. 1300s. The Yi taught Chinese classics in school and made neo-Confucianism state doctrine.

## Chapter 14 Test Form B, pp. 55–56

| | | | | |
|---|---|---|---|---|
| **1.** d | **6.** i | **11.** a | **16.** c | **21.** b |
| **2.** j | **7.** c | **12.** b | **17.** a | **22.** a |
| **3.** g | **8.** f | **13.** d | **18.** c | **23.** d |
| **4.** b | **9.** e | **14.** d | **19.** b | **24.** a |
| **5.** a | **10.** h | **15.** a | **20.** c | **25.** b |

**26a.** *Student essays will vary. Here is a sample:*
Japan includes four large, predominantly mountainous islands (and many smaller ones) about 100 miles off the coast of Korea. Its geography and location have affected its people in many ways. The sea that surrounds the islands has provided a natural barrier against invasion. Isolated from most of Asia, it developed with only limited cultural contact with the mainland of Asia. China was its primary outside influence. With little land suitable for farming, the Japanese had to turn to the sea for food production. The rugged mountain beauty also has given the inhabitants of Japan a reverence for nature. Its writers, artists, and religious scholars have been deeply influenced by the landscape.

**26b.** *Student essays will vary. Here is a sample:*
From about the A.D. 400s to the A.D. 1400s, religions of Indian origin were dominant in maritime Southeast Asia. Buddhism and Hinduism were brought by traders and scholars, and these beliefs predominated in the Srivijaya and Majapahit kingdoms. In the early A.D. 1200s, the religion of Islam began to take hold, first in Melaka on the Malay Peninsula, and continued to spread throughout the Indonesian islands. Eventually, Buddhism and Hinduism were supplanted by Islam in all of Indonesia with the exception of Bali.

## Chapter 15 Test Form A, pp. 57–58

| | | | | |
|---|---|---|---|---|
| **1.** d | **6.** j | **11.** c | **16.** a | **21.** b |
| **2.** b | **7.** a | **12.** d | **17.** a | **22.** b |
| **3.** c | **8.** g | **13.** d | **18.** d | **23.** a |
| **4.** h | **9.** f | **14.** d | **19.** b | **24.** d |
| **5.** i | **10.** e | **15.** a | **20.** c | **25.** c |

**26a.** *Student essays will vary. Here is a sample:*
The lifestyle of the Plains peoples was shaped by the natural resources available to them. Groups such as the Crow and Blackfoot had neither the ocean resources of the coastal Native American groups nor the plowable soil and water necessary to cultivate maize. They did have one resource in abundance—the herds of bison that roamed the area. The lifestyle of the Plains people reflected their focus on this resource. They used parts of the bison for food, clothing, and shelter, and they followed the herds as they migrated in search of grazing land.

**26b.** *Student essays will vary. Here is a sample:*
Religion permeated every aspect of Mayan society. Mayan rulers functioned as both political and religious leaders. The kings led the rituals and ceremonies conducted at the pyramids, which had been built especially for religious purposes. The Maya believed that their daily life was affected by the gods and spirits who inhabited the second level of existence, the Otherworld. Rituals such as bloodletting and human sacrifice were conducted regularly to appease these gods. The scientific breakthroughs of the Maya were accomplished by astronomer-priests who created astronomical charts that explained the changing positions of stars and planets as the movements of gods through the sky.

## Chapter 15 Test Form B, pp. 59–60

| | | | | |
|---|---|---|---|---|
| **1.** j | **6.** c | **11.** c | **16.** d | **21.** d |
| **2.** b | **7.** e | **12.** a | **17.** a | **22.** b |
| **3.** a | **8.** i | **13.** d | **18.** b | **23.** c |
| **4.** f | **9.** h | **14.** c | **19.** b | **24.** d |
| **5.** d | **10.** g | **15.** b | **20.** a | **25.** c |

**26a.** *Student essays will vary. Here is a sample:*
The Inca Empire was marked by a strong central government under the leadership of a powerful emperor. The emperor was seen as divine and was believed to have direct contact with the gods. He was owner of all land under the empire's control. Through his officials, he wielded a high level of control over the daily life of his subjects by regulating agriculture, food distribution, trade, and building projects. Local rulers of conquered territory were permitted to govern only as long as they remained loyal to the emperor.

**26b.** *Student essays will vary. Here is a sample:*
The Mayan civilization was centered in the Yucatán Peninsula of present-day Mexico. The

civilization reached its peak between A.D. 300 and A.D. 900. The accomplishments of the Maya were numerous. They developed sky charts and accurate calendars, and astronomers were able to predict eclipses. Mayan mathematicians developed a base-20 number system with symbols representing one, five, and zero. The Maya also developed a writing system and wrote in folded books made of bark and plaster.

## Chapter 16 Test Form A, pp. 61–62

| | | | | |
|---|---|---|---|---|
| 1. e | 6. a | 11. b | 16. d | 21. a |
| 2. h | 7. b | 12. d | 17. a | 22. c |
| 3. i | 8. d | 13. d | 18. b | 23. d |
| 4. g | 9. j | 14. b | 19. b | 24. c |
| 5. c | 10. f | 15. a | 20. c | 25. b |

**26a.** *Student essays will vary. Here is a sample:*

Two great Italian artists of the Renaissance were Leonardo da Vinci and Michelangelo Buonarroti. Leonardo da Vinci was a painter who is best known for the *Mona Lisa* and *The Last Supper*. A citizen of Florence, he exemplified the humanist ideal of participation in a variety of activities by excelling as a writer and scientist in addition to being an artist.

Michelangelo studied sculpture in Florence, where he created the famous marble statue of the biblical hero David. Later, he moved to Rome and sculpted *La Pietà*, which portrays the dead Jesus in Mary's arms. He also worked for the Vatican, painting biblical scenes and classical figures on the ceiling of the Sistine Chapel and designing the dome of St. Peter's Basilica.

**26b.** *Student essays will vary. Here is a sample:*

The Counter-Reformation was the response of the Catholic Church to the increasing spread of Protestant faith. The Church's effort included the attempt to eliminate corruption, reestablish papal authority, and combat Protestantism through missionary work.

The process was begun by Pope Paul III, who wanted to reform the Catholic Church and slow the spread of Protestantism. The full implementation of reforms did not begin until the 1540s, when the Church set up a court to try heretics and began to strengthen the pope's authority over church members. The process continued with the meetings of the Council of Trent to clarify and define Catholic doctrine.

Missionary activity by the Church was carried out by the Jesuits. This group, founded by Ignatius of Loyola, established universities throughout Europe and traveled the world to spread Catholic teachings.

## Chapter 16 Test Form B, pp. 63–64

| | | | | |
|---|---|---|---|---|
| 1. b | 6. j | 11. d | 16. d | 21. c |
| 2. f | 7. c | 12. a | 17. a | 22. b |
| 3. d | 8. a | 13. c | 18. c | 23. c |
| 4. i | 9. e | 14. d | 19. d | 24. b |
| 5. h | 10. g | 15. c | 20. d | 25. b |

**26a.** *Student essays will vary. Here is a sample:*

John Calvin believed in the idea of a theocracy, or church-run state. He tried to create a model theocracy in the Swiss city of Geneva.

In Geneva, Calvin set up a council of elders called the Consistory. This body was given the power to control almost every aspect of citizens' lives. Under the Consistory's leadership, citizens were expected to attend church services regularly and avoid sinful behavior. They were not allowed to hold non-Calvinist beliefs. Those who disobeyed the Consistory would be punished or executed. Visitors traveled from all over Europe to study Calvin's strict model community, which became known as the "City of God."

**26b.** *Student essays will vary. Here is a sample:*

The influence of ancient Greek and Roman ideals were reflected in the sculpture, architecture, and humanist philosophy of the Renaissance. Renaissance sculpture, such as that created by the Florentines, returned to the ideals of the Greek and Romans by depicting realistic human nudes. In contrast, work of the medieval period had often featured stylized figures.

Buildings of the Italian Renaissance displayed the desire of their architects to return to the simple forms of the classical age such as domes and columns. French architects mixed these Greek and Roman features into the design of country estates called châteaux.

Humanist scholars studied classical texts, and many adopted Greco-Roman values. These included the idea of seeking fulfillment in daily life and the value of participating in a wide variety of activities.

## Chapter 17 Test Form A, pp. 65–66

| | | | | |
|---|---|---|---|---|
| **1.** d | **6.** a | **11.** a | **16.** d | **21.** b |
| **2.** f | **7.** j | **12.** d | **17.** b | **22.** b |
| **3.** g | **8.** h | **13.** b | **18.** d | **23.** b |
| **4.** i | **9.** b | **14.** a | **19.** d | **24.** c |
| **5.** c | **10.** e | **15.** c | **20.** c | **25.** a |

**26a.** *Student essays will vary. Here is a sample:*

Ferdinand Magellan led a Spanish-sponsored expedition of five ships across the Atlantic in search of a route to Asia. After exploring the eastern coast of South America, he rounded the continent's southern tip through the narrow strait that now bears his name. The fleet, now down to three ships, sailed across the Pacific Ocean for four months before reaching the Philippines. Here Magellan was killed, but the surviving ship managed to return to Spain.

The three-year journey was significant because it established that the earth was indeed round and its oceans were connected. In addition, the lands discovered by Columbus were not part of Asia but a landmass previously unknown to Europeans.

**26b.** *Student essays will vary. Here is a sample:*

The triangular trade involved Europe, Africa, and the Americas. European ships traveled to Africa, where the captains traded manufactured goods for enslaved people. These enslaved people were brought across the Atlantic and sold in the American colonies, where the ship captains picked up agricultural products such as sugar, coffee, or tobacco and returned to Europe.

The colonists desired enslaved labor for the production of these commodities, as well as for working in the mines. These activities required intensive labor, and Europeans believed that Africans were physically suited to hard labor.

## Chapter 17 Test Form B, pp. 67–68

| | | | | |
|---|---|---|---|---|
| **1.** b | **6.** e | **11.** d | **16.** b | **21.** c |
| **2.** d | **7.** i | **12.** c | **17.** d | **22.** b |
| **3.** a | **8.** h | **13.** c | **18.** c | **23.** d |
| **4.** g | **9.** c | **14.** a | **19.** a | **24.** c |
| **5.** j | **10.** f | **15.** c | **20.** a | **25.** a |

**26a.** *Student essays will vary. Here is a sample:*

The European voyages of exploration in the Atlantic were made possible by advances in shipbuilding and navigation. European shipbuilders began to use the lateen sails favored by the Muslims. These triangular sails allowed ships to travel against and with the wind. Shipbuilders also abandoned the single-mast ship in favor of multiple masts and made ships more maneuverable by moving the rudder to the stern.

Improved navigation was a result of several factors. Europeans became acquainted with the technology of the Chinese and Arabs, which included the compass and a superior astrolabe. In addition, mapmaking had improved greatly by the 1300s. European cartographers adopted the use of coordinates of latitude and longitude developed by Ptolemy.

**26b.** *Student essays will vary. Here is a sample:*

The Spanish and Portuguese differed in what they hoped to achieve by overseas expansion. The Portuguese were more interested in trade than colonization and focused their efforts in Africa and Asia. They took over the islands off Africa's western coast, set up trading posts in China and Japan, and built naval bases along the Indian Ocean to control shipping and the spice trade. Their only colony in the Americas was Brazil.

The Spanish focused on exploiting the wealth of the Americas and converting its inhabitants to Christianity. To achieve their goals they set up colonies rather than mere trading or naval posts. Their possessions included much of the West Indies, Central America, the majority of South America, and parts of the present-day United States.

## Chapter 18 Test Form A, pp. 69–70

| | | | | |
|---|---|---|---|---|
| **1.** c | **6.** i | **11.** c | **16.** d | **21.** b |
| **2.** f | **7.** j | **12.** d | **17.** b | **22.** a |
| **3.** h | **8.** a | **13.** d | **18.** b | **23.** b |
| **4.** e | **9.** g | **14.** c | **19.** b | **24.** a |
| **5.** d | **10.** b | **15.** d | **20.** c | **25.** a |

**26a.** *Student essays will vary. Here is a sample:*

Partly because of the empire's size and diversity, the Muslim rulers of the Ottoman

Empire tolerated the practice of non-Islamic religions. Non-Muslims had special laws that applied to them, rather than Quranic law, and non-Muslim religious groups could choose their own local leaders.

Many Islamic leaders of the Mogul Empire, in contrast, persecuted their Hindu subjects, taxing those who would not convert to Islam and destroying their temples. A noted exception was Akbar, who advocated religious tolerance and encouraged the study of different faiths in his court.

**26b.** *Student essays will vary. Here is a sample:*
Tokugawa Ieyasu was a Japanese leader who continued the unification process begun by Oda Nobunaga. Founder of the Tokugawa shogunate, he used a variety of methods to control the daimyos, or feudal lords.

By reassigning land rights, he placed his relatives in productive lands near the capital and potential enemies far away in outlying areas. He also set up *sankin-kotai*. This system required the daimyos to come to the capital for half the year in his service. *Sankin-kotai* weakened the daimyos financially since they had to maintain multiple households, spend money traveling, and pay tribute to Tokugawa. Tokugawa also employed a group of officials called *metsuke*, who acted as spies and reported on potential uprisings or plots against him.

## Chapter 18 Test Form B, pp. 71–72

| | | | | |
|---|---|---|---|---|
| **1.** b | **6.** f | **11.** a | **16.** b | **21.** a |
| **2.** i | **7.** a | **12.** a | **17.** c | **22.** b |
| **3.** e | **8.** g | **13.** c | **18.** c | **23.** b |
| **4.** h | **9.** c | **14.** c | **19.** d | **24.** a |
| **5.** j | **10.** d | **15.** d | **20.** d | **25.** d |

**26a.** *Student essays will vary. Here is a sample:*
The Portuguese were the first European power active in Asia. To achieve control of the spice trade, the Portuguese seized Muslim ports on the Malay Peninsula and set up trading posts throughout Southeast Asia. In addition to economic activity, they tried, largely unsuccessfully, to convert the population to Catholicism. Eventually their control of the spice trade was challenged by the English and Dutch.

The Portuguese were also active in China, where they set up a trading base in Macao, and in Japan, where Portuguese merchants arrived in 1543. Like all other foreigners except the Dutch, the Portuguese were barred from Japan with the beginning of the Japanese seclusion policy.

**26b.** *Student essays will vary. Here is a sample:*
Several factors were involved in increased agricultural production during the rule of the Qing dynasty. The government itself made efforts to help farmers with public works and flood-control programs. Canal and irrigation systems were built to help farmers water their crops. Improvements in transport and infrastructure facilitated the distribution of food. Trade with the West also helped increase production. New crops introduced to China by traders fared well in poor soil that previously had been left untilled.

## Chapter 19 Test Form A, pp. 73–74

| | | | | |
|---|---|---|---|---|
| **1.** d | **6.** i | **11.** d | **16.** d | **21.** d |
| **2.** h | **7.** e | **12.** b | **17.** b | **22.** a |
| **3.** f | **8.** a | **13.** d | **18.** a | **23.** c |
| **4.** b | **9.** g | **14.** a | **19.** d | **24.** c |
| **5.** j | **10.** c | **15.** b | **20.** b | **25.** a |

**26a.** *Student essays will vary. Here is a sample:*
Russia needed access to the Baltic and Black Seas because Russia possessed few seaports, none ice-free year-round. Under Ivan the Terrible, Russia went to war with Poland, Lithuania, and Sweden over territory that would have given it Baltic access but failed to achieve its goals. Later, Russia won control of the eastern Baltic by defeating Sweden under Peter the Great. His attempt to gain a warm-water port on the Black Sea failed, however, when his forces were defeated by the Ottoman Turks. In the late 1700s Russia finally gained a warm-water port during the reign of Catherine the Great. To do so, Russia again battled the Turks, this time emerging victorious.

**26b.** *Student essays will vary. Here is a sample:*
The Huguenots were France's Protestant minority. Henry IV, a former Protestant who had converted to Catholicism, issued the Edict of Nantes, which granted the Huguenots civil rights and the freedom to worship in areas where they were in the majority.

During the period of Cardinal Richelieu's control of the French government, the Huguenots saw their military and territorial rights reduced. However, they were still allowed freedom to worship.

Louis XIV viewed the Huguenots as a threat and repealed the Edict of Nantes. Wanting all Huguenots to accept Catholicism, he did not allow them to practice their religion. As a result, many Huguenots immigrated to other parts of Europe and to England's American colonies.

## Chapter 19 Test Form B, pp. 75–76

| | | | | |
|---|---|---|---|---|
| **1.** b | **6.** d | **11.** b | **16.** d | **21.** b |
| **2.** g | **7.** c | **12.** c | **17.** a | **22.** b |
| **3.** f | **8.** j | **13.** c | **18.** a | **23.** c |
| **4.** a | **9.** i | **14.** d | **19.** a | **24.** b |
| **5.** h | **10.** e | **15.** c | **20.** c | **25.** d |

**26a.** *Student essays will vary. Here is a sample:*
The Thirty Years' War began when Ferdinand, a Catholic and heir to the Hapsburg throne, tried to suppress Czech Protestants in Bohemia. The war spread to include many other parties: Catholics such as Philip III of Spain sided with Ferdinand; Danes and then Swedes took up the Protestant cause. As the war continued, religious issues were replaced by political aims as motivating factors.

**26b.** *Student essays will vary. Here is a sample:*
The Hapsburgs were one of the most prominent royal families of Europe, and territories under their rule included Austria and other German states, Hungary, and Bohemia. Spain and its possessions were also ruled by Hapsburg monarchs until the death of Charles II.

The Hohenzollerns were a family of German rulers who became rivals to the Hapsburgs. They grew to prominence in the northeast German state of Brandenburg and eventually gained control of Prussia and surrounding areas. Under the rule of Frederick II, Prussia seized the Hapsburg-ruled province of Silesia, beginning the War of the Austrian Succession.

## Chapter 20 Test Form A, p. 77–78

| | | | | |
|---|---|---|---|---|
| **1.** d | **6.** b | **11.** d | **16.** a | **21.** c |
| **2.** c | **7.** a | **12.** b | **17.** c | **22.** b |
| **3.** h | **8.** j | **13.** a | **18.** a | **23.** d |
| **4.** g | **9.** e | **14.** c | **19.** a | **24.** b |
| **5.** f | **10.** i | **15.** a | **20.** b | **25.** d |

**26a.** *Student essays will vary. Here is a sample:*
Before Copernicus, the prevailing belief—one supported by the Catholic Church—was that the earth was at the center of the universe. Copernicus theorized that in fact, the earth revolved around the sun. To present an opinion in opposition to the traditional view would have been seen as questioning Church authority. Fearing the Church's response, he worked in privacy and did not publish his own work.

A century later, Galileo's astronomical observations convinced him that Copernicus was essentially correct. He did publish his work, but his book was banned by the Church and an outraged Pope Urban VIII convicted him of heresy. Faced with the threat of torture or execution, Galileo recanted many of his positions.

**26b.** *Student essays will vary. Here is a sample:*
Robert Boyle was a seventeenth-century Irish scientist who is considered responsible for establishing the modern science of chemistry. Before Boyle, chemistry was a quasi-science known as alchemy. Alchemists subscribed to the belief that all matter was made up of four elements, one of which was air. Boyle criticized the alchemists and this theory of elements. He redefined *element* as a material that could not be broken down into simpler parts and proved that air could not be an element since it was composed of several gases.

## Chapter 20 Test Form B, p. 79–80

| | | | | |
|---|---|---|---|---|
| **1.** b | **6.** c | **11.** a | **16.** c | **21.** b |
| **2.** e | **7.** a | **12.** a | **17.** d | **22.** c |
| **3.** d | **8.** i | **13.** d | **18.** b | **23.** d |
| **4.** j | **9.** f | **14.** d | **19.** a | **24.** c |
| **5.** h | **10.** g | **15.** c | **20.** c | **25.** d |

**26a.** *Student essays will vary. Here is a sample:*
The term *enlightened despots* refers to European monarchs who were influenced by and tried to implement the ideas of the Enlightenment. Two of the enlightened despots were Frederick II of Prussia and Maria Theresa of Austria. Frederick, a friend of Voltaire, became known as a thinking ruler who tried to raise the economic and intellectual standards of his subjects. He established elementary schools and gave away seeds to improve the life of the peasantry. Similarly, Maria Theresa tried to improve life for her subjects. She freed the peasants on royal land and also set up elementary schools.

**26b.** *Student essays will vary. Here is a sample:*
Two people who disagreed with the Enlightenment's emphasis on reason were Jean-Jacques Rousseau and John Wesley. Rousseau, a French philosopher, argued that reason should be subordinate to instinct and emotion. He believed that the arts and the sciences had a corrupting influence on people, and he emphasized the value of a simple, preferably rural, existence.
Wesley, an English religious leader, argued for the value of personal religious experience. His Methodist movement presented an alternative to the Enlightenment-era religious philosophy of deism, which had attempted to apply reason and the concept of natural law to religious belief.

## Chapter 21 Test Form A, pp. 81–82

| | | | | |
|---|---|---|---|---|
| **1.** c | **6.** b | **11.** b | **16.** d | **21.** c |
| **2.** d | **7.** i | **12.** c | **17.** c | **22.** d |
| **3.** e | **8.** j | **13.** d | **18.** a | **23.** b |
| **4.** a | **9.** f | **14.** a | **19.** a | **24.** c |
| **5.** g | **10.** h | **15.** b | **20.** b | **25.** d |

**26a.** *Student essays will vary. Here is a sample:*
The Declaration of Independence and the Constitution of the United States were heavily influenced by the work of Baron de Montesquieu and John Locke. The political system set up by the Constitution divided central political authority among executive, legislative, and judicial branches. This system was recommended by Montesquieu in *The Spirit of Laws*.
The Declaration of Independence demonstrates Thomas Jefferson's admiration for Enlightenment thinkers, particularly John Locke.

Reflecting Locke's theory of a social contract between the rulers and the ruled, it argues that Great Britain had abused its authority and that therefore the colonists had a right to rebel.

**26b.** *Student essays will vary. Here is a sample:*
Oliver Cromwell was military commander of the pro-Parliament forces during the English Civil War. Under his leadership, these forces forced the surrender of the royalist armies and captured and executed King Charles. After leading the defeat of the Scottish and Irish rebellions, Cromwell dismissed Parliament and ruled England for five years. Cromwell ruled as a dictator, and his tenure was notable for the enforcement of strict Puritan rules of behavior.

## Chapter 21 Test Form B, pp. 83–84

| | | | | |
|---|---|---|---|---|
| **1.** i | **6.** j | **11.** c | **16.** b | **21.** a |
| **2.** g | **7.** b | **12.** b | **17.** d | **22.** c |
| **3.** d | **8.** c | **13.** c | **18.** a | **23.** a |
| **4.** e | **9.** f | **14.** b | **19.** c | **24.** d |
| **5.** a | **10.** h | **15.** b | **20.** a | **25.** d |

**26a.** *Student essays will vary. Here is a sample:*
Between 1781 and 1787, the former colonies were organized into a loose union of independent states, or a confederation. This union was governed by an agreement called the Articles of Confederation. Faced with the problems of mounting debt—the confederation had little central authority and could not collect taxes—and economic competition among the independent states, Congress called a convention to replace the Articles of Confederation with a new constitution.
The Constitution replaced the confederation with a federal system with shared power between central and regional governments. The central government was split into three branches: executive, legislative, and judicial. In 1789, George Washington was elected first President of the United States.

**26b.** *Student essays will vary. Here is a sample:*
The Bill of Rights was passed by the English Parliament in 1689, shortly after William III gained the British throne. Limiting royal power, the Bill of Rights strengthened the role of Parliament by prohibiting a king from suspending laws, raising taxes, or maintaining an army

without its consent. It also provided legal protection to individuals by guaranteeing the right to a jury trial and by prohibiting cruel and unusual punishment.

## Chapter 22 Test Form A, pp. 85–86

| | | | | |
|---|---|---|---|---|
| **1.** j | **6.** g | **11.** c | **16.** d | **21.** c |
| **2.** i | **7.** h | **12.** a | **17.** d | **22.** a |
| **3.** a | **8.** e | **13.** c | **18.** b | **23.** b |
| **4.** c | **9.** b | **14.** d | **19.** b | **24.** d |
| **5.** f | **10.** d | **15.** a | **20.** a | **25.** a |

**26a.** *Student essays will vary. Here is a sample:*

Three related factors led to military conflict between France and its neighbors during the revolutionary period. The first factor was the worry of European monarchs that the overthrow of royalty in France could spread to their own domains. French émigrés, members of the nobility who had fled to other countries, encouraged this fear. Desiring a return to their privileged prerevolutionary lifestyles, they tried to convince the monarchs to use their armies to destroy the revolutionary forces. Leaders of the revolution in France were motivated to fight by both the desire to spread revolutionary ideals and the need to preempt the attacks of anti-revolutionary monarchs.

**26b.** *Student essays will vary. Here is a sample:*

Two ways European leaders tried to reestablish the prerevolutionary order were by restoring monarchies to power and diminishing the power of France.

At the Congress of Vienna, European leaders examined claims to the throne and restored many of Europe's royal dynasties, including those of France, Spain, and Portugal. To prevent France from regaining the power it had held under Napoleon or again spreading revolution, several steps were taken. France was reduced to its 1790 borders, and buffer states, or neutral territories, were set up to surround it. The country was also forced to pay a large indemnity for war damages it had caused.

## Chapter 22 Test Form B, pp. 87–88

| | | | | |
|---|---|---|---|---|
| **1.** h | **6.** a | **11.** b | **16.** b | **21.** a |
| **2.** d | **7.** g | **12.** a | **17.** b | **22.** a |
| **3.** i | **8.** b | **13.** c | **18.** b | **23.** a |
| **4.** j | **9.** e | **14.** b | **19.** c | **24.** d |
| **5.** f | **10.** c | **15.** d | **20.** d | **25.** c |

**26a.** *Student essays will vary. Here is a sample:*

Prerevolutionary France had a highly stratified society divided into three classes, or estates. The First Estate was made up of the Catholic clergy and comprised about 1 percent of the population. The Second Estate was made up of the nobles and totaled about 2 percent of the population. The Third Estate included everyone else in France. This structure fostered great social discord since the first two estates enjoyed a variety of privileges but paid no taxes. Members of the Third Estate—mainly peasant farmers but also doctors, lawyers, artisans, and traders—were burdened by feudal dues, tithes, and/or taxes but had few privileges and no ability to join the first two echelons of society.

**26b.** *Student essays will vary. Here is a sample:*

The French Revolution had great influence in many places outside the country's boundaries.

Almost immediately, the revolt of the French and their adoption of a bill of rights encouraged other peoples around the world to rebel. For example, enslaved Africans in the French colony of Saint Domingue revolted against the plantation owners there.

The revolution also caused a permanent weakening in the authority of Europe's absolute monarchies. Despite post-Napoleonic efforts to restore prerevolutionary ruling systems, European monarchies never again achieved the level of power they previously controlled.

Two other lasting effects of the revolution can be traced to the rise of Napoleon. Nationalist feelings generated by Napoleon's conquests continued to affect Europe's politics and history long after his defeat. In addition, despite his dictatorial rule, his reign contributed to the spread of liberal and democratic ideas across the continent.

# Chapter 23 Test Form A, pp. 89–90

| | | | | |
|---|---|---|---|---|
| **1.** d | **6.** a | **11.** d | **16.** d | **21.** b |
| **2.** i | **7.** f | **12.** c | **17.** a | **22.** a |
| **3.** g | **8.** b | **13.** b | **18.** c | **23.** d |
| **4.** j | **9.** c | **14.** d | **19.** a | **24.** b |
| **5.** h | **10.** e | **15.** d | **20.** c | **25.** a |

**26a.** *Student essays will vary. Here is a sample:*

Mass production involved the use of machines to replace, as much as possible, human labor in factories and to produce great quantities of identical goods. Two people who contributed to the development of mass production were Frederick Taylor and Henry Ford.

Taylor helped manufacturers increase their efficiency by encouraging them to divide large tasks into smaller parts and implement step-by-step procedures in their production processes. Manufacturers who followed Taylor's advice created assembly lines on which products moved from worker to worker, each of whom performed one specialized task. Henry Ford borrowed and improved the assembly-line methods to mass-produce great quantities of cars with small amounts of labor.

**26b.** *Student essays will vary. Here is a sample:*

The Industrial Revolution brought about great change in the lives of many middle-class and working-class women. Middle-class women enjoyed increased prosperity. While a great part of their lives revolved around the maintenance of the home and the raising of children, the ability to hire domestic help freed women from many tasks and allowed them to become involved in pursuits such as crafts and educational endeavors.

The changes in the lives of working-class women were quite different. Rather than laboring in the fields to produce food, many women were employed in factories for long hours under difficult and dangerous conditions. Few women received wages equal to their male counterparts. Nonetheless, the ability to earn a living meant increased freedom, since most women had limited choices before the industrial era.

# Chapter 23 Test Form B, pp. 91–92

| | | | | |
|---|---|---|---|---|
| **1.** f | **6.** c | **11.** d | **16.** c | **21.** a |
| **2.** b | **7.** j | **12.** d | **17.** c | **22.** b |
| **3.** a | **8.** g | **13.** d | **18.** b | **23.** c |
| **4.** e | **9.** i | **14.** b | **19.** b | **24.** c |
| **5.** h | **10.** d | **15.** c | **20.** a | **25.** b |

**26a.** *Student essays will vary. Here is a sample:*

Three key factors in Great Britain's early industrial success were its abundance of capital, natural resources, and available labor. Industrialism required capital for building factories, hiring labor, and purchasing raw materials. Great Britain had an abundance of capital due to the prosperity of its landowners and the success of its overseas pursuits including the lucrative slave trade. Its natural resources included a network of rivers that provided power for factories and transport for materials and goods. The labor supply was provided by a large number of people who had been forced out of agriculture by the enclosure movement. The benefits of large-scale agriculture had also helped the population to grow and become healthier.

**26b.** *Student essays will vary. Here is a sample:*

Many factory workers of the early industrial era worked long hours in dangerous conditions. Workplaces generally had poor ventilation, which contributed to the spread of disease, and the performance of monotonous tasks using heavy machinery often resulted in injury to employees. Employers, interested only in profits, had no incentive to improve working conditions, and governments did little. An individual worker had no leverage against his or her employer. To fight for higher wages and improved working conditions, workers in specific industries joined together in associations. These associations developed into labor unions, and despite opposition by factory owners and government, they succeeded in achieving major gains.

## Chapter 24 Test Form A, pp. 93–94

| | | | | |
|---|---|---|---|---|
| **1.** d | **6.** c | **11.** c | **16.** c | **21.** d |
| **2.** h | **7.** a | **12.** d | **17.** a | **22.** b |
| **3.** i | **8.** f | **13.** d | **18.** b | **23.** c |
| **4.** g | **9.** b | **14.** c | **19.** c | **24.** b |
| **5.** j | **10.** e | **15.** a | **20.** a | **25.** a |

**26a.** *Student essays will vary. Here is a sample:*

During the 1800s, agriculture became more mechanized, and many people were unable to find work on farms. The growth of industry in the cities provided more opportunities. As a result, a vast shift in the population distribution of the industrialized countries occurred. Far more people lived in cities than in the rural areas. Britain led the way, with 80 percent of its inhabitants living in cities, but the same trend occurred in Germany, France, and the United States.

The rapid growth of cities led to a variety of problems. Housing was in short supply and often substandard, and industry polluted the urban environment. Inadequate waste-disposal facilities led to epidemics, and crowded conditions made fire a constant threat.

**26b.** *Student essays will vary. Here is a sample:*

According to Marx, class struggle was the basic conflict that propelled historical events. Once people developed the ability to produce more than they needed to survive, a struggle began between those who controlled this surplus and those who did not. Marx predicted a battle between those who produced goods—the workers, or proletariat—and those he considered non-productive—the middle class, or bourgeoisie. At the end of this struggle, a new society would emerge, one without private property or class distinction.

## Chapter 24 Test Form B, pp. 95–96

| | | | | |
|---|---|---|---|---|
| **1.** f | **6.** j | **11.** a | **16.** c | **21.** c |
| **2.** i | **7.** d | **12.** d | **17.** b | **22.** d |
| **3.** e | **8.** b | **13.** b | **18.** b | **23.** b |
| **4.** g | **9.** h | **14.** d | **19.** b | **24.** c |
| **5.** a | **10.** c | **15.** d | **20.** b | **25.** a |

**26a.** *Student essays will vary. Here is a sample:*

Many factors contributed to the emigration from Europe during the end of the nineteenth century. Economic motivation was probably the primary cause. Many European emigrants hoped to escape from overcrowded cities and to find higher-paying jobs in the Americas, Australia, and South Africa. Overseas industrialists in search of labor encouraged these hopes through recruiters, who promised prosperity to potential emigrants. Many other emigrants were fleeing persecution by their government. Emigration was facilitated during this period by people's improved mobility. Railroads made transportation easier, and steamships offered low fares to transatlantic passengers.

**26b.** *Student essays will vary. Here is a sample:*

Two artistic styles that developed during the nineteenth century were realism and impressionism. In painting and literature, realism involved a rejection of romanticism and an emphasis on representing life as it actually was. For the French painter Gustave Courbet, this meant the depiction of scenes of peasant life and the suffering endured by the less fortunate members of society. Impressionism, which developed later, tended to focus on color and light. While impressionists used the real world as their subject matter, they were primarily interested in the impact that it made on the senses. Perhaps the most famous impressionist was Claude Monet, who often painted the same subject in different seasons and at different times of the day.

## Chapter 25 Test Form A, pp. 97–98

| | | | | |
|---|---|---|---|---|
| **1.** c | **6.** d | **11.** d | **16.** c | **21.** b |
| **2.** a | **7.** b | **12.** b | **17.** d | **22.** c |
| **3.** e | **8.** i | **13.** d | **18.** b | **23.** a |
| **4.** g | **9.** j | **14.** d | **19.** a | **24.** b |
| **5.** h | **10.** f | **15.** b | **20.** c | **25.** d |

**26a.** *Student essays will vary. Here is a sample:*

The Catholic Church and the colonial governments cooperated very closely in Spain and Portugal's Latin American colonies. Catholic priests encouraged the governments to support their efforts as they went about converting native peoples to Catholicism. Colonial governments often had many clergymen in positions of power, and the Church benefited economically from the intertwined relationship, controlling about half the wealth of Latin America by 1800.

To some extent this relationship broke down during the period of revolutionary activity against the colonial governments. For example, Catholic priests were the leaders of several uprisings against Spanish rule in Mexico.

**26b.** *Student essays will vary. Here is a sample:*
In England, the battle for greater rights grew during the mid- to late 1800s. Led by women's rights activists, women fought for control of their own property and achieved it through two parliamentary acts. They gained the right to vote in local elections in 1869. National voting rights were not won until 1918, after a fight led by Emmeline Pankhurst. Women's voting rights advocates were known as suffragettes.

In America from the late 1800s on, women's voting rights advocates traveled across the country speaking in support of their cause. A major leader was Elizabeth Cady Stanton, who formed the National Woman Suffrage Association. Voting rights were gradually achieved in individual states beginning in the West. The right to vote was guaranteed nationally in 1920 by the Nineteenth Amendment.

## Chapter 25 Test Form B, pp. 99–100

| | | | | |
|---|---|---|---|---|
| **1.** i | **6.** b | **11.** b | **16.** a | **21.** c |
| **2.** a | **7.** j | **12.** b | **17.** b | **22.** d |
| **3.** c | **8.** h | **13.** a | **18.** b | **23.** c |
| **4.** d | **9.** f | **14.** c | **19.** b | **24.** a |
| **5.** e | **10.** g | **15.** a | **20.** d | **25.** a |

**26a.** *Student essays will vary. Here is a sample:*
A revolutionary from Argentina, José de San Martín led armies into Chile and defeated the Spanish there with the help of Bernardo O'Higgins. In 1820 he headed into Peru, and liberated that country, before ceding his revolutionary leadership to Simón Bolívar.

Born in Venezuela, Bolívar had fought against Spanish rule in Caracas and crushed Spain's power at the Battle of Boyacá in 1819. He continued to lead forces against the Spanish throughout Latin America, eventually liberating the territories that form present-day Venezuela, Colombia, Panama, Bolivia, and Ecuador.

**26b.** *Student essays will vary. Here is a sample:*
The original home of a people known as the Maori, New Zealand became attractive to Europeans because of its hunting, whaling, and logging resources. Settlers began to arrive in the late eighteenth century. The British achieved political sovereignty over New Zealand in 1840 by signing the Treaty of Waitangi with Maori chiefs. The colony was granted a constitution by Britain in 1852, but the Waitangi treaty, which was supposed to protect Maori land rights, was repeatedly violated by settlers and the colonial government. New Zealand achieved dominion status in 1907.

## Chapter 26 Test Form A, pp. 101–102

| | | | | |
|---|---|---|---|---|
| **1.** d | **6.** b | **11.** d | **16.** c | **21.** c |
| **2.** g | **7.** i | **12.** b | **17.** a | **22.** b |
| **3.** c | **8.** f | **13.** b | **18.** a | **23.** d |
| **4.** h | **9.** a | **14.** d | **19.** c | **24.** a |
| **5.** j | **10.** e | **15.** d | **20.** c | **25.** b |

**26a.** *Student essays will vary. Here is a sample:*
As adviser to King Victor Emmanuel II, Count Camillo di Cavour masterminded Sardinia's role in furthering Italian unification. After establishing Sardinian influence by having the country side with France during the Crimean War, Cavour made a deal with Napoleon III for French aid in expelling Austria from the Italian Peninsula. With this support, Sardinia gained control of Lombardy. Sardinia's victory encouraged inhabitants of other Italian territories to overthrow their rulers and join the unified kingdom. Cavour then sent an army to defeat papal forces at Castelfidaro. Southern Italians, in territory recently won by Garibaldi, were inspired to join the Sardinian-ruled kingdom. With Garibaldi's agreement to surrender this territory, Cavour created a united Italy under Sardinian rule.

**26b.** *Student essays will vary. Here is a sample:*
Two radical Russian political groups were the populists and the Bolsheviks. The populist movement began in the 1870s and was based on the belief that socialism would be installed in Russia by a peasant-led revolution against the czar. Populism was spread by intellectuals and students who went from village to village preparing the peasantry for their role as revolutionaries. The Bolsheviks, led by Lenin, emerged in the early twentieth century. They also wanted to bring about a socialist society, but unlike the populists thought that it could be established by a small party of professional revolutionaries.

## Chapter 26 Test Form B, pp. 103–104

| | | | | |
|---|---|---|---|---|
| **1.** b | **6.** i | **11.** b | **16.** a | **21.** a |
| **2.** a | **7.** d | **12.** b | **17.** b | **22.** d |
| **3.** f | **8.** e | **13.** d | **18.** c | **23.** c |
| **4.** g | **9.** h | **14.** a | **19.** a | **24.** c |
| **5.** j | **10.** c | **15.** b | **20.** b | **25.** c |

**26a.** *Student essays will vary. Here is a sample:*

Nationalism presented a threat to the stability of the Austro-Hungarian Empire because of the many different peoples within its population. The dual monarchy set up by Francis Joseph provided political representation to the German speakers of Austria and the Magyars of Hungary, but the majority of the empire's people were unrepresented Slavs. Austro-Hungarian rulers feared that Slavic nationalist feeling could lead to a breakaway of the Slavs from their empire, a fear heightened by Russian support for Slavic nationalism and the achievement of independence by Serbia and Bulgaria.

**26b.** *Student essays will vary. Here is a sample:*

A major reason Russia's level of industrialization lagged behind that of western Europe was its delay in abandoning a feudal-era agricultural system. Many peasants in Russia were still bound as serfs to the land. They were not emancipated until 1861, by the decree of Alexander II, and even then peasants were not allowed to leave the land until landlords had been compensated for property lost to village communities. Without the pool of workers provided in other countries by former peasants, Russian industrialists did not have the access to labor needed for the growth of an industrial economy.

## Chapter 27 Test Form A, pp. 105–106

| | | | | |
|---|---|---|---|---|
| **1.** f | **6.** i | **11.** d | **16.** b | **21.** d |
| **2.** b | **7.** d | **12.** a | **17.** c | **22.** d |
| **3.** g | **8.** e | **13.** d | **18.** b | **23.** c |
| **4.** c | **9.** j | **14.** d | **19.** a | **24.** c |
| **5.** a | **10.** h | **15.** b | **20.** a | **25.** d |

**26a.** *Student essays will vary. Here is a sample:*

The Dutch began to arrive in southern Africa in the mid-seventeenth century. Known as Afrikaners, these settlers controlled the region known as the Cape Colony until the British gained control of the region in the nineteenth century. Unhappy with British rule, Afrikaners migrated north and came into conflict with the Zulu nation. Neither side achieved dominance, but eventually the British attacked and defeated the Zulu. In the late nineteenth century, increased British settlement in the north brought the British into conflict with the Afrikaners. A war ensued, and after the British victory, the southern African territories were united into the Union of South Africa. The white-dominated state that resulted began to generate opposition from the nonwhite inhabitants of the Union.

**26b.** *Student essays will vary. Here is a sample:*

The Panama Canal had long been dreamed of as a way to cut travel time between the Pacific and Atlantic Oceans. A French effort to build it in the late nineteenth century failed, but in the early twentieth century, President Theodore Roosevelt instigated an American plan for its construction. At that time, Panama was part of Colombia, but Colombia refused to sign a treaty allowing the canal to be built in its territory. With American encouragement and military support, the Panamanians revolted against the Colombians and created a separate nation, one willing to grant the United States the land to build the canal. Construction was difficult and took ten years, but in 1914 the canal was finally completed.

## Chapter 27 Test Form B, pp. 107–108

| | | | | |
|---|---|---|---|---|
| **1.** c | **6.** a | **11.** d | **16.** b | **21.** b |
| **2.** d | **7.** i | **12.** c | **17.** a | **22.** a |
| **3.** g | **8.** j | **13.** c | **18.** a | **23.** d |
| **4.** e | **9.** b | **14.** b | **19.** c | **24.** a |
| **5.** h | **10.** f | **15.** d | **20.** d | **25.** d |

**26a.** *Student essays will vary. Here is a sample:*

The Industrial Revolution encouraged the growth of European imperialism in several ways. During the period of industrialization, the demand for raw materials increased. Factories in newly industrialized Europe needed commodities such as rubber, copper, tin, and jute for production. In addition, citizens made prosperous by the growing economies of Europe demanded imported products such as exotic fruits. To gain access to these materials, European nations fought for colonies and trading rights in the regions that produced them—Asia, Africa, and South America. In addition, European countries needed to find new markets for manufactured goods. The inhabitants of the regions they dominated provided greater markets.

**26b.** *Student essays will vary. Here is a sample:*

Two African countries that avoided colonization by the European powers during the nineteenth century were Ethiopia and Liberia. Liberia's historical relationship with the United States discouraged interference by the European powers. The country was established by former enslaved Africans, became independent in 1847, and continued to receive the support of the United States during the period in which Africa was being divided by the Europeans.

Ethiopia maintained its independence largely because of the determination of its ruler Menelik II. His armies crushed an attempted Italian invasion so thoroughly that other Europeans did not even make an attempt on his territory.

## Chapter 28 Test Form A, pp. 109–110

| | | | | |
|---|---|---|---|---|
| **1.** e | **6.** i | **11.** b | **16.** c | **21.** c |
| **2.** j | **7.** b | **12.** a | **17.** c | **22.** d |
| **3.** h | **8.** a | **13.** a | **18.** b | **23.** b |
| **4.** d | **9.** g | **14.** b | **19.** b | **24.** d |
| **5.** c | **10.** f | **15.** d | **20.** a | **25.** a |

**26a.** *Student essays will vary. Here is a sample:*

Under the agreements made after World War I, the states that formed the Central Powers lost great portions of the territory they had controlled before the war. Germany lost all of its overseas colonies. It also lost Alsace-Lorraine to the French and portions of its territory to newly independent Poland. The Austro-Hungarian Empire was broken up, and territories it had controlled were granted to Italy, to newly independent states in eastern Europe, and to the new South Slavic nation of Yugoslavia. That which remained of the Ottoman Empire was divided and placed under the control of Great Britain and France.

**26b.** *Student essays will vary. Here is a sample:*

World War I brought about the abandonment of cavalry-based military tactics and the introduction of new technology and methods. The British introduced tank warfare at the Battle of the Somme, although their early armored vehicles were primitive and slow. The Germans produced poisonous chlorine gas that was released and carried by wind into the trenches of enemy troops. The Germans also changed the rules of naval warfare. In their attempt to break British control of the seas, they would not issue warnings when attacking nonmilitary targets and provided no opportunity for passengers to evacuate. In response, the Allies developed their own naval tactics, including the use of underwater mines and the use of the convoy system, in which merchant ships travel only in warship-escorted groups. Airplanes began to be used for bombing enemy positions as well as for air reconnaissance.

## Chapter 28 Test Form B, pp. 111–112

| | | | | |
|---|---|---|---|---|
| **1.** c | **6.** j | **11.** d | **16.** c | **21.** b |
| **2.** e | **7.** h | **12.** d | **17.** d | **22.** b |
| **3.** f | **8.** b | **13.** d | **18.** a | **23.** d |
| **4.** g | **9.** i | **14.** a | **19.** a | **24.** c |
| **5.** a | **10.** d | **15.** a | **20.** b | **25.** b |

**26a.** *Student essays will vary. Here is a sample:*

The Fourteen Points was a peace plan first put forward by American President Woodrow Wilson before the defeat of the Central Powers by the Allies. Designed to serve as a framework for a peace settlement and provide for international stability in the future, it included proposals for limitations on arms, a prohibition on secret alliances, guarantees of freedom for trade and seafaring, and the establishment of an assembly of nations to deal with international problems. The majority of the points were not adopted at the Paris Peace Conference, which established the terms of the war's end. However, an international assembly, the League of Nations, was created.

**26b.** *Student essays will vary. Here is a sample:*

World War I led directly to the end of czarist rule in Russia. The Russians suffered huge military losses to Germany during the war. Its troops were demoralized by defeat and their lack of sufficient weaponry, and attempts to provide supplies for the army caused shortages and suffering for the civilian population. These shortages led to public uprisings against the czar, and

many unhappy soldiers joined civilian protesters. Faced with the inability to control the army
and use it to crush the rebellion, the czar was
forced to abdicate.

## Chapter 29 Test Form A, pp. 113–114

| | | | | |
|---|---|---|---|---|
| **1.** e | **6.** a | **11.** c | **16.** d | **21.** c |
| **2.** h | **7.** c | **12.** a | **17.** b | **22.** a |
| **3.** i | **8.** j | **13.** d | **18.** a | **23.** c |
| **4.** b | **9.** d | **14.** d | **19.** b | **24.** a |
| **5.** f | **10.** g | **15.** a | **20.** c | **25.** b |

**26a.** *Student essays will vary. Here is a sample:*
There are several reasons why the United
States emerged from World War I in stronger
economic condition than the European nations.
Because there was no military conflict on
American soil, the country's forests, farmland,
cities, and factories did not suffer the devastation of war as those of Europe did. American
industry also benefited by capturing markets
that had been supplied by Europe before the
war. Because of America's late entry into the
war, American casualties were fewer, and its
wartime expenses were smaller. In fact, the war
changed America from a debtor nation to a cred-
itor nation, whereas European countries were
left deeply burdened by war debts. Germany
faced the additional expense of paying reparations.

**26b.** *Student essays will vary. Here is a sample:*
Totalitarian governments had a chilling
effect on artistic and intellectual freedom in both
Germany and Russia. In Germany, Hitler eliminated guarantees of free speech and tried to
bring all intellectual and artistic activity under
the control of the Third Reich. Desiring the cele-
bration of Nazism, he used the arts and media to
spread propaganda and caused intellectuals and
artists to flee the country. In Russia, Stalin used
the secret police to quell intellectual freedom
and, like Hitler, believed that all cultural activities should promote the ideals of the government. Under his rule, Socialist realism became
the mandatory artistic style, and artists who
didn't produce work that glorified Communist
ideals were exiled or imprisoned.

## Chapter 29 Test Form B, pp. 115–116

| | | | | |
|---|---|---|---|---|
| **1.** i | **6.** d | **11.** a | **16.** d | **21.** c |
| **2.** b | **7.** c | **12.** d | **17.** c | **22.** d |
| **3.** h | **8.** g | **13.** b | **18.** b | **23.** c |
| **4.** f | **9.** j | **14.** d | **19.** c | **24.** a |
| **5.** a | **10.** e | **15.** c | **20.** d | **25.** a |

**26a.** *Student essays will vary. Here is a sample:*
The two men who battled to follow Lenin as
leader of the Soviet Union were Leon Trotsky
and Joseph Stalin. Trotsky was the leader of the
Red Army as well as a prominent Marxist
scholar. Like Lenin, Trotsky believed that
Russian socialism could succeed only if accompanied by Communist revolutions in other parts
of the world. Stalin was a Communist adminis-
trator who became general secretary of the
Communist party. Unlike Trotsky and Lenin, he
believed that the building of a Socialist society in
Russia did not depend on simultaneous international revolution. Stalin won the battle for leadership by achieving control of the party bureaucracy and then having Trotsky exiled and assassinated.

**26b.** *Student essays will vary. Here is a sample:*
Two forms of technology that had an impact
on American culture in the post-World War I era
were radio and film. The increased use of radio
by the American public helped produce a more
homogeneous culture as people in different
areas listened to the same programs. By broad-
casting advertisements, radio also stimulated
people's interest in buying consumer goods. In
the late 1920s, the popularity of motion pictures
increased when sound was added to the films.
The movies grew as a vehicle for spreading ideas
and provided cheap entertainment during the
Great Depression.

## Chapter 30 Test Form A, pp. 117–118

| | | | | |
|---|---|---|---|---|
| **1.** f | **6.** b | **11.** b | **16.** a | **21.** b |
| **2.** h | **7.** i | **12.** d | **17.** a | **22.** c |
| **3.** d | **8.** c | **13.** c | **18.** b | **23.** a |
| **4.** j | **9.** g | **14.** b | **19.** b | **24.** b |
| **5.** e | **10.** a | **15.** c | **20.** c | **25.** d |

**26a.** *Student essays will vary. Here is a sample:*
Under Kemal Atatürk's rule, Turkey became a modern nation. After repelling a Greek invasion, Kemal transformed the old center of the Ottoman Empire into the Republic of Turkey and set about the process of modernization. He laid the groundwork for industrialization, reformed the legal code, and created a separation between church and state. While encouraging the adoption of the Western calendar and Latin alphabet, he also encouraged nationalist pride by urging Turks to rid their language of foreign influences.

**26b.** *Student essays will vary. Here is a sample:*
During World War I, the British received tremendous support from their overseas colonies as well as from peoples of the Middle East. Thousands of Kenyans, for example, died while fighting for the British side. India provided Great Britain with needed food and raw materials, and more than a million soldiers. Arabs in Ottoman territories supported the British in return for the promise of independence after the war.

In general, these efforts went unrewarded, and British promises were broken. Returning Kenyans were greeted by land seizures rather than increased freedoms. Instead of gradual development toward self-rule, Indians suffered under harsh new laws and saw the weapons of British soldiers turned against them. In Palestine, the British delivered independence to neither the Arabs nor the Jews.

## Chapter 30 Test Form B, pp. 119–120

| | | | | |
|---|---|---|---|---|
| **1.** f | **6.** g | **11.** d | **16.** d | **21.** c |
| **2.** i | **7.** h | **12.** c | **17.** b | **22.** b |
| **3.** b | **8.** j | **13.** a | **18.** c | **23.** b |
| **4.** a | **9.** e | **14.** d | **19.** c | **24.** c |
| **5.** c | **10.** d | **15.** d | **20.** a | **25.** d |

**26a.** *Student essays will vary. Here is a sample:*
Two factors that contributed to the growth of militarism in Japan were economic depression and opposition to Western influence. Despite Japan's rapid industrial growth during the 1920s, the economy was devastated by the Great Depression. Poor farmers and unemployed workers were open to the idea that strong military leaders could lead the country out of its problems. In addition, many Japanese resented Western policies toward Japan, which they regarded as discriminatory, and were opposed to the growth of Western influence and lifestyles during the period of industrialization. Militarist lifestyle and dress were seen as a way to return to Japanese tradition and to turn away from the West.

**26b.** *Student essays will vary. Here is a sample:*
United States policy toward Latin America changed significantly beginning in the late 1920s. Earlier in the twentieth century, the United States had repeatedly intervened in the economic, political, and military affairs of Latin America, often fueling Latin American resentment and nationalism. The Hoover administration attempted to change Latin American perception of the United States with a goodwill tour, and his secretary of state clarified the meaning of the Monroe Doctrine, determining that it did not support the unlimited right of the United States to interfere in Latin America. President Roosevelt further changed the United States' relationship with Latin America with his Good Neighbor policy and his withdrawal of troops from Haiti and Nicaragua.

## Chapter 31 Test Form A, pp. 121–122

| | | | | |
|---|---|---|---|---|
| **1.** d | **6.** h | **11.** a | **16.** b | **21.** d |
| **2.** i | **7.** e | **12.** d | **17.** c | **22.** c |
| **3.** f | **8.** g | **13.** b | **18.** c | **23.** b |
| **4.** j | **9.** a | **14.** a | **19.** a | **24.** b |
| **5.** b | **10.** c | **15.** c | **20.** d | **25.** a |

**26a.** *Student essays will vary. Here is a sample:*
The early stages of the war in the Pacific were marked by great Japanese success. With the British withdrawal of forces from Singapore, the fall of the French government, and the attack on Pearl Harbor, the Japanese were able to expand rapidly and seize territory previously controlled by European powers and the United States.

In 1942 the United States began to achieve naval success against the Japanese and began a series of island battles that gradually shrank the area under Japanese control. By 1945, although the Japanese continued to fight, the eventual success of the Allies became inevitable. After the U.S. demand for unconditional surrender was rejected, President Truman ordered the dropping of atomic bombs on Hiroshima and then Nagasaki. On August 14, Japanese Emperor Hirohito surrendered.

**26b.** *Student essays will vary. Here is a sample:*

In the "New Order" envisioned by Hitler, Europe would be ruled by a German "master race," and "lesser" races would be enslaved or exterminated. The Nazis carried out their plan in the territories they occupied, sending millions of conquered peoples into labor, concentration, and death camps. The greatest victims of Nazi genocide were the Jewish people, of whom six million were killed at death camps such as Auschwitz and Dachau. Gypsies and Slavs were among the other groups exterminated in large numbers.

## Chapter 31 Test Form B, pp. 123–124

| | | | | |
|---|---|---|---|---|
| **1.** j | **6.** e | **11.** c | **16.** b | **21.** d |
| **2.** h | **7.** d | **12.** c | **17.** b | **22.** a |
| **3.** g | **8.** c | **13.** c | **18.** c | **23.** a |
| **4.** b | **9.** f | **14.** d | **19.** a | **24.** b |
| **5.** a | **10.** i | **15.** b | **20.** c | **25.** b |

**26a.** *Student essays will vary. Here is a sample:*

The League of Nations proved ineffective in its attempts to respond to Japanese and Italian expansionism. When the Japanese occupied Manchuria and the Chinese protested to the League, the League set up a commission to investigate. When the commission found Japan at fault, Japan simply withdrew from the League. The League had no means to force Japan to return Manchuria to China. Its ineffectiveness was also revealed by its response to the Italian invasion of Ethiopia. After the Ethiopian ruler appealed for League help, the League imposed weak sanctions on Italy, not ones that would have crippled its ability to wage war. Italy ignored the League's feeble response and formally annexed Ethiopia.

**26b.** *Student essays will vary. Here is a sample:*

Hitler used the cause of German unity to justify German expansion into Austria and Czechoslovakia. In 1938 he sent troops into Austria and proclaimed it part of Germany, fulfilling his dream of *Anschluss*. Hitler claimed he was merely unifying German-speaking people rather than engaging in aggressive territorial expansion. He used a similar line of reasoning with regard to Czechoslovakia, saying that the country's three million Germans had a right to self-determination. Yet even after the Munich Agreement gave Germany control of the ethnic German region, Hitler invaded the country.

## Chapter 32 Test Form A, pp. 125–126

| | | | | |
|---|---|---|---|---|
| **1.** b | **6.** h | **11.** c | **16.** a | **21.** b |
| **2.** g | **7.** e | **12.** d | **17.** b | **22.** d |
| **3.** j | **8.** a | **13.** b | **18.** a | **23.** a |
| **4.** f | **9.** d | **14.** d | **19.** d | **24.** c |
| **5.** c | **10.** i | **15.** c | **20.** c | **25.** a |

**26a.** *Student essays will vary. Here is a sample:*

Two problems that plagued the American economy in the 1970s were the inflationary effects of the oil embargo and the growth of a large trade deficit. In 1973 the oil-producing nations that formed OPEC exercised their control of the oil industry by refusing to ship oil to foreign customers. The price of the oil that the United States needed for its industrial production soared, as did the cost of manufacturing goods.

The United States also began to experience a trade deficit. Although the country emerged from World War II as the world's manufacturing leader, other nations became more industrialized, and American factories moved abroad to take advantage of lower labor costs. By the 1970s America was importing more goods than it exported.

**26b.** *Student essays will vary. Here is a sample:*

Two international organizations that arose in the postwar period were NATO and the Common Market. NATO, the North Atlantic Treaty Organization, was formed by the United States and Western European countries in 1949 as a reaction to increasing concern about the intentions and military power of the Soviet Union. Organization members agreed to defend one another in the event of Soviet attack.

The Common Market emerged as Western European nations recognized the benefits of greater unity and economic integration. Striving to create a tariff-free market for European products, they initially established the coordinating body of the European Coal and Steel Community in 1952. Five years later they expanded it to become the European Economic Community or Common Market.

## Chapter 32 Test Form B, pp. 127–128

| | | | | |
|---|---|---|---|---|
| **1.** h | **6.** c | **11.** d | **16.** a | **21.** b |
| **2.** b | **7.** j | **12.** c | **17.** d | **22.** d |
| **3.** i | **8.** f | **13.** b | **18.** d | **23.** b |
| **4.** a | **9.** d | **14.** c | **19.** b | **24.** c |
| **5.** g | **10.** e | **15.** d | **20.** d | **25.** a |

**26a.** *Student essays will vary. Here is a sample:*

After World War II, Canada began to weaken its traditional ties with Great Britain and assert its Canadian identity. The country strengthened its social welfare programs, took a more active role in international affairs, and replaced the Union Jack with a new flag featuring the maple leaf. As it became close to and influenced by its larger and more powerful neighbor, the United States, some Canadians began to worry about the growing Americanization of the country.

Another threat to the formation of a distinct and united Canada was its multicultural character. Postwar immigration helped diversify the population, and Canada's large proportion of French speakers became active in demanding the protection of their language, rights, and culture. Despite the passage of the Official Languages Act, a French separatist movement grew powerful in Quebec province.

**26b.** *Student essays will vary. Here is a sample:*

The Soviet Union was led by Joseph Stalin until his death in 1953. His postwar rule was characterized by the extension of Soviet control in Eastern Europe and the view that conflict with the West was inevitable.

During the 1950s, Nikita Khrushchev assumed control of the Soviet government, and while he continued economic and military competition, his tenure was marked by a gradual "thaw" in tensions with the West, at least until the crises of the early 1960s. Khrushchev was succeeded by Leonid Brezhnev, who looked to reduce Soviet military spending, helped to improve U.S.-Soviet relations in the 1970s by meeting with Nixon, and inaugurated the policy of detente.

## Chapter 33 Test Form A, pp. 129–130

| | | | | |
|---|---|---|---|---|
| **1.** g | **6.** b | **11.** b | **16.** d | **21.** a |
| **2.** h | **7.** f | **12.** d | **17.** d | **22.** a |
| **3.** e | **8.** c | **13.** b | **18.** b | **23.** b |
| **4.** a | **9.** d | **14.** c | **19.** d | **24.** d |
| **5.** j | **10.** i | **15.** b | **20.** a | **25.** c |

**26a.** *Student essays will vary. Here is a sample:*

After a civil war won by the Mao Zedong-led Communists, the defeated Nationalist forces retreated to Taiwan. Chiang Kai-shek set up a rival government on the island and under his rule, the country prospered economically. According to both the government of mainland China and that of Taiwan, the island is still a province of China. Both governments claim to be legitimate rulers of a unified China. While relations between the two governments improved somewhat beginning in the 1980s, many Taiwanese now would prefer that the island become an independent country.

**26b.** *Student essays will vary. Here is a sample:*

The United States played a major role in the reconstruction of Japan after World War II. The United States set up an occupation government, SCAP, directed by General Douglas MacArthur. Under SCAP rule, Japan accepted a new constitution that established a democratic political system. SCAP also carried out economic reforms including the decentralization of agriculture. In the 1950s, the United States helped the Japanese economy with a huge aid package and trained the Japanese in management skills. In addition, the constitutional prohibition against the creation of a Japanese military, as well as its continued military protection, allowed Japan to focus its resources on industrial development.

## Chapter 33 Test Form B, pp. 131–132

| | | | | |
|---|---|---|---|---|
| **1.** i | **6.** c | **11.** c | **16.** a | **21.** d |
| **2.** g | **7.** j | **12.** c | **17.** c | **22.** b |
| **3.** h | **8.** b | **13.** a | **18.** b | **23.** b |
| **4.** f | **9.** d | **14.** c | **19.** a | **24.** d |
| **5.** a | **10.** e | **15.** a | **20.** a | **25.** d |

**26a.** *Student essays will vary. Here is a sample:*
  Cambodia suffered greatly from the war in Vietnam despite the attempts of its ruler, King Sihanouk, to remain neutral. In 1969 the country was bombed by the United States in an effort to eliminate Viet Cong bases inside its borders. Although the bombing failed, it helped to trigger a civil war that was won by the Communist Khmer Rouge. Millions of Cambodians died during Khmer Rouge rule, and the country was devastated economically. After the Khmer Rouge's ouster by the Vietnamese, the country continued to be torn by conflict.

**26b.** *Student essays will vary. Here is a sample:*
  In 1947 majority Muslim areas in ex-British India became the nation of Pakistan. This country was divided in two parts, East Pakistan and West Pakistan, separated by a large section of Indian territory. In 1971 civil war broke out between the two distant territories that had little in common. After the intervention of India, the East Pakistan side emerged victorious, and became the independent nation of Bangladesh.

## Chapter 34 Test Form A, pp. 133–134

| | | | | |
|---|---|---|---|---|
| **1.** e | **6.** f | **11.** c | **16.** d | **21.** d |
| **2.** h | **7.** g | **12.** d | **17.** b | **22.** b |
| **3.** i | **8.** j | **13.** c | **18.** b | **23.** c |
| **4.** a | **9.** b | **14.** b | **19.** b | **24.** a |
| **5.** c | **10.** d | **15.** d | **20.** d | **25.** a |

**26a.** *Student essays will vary. Here is a sample:*
  South Africa's apartheid policies were an attempt by white South Africans to institutionalize their supremacy over the country's nonwhite inhabitants. Legalized by the Afrikaner government that took power in 1948, the laws grew to cover most aspects of black South Africans' lives. Apartheid defined where nonwhites could live and work and whom they could marry. It denied them the right to vote or own property. Some apartheid laws were weakened in the 1980s as the government began to respond to international pressure and the resistance of the African National Congress. The last apartheid laws were repealed as negotiations between the government and the ANC began in the 1990s.

**26b.** *Student essays will vary. Here is a sample:*
  The battle for independence in Kenya grew in intensity after World War II, motivated in part by the discriminatory policies of European colonialists. One of the movement's leaders was Jomo Kenyatta, who founded the Kenya African Union in 1947.
  In the 1950s, an underground freedom movement spread through the country. The British suppressed the uprising, jailing nationalist leaders, including Kenyatta. They were unable, however, to stem nationalist feeling and granted the country independence in 1963. Kenyatta became the country's first president.

## Chapter 34 Test Form B, pp. 135–136

| | | | | |
|---|---|---|---|---|
| **1.** g | **6.** j | **11.** d | **16.** c | **21.** b |
| **2.** f | **7.** b | **12.** c | **17.** c | **22.** a |
| **3.** e | **8.** d | **13.** c | **18.** d | **23.** b |
| **4.** h | **9.** a | **14.** a | **19.** c | **24.** b |
| **5.** i | **10.** c | **15.** d | **20.** c | **25.** b |

**26a.** *Student essays will vary. Here is a sample:*
  Two African countries that have been plagued by ethnic conflict are Nigeria and Rwanda. Nigeria's large population is divided into hundreds of ethnic groups. In the 1960s, conflict among them motivated the Ibo to secede from Nigeria and set up the independent state of Biafra. Thousands died in the ensuing war, and Biafra was taken back as part of Nigeria.
  Rwanda has two major ethnic groups, the Hutu and the Tutsi. Antagonism between them was fostered by the policies of the country's colonial ruler, Belgium. Competition and hostility continued after independence. In the 1990s, full-scale civil war broke out between the two groups, leading to the death of hundreds of thousands of people and charges of genocide against the Hutu.

**26b.** *Student essays will vary. Here is a sample:*
  One economic problem confronting African countries is overreliance on a single crop or raw material for much of their income. Countries like Ghana, which relies on cocoa, and Nigeria, which relies on oil, see their income drop dramatically when demand for their particular commodity decreases and world market prices fall.
  A second problem is the challenge of feeding a rapidly growing population. One-product economies, the shrinkage in arable land due to drought and desertification, and the emphasis on industrializing rather than developing agriculture are all factors that make it difficult for

some African countries to produce enough food as their populations increase.

## Chapter 35 Test Form A, pp. 137–138

| | | | | |
|---|---|---|---|---|
| **1.** b | **6.** i | **11.** a | **16.** b | **21.** b |
| **2.** h | **7.** a | **12.** c | **17.** a | **22.** b |
| **3.** e | **8.** c | **13.** b | **18.** a | **23.** c |
| **4.** j | **9.** d | **14.** d | **19.** a | **24.** a |
| **5.** f | **10.** g | **15.** d | **20.** b | **25.** a |

**26a.** *Student essays will vary. Here is a sample:*
The Suez Crisis developed out of a deterioration in the relationship between Egypt and the West. Angered by the withdrawal of a U.S. loan package to build the Aswan Dam, Egypt nationalized the Suez Canal. Fearing a cutoff in oil shipments through the canal, Great Britain and France invaded Egypt and were joined by Israel. The United States had tried to negotiate an end to the crisis and opposed the invasion. Facing international criticism, the invaders were forced to withdraw their armies.

**26b.** *Student essays will vary. Here is a sample:*
After the British withdrew from Palestine, the UN spent months trying to decide how that territory should be governed. In 1947 the General Assembly approved a partition plan dividing the territory into two parts, Israeli and Arab. Jerusalem would be administered by the UN. Jewish leaders accepted partition and proclaimed Israel's independence in the territory allotted under the plan. Arabs refused to accept partition and within 24 hours of its creation, neighboring Arab states had attacked the newly formed state.

## Chapter 35 Test Form B, pp. 139–140

| | | | | |
|---|---|---|---|---|
| **1.** c | **6.** d | **11.** a | **16.** b | **21.** b |
| **2.** e | **7.** h | **12.** d | **17.** c | **22.** a |
| **3.** b | **8.** i | **13.** c | **18.** c | **23.** a |
| **4.** f | **9.** j | **14.** d | **19.** b | **24.** b |
| **5.** g | **10.** a | **15.** c | **20.** d | **25.** d |

**26a.** *Student essays will vary. Here is a sample:*
The two major peace agreements made between Israelis and Arabs are the Camp David Accords of the late 1970s and the 1993 Israeli-Palestinian agreements. With the Camp David Accords, Egypt and Israel made a historic peace.

Egypt became the first Arab nation to recognize Israel's right to exist, and Israel returned Egyptian land, including the Sinai Peninsula.
The 1993 agreements provided mutual recognition between Israel and the PLO for the first time. They also called for increasing Palestinian self-government in the West Bank and Gaza and for Israeli withdrawal from those territories.

**26b.** *Student essays will vary. Here is a sample:*
Two natural resources vital to the Middle East are oil and water. Abundant oil resources have provided the basis for economic growth in several Middle Eastern countries including Iran, Iraq, Saudi Arabia, and Kuwait. Oil-producing nations have also shared their wealth with non-producing nations, though to a limited extent. In addition, oil has brought increased political influence to the Middle East, demonstrated during the oil embargo of the 1970s.
Water is just as vital as oil, but for the opposite reason—it is a regional commodity in very short supply. As the Middle Eastern population has soared, demand for water has increased to supply growing cities and industry and to irrigate arid but fertile areas.

## Chapter 36 Test Form A, pp. 141–142

| | | | | |
|---|---|---|---|---|
| **1.** d | **6.** i | **11.** a | **16.** d | **21.** b |
| **2.** j | **7.** a | **12.** a | **17.** c | **22.** d |
| **3.** f | **8.** g | **13.** c | **18.** c | **23.** b |
| **4.** h | **9.** c | **14.** c | **19.** a | **24.** a |
| **5.** b | **10.** e | **15.** d | **20.** c | **25.** b |

**26a.** *Student essays will vary. Here is a sample:*
Relations between Cuba and the United States have been poor since Fidel Castro took power in Cuba. Initially, the U.S. government became angered by the Cuban leader's seizure of American-owned property and disregard for civil liberties. Relations grew worse when Cuba became allied with the Soviet Union and began to support revolutionary movements throughout Latin America. The United States has made repeated attempts to topple Castro's government and has imposed trade and travel embargoes.

**26b.** *Student essays will vary. Here is a sample:*
A major cause of the conflict in El Salvador was the unequal distribution of the country's wealth. Although the country became industrial-

ized during the 1960s and 1970s, the economy was controlled by a tiny elite, while the peasant majority suffered. Landowners, with government support, responded to demands for reform by unleashing death squads throughout the countryside. Eventually, growing conflict turned into a civil war between the U.S.-supported government and a coalition of guerrilla groups.

## Chapter 36 Test Form B, pp. 143–144

| | | | | |
|---|---|---|---|---|
| **1.** d | **6.** i | **11.** c | **16.** a | **21.** d |
| **2.** e | **7.** b | **12.** c | **17.** a | **22.** c |
| **3.** h | **8.** c | **13.** d | **18.** a | **23.** d |
| **4.** a | **9.** j | **14.** b | **19.** b | **24.** b |
| **5.** f | **10.** g | **15.** c | **20.** c | **25.** c |

**26a.** *Student essays will vary. Here is a sample:*
Many Latin American countries borrowed heavily to finance industrialization during the 1970s and 1980s. When recession struck and interest rates rose, some countries, notably Mexico, had difficulty repaying the loans. The failure of Latin American countries to meet their obligations, or their decision to suspend payment, has had a great impact on American banks because many had extended credit in the region. For that reason, the U.S. government has been active in providing economic aid and encouraging the rescheduling of debt payment. The debt problem may be easing as Latin America experiences renewed growth and stability in the 1990s.

**26b.** *Student essays will vary. Here is a sample:*
For three decades the Duvalier family ruled Haiti as dictators. After Jean-Claude Duvalier was overthrown in 1986, the country entered a period of unrest. Jean Bertrand Aristide, a priest and reformer, was elected president in 1990 but was quickly forced to flee the country after a military coup. With the help of the United States, Aristide returned as president in 1994 and in 1995 was succeeded by René Preval in democratic elections.

## Chapter 37 Test Form A, pp. 145–146

| | | | | |
|---|---|---|---|---|
| **1.** g | **6.** a | **11.** c | **16.** d | **21.** c |
| **2.** h | **7.** b | **12.** c | **17.** a | **22.** a |
| **3.** j | **8.** f | **13.** c | **18.** a | **23.** b |
| **4.** i | **9.** c | **14.** b | **19.** b | **24.** d |
| **5.** d | **10.** e | **15.** a | **20.** a | **25.** d |

**26a.** *Student essays will vary. Here is a sample:*
The relationship between the United States and the Soviet Union improved markedly during the 1980s. At the beginning of the decade, the cold war had intensified because of President Reagan's dramatic increase in the American military budget and hard-line stance against what he referred to as the "evil empire." With the rise to leadership of Mikhail Gorbachev by mid-decade, however, relations began to improve. Gorbachev and Reagan developed a friendly relationship made possible by the Soviet leader's reform policies and willingness to make military cutbacks and enter arms-control agreements. Relations were also improved by Soviet withdrawal from Afghanistan.

**26b.** *Student essays will vary. Here is a sample:*
Two examples of the increasing interdependence of individual nations are global environmental problems and the integration of the world's economy. Increased trade among countries means that individual nations are more dependent on the economy of the world as a whole. Economic problems in one region can reduce trade with another, affecting the economies of many nations.
Environmental issues are increasingly global rather than national in scope. Problems such as the pollution of the world's oceans and the loss of the world's protective ozone layer cross national boundaries and can be solved only by international cooperation.

## Chapter 37 Test Form B, pp. 147–148

| | | | | |
|---|---|---|---|---|
| **1.** f | **6.** e | **11.** a | **16.** d | **21.** a |
| **2.** j | **7.** b | **12.** c | **17.** d | **22.** b |
| **3.** i | **8.** g | **13.** b | **18.** b | **23.** d |
| **4.** h | **9.** a | **14.** b | **19.** d | **24.** b |
| **5.** d | **10.** c | **15.** c | **20.** c | **25.** a |

**26a.** *Student essays will vary. Here is a sample:*
Both England and France experienced stable leadership during the 1980s, but their respective ruling parties represented opposite ends of the political spectrum. France was governed by the Socialists led by François Mitterrand. During his rule, the government nationalized private industry and increased spending on social welfare.
England was governed by the Conservative party led by Prime Minister Margaret Thatcher. Thatcher was a free-market advocate who tried

to promote economic growth by privatizing state-owned industries and dismantling social welfare programs.

**26b.** *Student essays will vary. Here is a sample:*

The fall of communism played a major role in the creation of many new states in Eastern Europe and central Asia. Many of the republics within the USSR resented rule by Russia, and the union was held together only by the Communist government's military power and suppression of nationalist feeling. After the collapse of that government, the republics in Eastern Europe and central Asia seized the opportunity to declare their independence.

Communist rule had also checked nationalism in the historically volatile Balkan region. After the death of longtime Yugoslavian leader Tito and the country's move away from communism, ethnic rivalries reemerged. Yugoslavia fractured into several independent states as it descended into civil war.

## Unit 1 Test, pp. 149–152

| | | | | |
|---|---|---|---|---|
| **1.** e | **12.** r | **23.** b | **34.** b | **45.** c |
| **2.** a | **13.** b | **24.** c | **35.** a | **46.** b |
| **3.** n | **14.** k | **25.** d | **36.** c | **47.** d |
| **4.** j | **15.** c | **26.** d | **37.** c | **48.** a |
| **5.** g | **16.** s | **27.** b | **38.** a | **49.** b |
| **6.** q | **17.** m | **28.** b | **39.** b | **50.** d |
| **7.** h | **18.** o | **29.** d | **40.** c | **51.** a |
| **8.** l | **19.** f | **30.** b | **41.** d | **52.** b |
| **9.** d | **20.** p | **31.** a | **42.** d | **53.** d |
| **10.** t | **21.** d | **32.** d | **43.** b | **54.** c |
| **11.** i | **22.** a | **33.** b | **44.** c | **55.** a |

**56a.** *Student essays will vary. Here is a sample:*

Both the Persians and Assyrians developed vast Fertile Crescent empires. Each empire had great accomplishments, yet their ruling styles differed markedly.

The Assyrians developed a powerful army, known for cruelty in battle, and they became legendary for their harsh treatment of the people they conquered. At its peak, the empire reached Asia Minor in the north and Egypt in the south. They facilitated transportation and communication across their territory by constructing an extensive network of roads.

Although the Persians were also proficient in battle, they administered conquered territories more tolerantly than the Assyrians, respecting the language and traditions of local people. They employed the talents of local artisans to build their own magnificent capital, the city of Persepolis. The Persians utilized the Assyrian road network but improved it, speeding transportation in an empire that was even larger, stretching from the Nile to the Indus River. The religion of the late Persian Empire also had a lasting influence, unlike that of the Assyrians, as the principles of Zoroaster may have influenced Judaism, Christianity, and Islam.

**56b.** *Student essays will vary. Here is a sample:*

The Egyptian system of hieroglyphics involved inscribing picture symbols onto slate or papyrus. These symbols represented ideas, objects, or sounds.

The Chinese script contained characters that also represented ideas, objects, or sounds. These characters were written in vertical columns. Because of the great number of symbols and strokes to learn, both hieroglyphics and Chinese writing were utilized mainly by priests and professional scribes.

The Phoenicians used a concise 22-character alphabet, each character representing a different consonant. Because of the small number of characters, it was easier to master than the Chinese and Egyptian systems and was used by a larger portion of the population.

## Unit 2 Test, pp. 153–156

| | | | | |
|---|---|---|---|---|
| **1.** t | **12.** g | **23.** a | **34.** d | **45.** c |
| **2.** k | **13.** i | **24.** a | **35.** b | **46.** b |
| **3.** q | **14.** c | **25.** a | **36.** a | **47.** d |
| **4.** f | **15.** p | **26.** a | **37.** d | **48.** a |
| **5.** s | **16.** b | **27.** d | **38.** a | **49.** a |
| **6.** h | **17.** l | **28.** a | **39.** b | **50.** d |
| **7.** n | **18.** a | **29.** c | **40.** d | **51.** c |
| **8.** r | **19.** m | **30.** a | **41.** c | **52.** d |
| **9.** d | **20.** e | **31.** d | **42.** b | **53.** b |
| **10.** o | **21.** b | **32.** d | **43.** b | **54.** c |
| **11.** j | **22.** c | **33.** c | **44.** c | **55.** d |

**56a.** *Student essays will vary. Here is a sample:*

The Chinese civil service system originated under the Han dynasty ruler Wudi. Before Wudi, government officials were chosen from the associates of Chinese emperors, and corruption was common. Under Wudi, candidates for public service had to pass difficult written examinations. The civil service was heavily influenced by Confucian teachings about order, duty, and ethical behavior. Study of these teachings was a requirement for entry, and books of Confucian thought were used as problem-solving resources.

In theory, public service was open to all except the despised merchant class. In practice, entrance depended on one's ability to afford education, so few members of the peasantry were eligible. The well-educated civil servants became a respected segment of society known as mandarins and ran the Chinese government until the 1900s.

**56b.** *Student essays will vary. Here is a sample:*
Both trade and government policy played an important role in the spread of Islam through Africa. Merchants from Persia and the Arabian Peninsula helped bring Islamic religion and culture to the East African coast as they established trading settlements there. The introduction of Islam into West Africa occurred as salt and gold caravans plied the trade routes between North Africa and Ghana. The establishment of Islam in West Africa was further assisted by the policies of the West African kings Mansa Musa and Askia Muhammad. Mansa Musa encouraged Islamic scholarship and made Timbuktu a center of Islamic learning. Muhammad made the laws of the Songhai Empire subject to the teachings of the Quran.

## Unit 3 Test, pp. 157–160

| | | | | |
|---|---|---|---|---|
| **1.** j | **12.** b | **23.** a | **34.** a | **45.** a |
| **2.** c | **13.** d | **24.** c | **35.** c | **46.** b |
| **3.** g | **14.** n | **25.** d | **36.** b | **47.** a |
| **4.** p | **15.** l | **26.** c | **37.** a | **48.** a |
| **5.** i | **16.** s | **27.** d | **38.** c | **49.** d |
| **6.** h | **17.** t | **28.** d | **39.** d | **50.** a |
| **7.** f | **18.** e | **29.** d | **40.** d | **51.** b |
| **8.** q | **19.** a | **30.** c | **41.** a | **52.** a |
| **9.** r | **20.** k | **31.** d | **42.** b | **53.** d |
| **10.** m | **21.** b | **32.** d | **43.** b | **54.** b |
| **11.** o | **22.** b | **33.** a | **44.** c | **55.** c |

**56a.** *Student essays will vary. Here is a sample:*
Beginning with Muhammad's revelations in the A.D. 600s, Islam quickly spread from Makkah

through the Arabian Peninsula. After Muhammad's death, Arab armies under the Rightly Guided Caliphs brought most of the Middle East including large parts of the Byzantine and Persian Empires under Muslim control. During the rule of the Umayyad dynasty, Islam spread west through North Africa and into the Iberian Peninsula and eastward to the borders of China and India. Around A.D. 1200, Islam was introduced by traders from India and the Middle East into the maritime areas of Southeast Asia. Within a few centuries, the people of the Malay Peninsula and Indonesia were predominantly Muslim.

**56b.** *Student essays will vary. Here is a sample:*
Several factors contributed to the growth of European cities during the Middle Ages. The Crusades led to the rebuilding of transportation infrastructure and increased contact between Europe and the Middle East. A resulting increase in trade, both within Europe and between Europe and other regions, led to the growth of many European cities as trading centers and trade route stops. The cultural contact with the Middle East also renewed interest in literature and art, contributing to the growth of cities as centers of scholarship and culture.

Cities also swelled due to the influx of farmers leaving their land and serfs who had bought their freedom from feudal lords. Wars had impoverished the feudal lords—they had provided the soldiers and supplies—and also destroyed farmland, encouraging this pattern of urban immigration.

## Unit 4 Test, pp. 161–164

| | | | | |
|---|---|---|---|---|
| **1.** b | **12.** j | **23.** b | **34.** c | **45.** a |
| **2.** m | **13.** f | **24.** a | **35.** c | **46.** b |
| **3.** s | **14.** p | **25.** a | **36.** d | **47.** b |
| **4.** r | **15.** i | **26.** d | **37.** d | **48.** a |
| **5.** o | **16.** k | **27.** c | **38.** b | **49.** d |
| **6.** l | **17.** e | **28.** a | **39.** b | **50.** b |
| **7.** g | **18.** t | **29.** d | **40.** a | **51.** b |
| **8.** a | **19.** n | **30.** c | **41.** d | **52.** c |
| **9.** d | **20.** c | **31.** a | **42.** c | **53.** c |
| **10.** q | **21.** a | **32.** c | **43.** a | **54.** a |
| **11.** h | **22.** d | **33.** c | **44.** c | **55.** d |

**56a.** *Student essays will vary. Here is a sample:*

Situated in the Adriatic Sea in northeastern Italy, Venice rose to prosperity based on its control of Mediterranean trade with Asia. By the late Renaissance, it was the most powerful Italian city-state and possessed a monopoly on trade between Europe and the East.

Its success, along with political instability along the Asian land routes, helped motivate other European powers to search for alternative routes to Asia via the Atlantic. By the 1600s, the focus of European economic activity had shifted to those countries that had developed colonies as a result of their explorations. The importance of Venice, and other Mediterranean trading cities, was diminished by the resulting growth of Atlantic sea trade. Europe no longer needed its link to the Asian land routes.

**56b.** *Student essays will vary. Here is a sample:*

The Jesuits, as members of the Society of Jesus came to be known, were founded by Ignatius of Loyola in 1540. Part of the effort to reform Catholicism and slow the spread of the Protestant faith, Jesuits swore obedience to the pope and worked as missionaries, preaching, setting up schools, and traveling in service of the Church.

Jesuits were valued as advisers in many countries because of their academic and scientific knowledge. The first Jesuit in Japan was a priest named Francis Xavier, who quickly won support of local lords. Adapting to Japanese customs, the Jesuits were successful at converting many to Catholicism—300,000 within a few decades. Eventually, Japan's rulers began to fear Christian influence. The Jesuit presence in Japan was outlawed, and converts were persecuted, exiled, or killed.

## Unit 5 Test, pp. 165–168

| | | | | |
|---|---|---|---|---|
| **1.** s | **10.** m | **19.** b | **28.** c | **37.** d |
| **2.** g | **11.** a | **20.** l | **29.** a | **38.** c |
| **3.** q | **12.** i | **21.** b | **30.** c | **39.** b |
| **4.** n | **13.** e | **22.** c | **31.** b | **40.** b |
| **5.** t | **14.** r | **23.** b | **32.** a | **41.** a |
| **6.** p | **15.** c | **24.** b | **33.** a | **42.** d |
| **7.** j | **16.** d | **25.** b | **34.** d | **43.** c |
| **8.** k | **17.** o | **26.** c | **35.** a | **44.** b |
| **9.** h | **18.** f | **27.** d | **36.** a | **45.** b |

| | | | | |
|---|---|---|---|---|
| **46.** a | **48.** a | **50.** d | **52.** d | **54.** c |
| **47.** d | **49.** d | **51.** c | **53.** c | **55.** a |

**56a.** *Student essays will vary. Here is a sample:*

Two acts of the British government that stirred the opposition of the American colonists were the Stamp Act and the tax placed on tea. The Stamp Act of 1765 required a direct tax to be paid to the British government on all printed materials. These materials, such as newspapers and shipping documents, had to be stamped in order to show that the tax had been paid. Colonists were outraged and reacted with a boycott of British goods and attacks on British stamp agents.

The British tax on incoming tea also angered the colonists. Although the British East India Company's tea could be sold more cheaply than others, it still included a tax. Some ships were turned away. Colonists in Boston reacted by dumping tea from British ships into Boston Harbor, an event known as the Boston Tea Party.

**56b.** *Student essays will vary. Here is a sample:*

At the height of his power, Napoleon controlled most of continental Europe, and France's boundaries extended as far as the Russian border. Napoleon's success, however, led to resentment among the people living in conquered territories. He had destroyed many local governments and institutions, and people objected to paying taxes to France and being forced into service in Napoleon's armies. This resentment grew into nationalist feeling and movements as people desired a return to their own traditions and the rule of local government rather than that of the French.

## Unit 6 Test, pp. 169–172

| | | | | |
|---|---|---|---|---|
| **1.** n | **10.** a | **19.** e | **28.** a | **37.** d |
| **2.** d | **11.** k | **20.** t | **29.** c | **38.** b |
| **3.** q | **12.** r | **21.** c | **30.** b | **39.** d |
| **4.** c | **13.** b | **22.** d | **31.** b | **40.** a |
| **5.** o | **14.** m | **23.** d | **32.** a | **41.** b |
| **6.** g | **15.** h | **24.** d | **33.** a | **42.** a |
| **7.** f | **16.** j | **25.** d | **34.** b | **43.** b |
| **8.** s | **17.** p | **26.** c | **35.** b | **44.** a |
| **9.** i | **18.** l | **27.** d | **36.** d | **45.** c |

| 46. c | 48. b | 50. a | 52. c | 54. c |
|---|---|---|---|---|
| 47. a | 49. c | 51. d | 53. a | 55. d |

**56a.** *Student essays will vary. Here is a sample:*
Otto von Bismarck was a German prime minister in the 1860s and adviser to the Prussian king William I. Espousing a policy of realpolitik—the right of a state to use any means necessary to achieve its objectives—and the buildup of the Prussian army, he waged war several times to bring most German states under Prussian control and simultaneously weaken Austria's influence among them. First he made an alliance with Austria to end Danish control of Schleswig and Holstein. Shortly thereafter he forged alliances with other European powers, invaded Holstein, and defeated his former ally. Through the Franco-Prussian War, Bismarck gained the support of the southern German states that had remained outside Prussia's rule. William I then became the first emperor of the newly united German Empire, with Bismarck as his chief minister.

**56b.** *Student essays will vary. Here is a sample:*
The Scottish economist Adam Smith was an early advocate of laissez-faire economics—the theory that governments should not interfere in the economy. According to Smith, the major economic force was the self-interest of individuals, and he believed that this competition between individuals—unconstrained by government policy—was both natural and desirable for society.
One critic of laissez-faire economics was the British philosopher John Stuart Mill. Mill argued that society could benefit from government activity in the economy and that the government should make laws to prevent the formation of monopolies and to redistribute wealth through taxation.

## Unit 7 Test, pp. 173–176

| 1. t | 9. c | 17. r | 25. d | 33. d |
|---|---|---|---|---|
| 2. a | 10. l | 18. j | 26. c | 34. b |
| 3. p | 11. d | 19. h | 27. d | 35. c |
| 4. b | 12. k | 20. f | 28. c | 36. a |
| 5. i | 13. q | 21. b | 29. c | 37. b |
| 6. s | 14. n | 22. b | 30. d | 38. a |
| 7. g | 15. e | 23. b | 31. c | 39. d |
| 8. o | 16. m | 24. b | 32. a | 40. d |

| 41. a | 44. c | 47. b | 50. b | 53. c |
|---|---|---|---|---|
| 42. a | 45. a | 48. a | 51. c | 54. c |
| 43. a | 46. b | 49. c | 52. a | 55. d |

**56a.** *Student essays will vary. Here is a sample:*
The Spanish Civil War began soon after the country became a republic. The republican government tried to introduce reforms that angered right-wing groups in the country. Led by General Francisco Franco, these groups began an uprising against the Republicans that turned into a civil war.
Many forces from outside the country took sides in the conflict, viewing the war as a battleground for the ideals of democracy, communism, or fascism. The Germans and Italians supported the right-wing military, while the Soviets and many international volunteers supported the Republicans. Most Western governments remained neutral. In the end, Franco's forces won the war, and the government of Spain became a dictatorship.

**56b.** *Student essays will vary. Here is a sample:*
Germany, Italy, and Japan were all dissatisfied by the peace settlements made after World War I. Germany had lost much territory, including all of its overseas colonies. In addition, it bore responsibility for repaying countries for damages caused during the war and faced constraints on its military power. Japan, despite its gain of former German possessions, was angered by the refusal of the newly created League of Nations to adopt a statement of racial equality. Italy had hoped to receive large portions of territory from the defeated Central Powers in the settlements. Instead, it gained only a small piece of Austrian territory.

## Unit 8 Test, pp. 177–180

| 1. r | 10. j | 19. n | 28. c | 37. a |
|---|---|---|---|---|
| 2. c | 11. b | 20. e | 29. b | 38. b |
| 3. o | 12. d | 21. d | 30. a | 39. b |
| 4. s | 13. p | 22. a | 31. a | 40. d |
| 5. q | 14. g | 23. c | 32. a | 41. b |
| 6. i | 15. l | 24. d | 33. c | 42. a |
| 7. a | 16. h | 25. b | 34. d | 43. b |
| 8. m | 17. f | 26. b | 35. c | 44. a |
| 9. t | 18. k | 27. d | 36. b | 45. c |

**46.** b    **48.** d    **50.** a    **52.** b    **54.** c

**47.** a    **49.** b    **51.** d    **53.** b    **55.** d

**56a.** *Student essays will vary. Here is a sample:*

As the continent returned to prosperity in the postwar period, European countries began the process of achieving greater political and economic integration. In the 1950s the objective of a tariff-free Europe led to the creation of the Common Market. That organization's membership and scope of authority increased, and momentum grew toward the development of a truly united Europe. With the signing of the Treaty of Maastricht and the Single Europe Act, member countries agreed to cooperate on issues such as defense and immigration and to remove remaining obstacles to free trade and movement. Future plans include the development of a central European bank and common European currency.

**56b.** *Student essays will vary. Here is a sample:*

Social inequality and the cold war both played major roles in the civil conflicts of postwar Latin America. In many countries, power and wealth were traditionally controlled by a small elite. The great disparity between rich and poor often led to unrest. The wealthy turned to military governments to protect their privileges; the poor often supported radical movements for social reform.

Tension between the Soviet Union and the United States contributed to these conflicts. The United States, desiring to check the spread of communism in the Western Hemisphere, tended to support and intervene on behalf of military governments, such as those in Chile and El Salvador. It also aided anti-Communist rebels such as the Nicaraguan contras. The Soviet Union supported Communist governments such as those of Cuba and Nicaragua and used its influence to support Communist movements in other nations.

# Teacher's Notes

# Teacher's Notes

# Teacher's Notes

# Teacher's Notes

# Teacher's Notes